The Yearbook of Agriculture 1971

92D CONGRESS, 1ST SESSION
HOUSE DOCUMENT NO. 29

A good life
for
more people

With a big increase in population a possibility by the turn of the century, our nation faces a choice between continuing to crowd people into jammed urban areas . . . or using space for living in the countryside.

Country areas offer sites and workers for industry, and land for homebuilding. Jobs and programs such as self-help housing will mean a new life for millions of impoverished rural people who in the past have seen no way out except the uncertainties of moving to the city.

Essential services for a fast-growing America include
vocational training, feeding programs for the
young, child day care centers, and imaginative teaching.

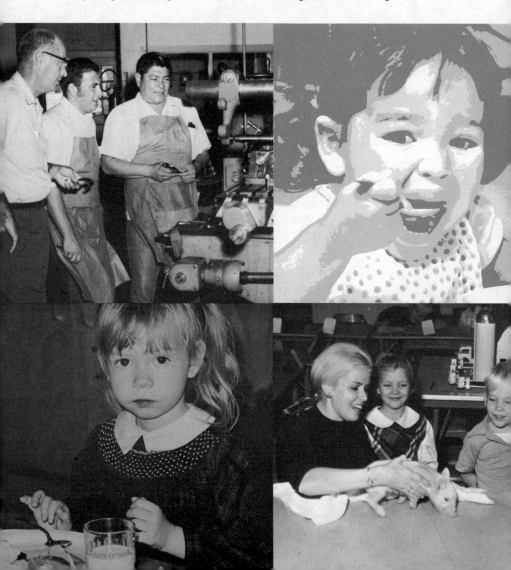

Over 10 million persons already participate in the food stamp
program. This is one way of supplementing the incomes of
families at the bottom of the economic ladder.

For America's next generation, readily-available data through computers will become increasingly vital. Extension staffers will broadcast fast-paced information from their cars.

Rising demands will be made for water, and other community services such as skilled fire protection. Four-H programs will help enrich the lives of city youth, as well as those of rural young people.

Our food industry must gear up for greater
production by the turn of the century
while preserving the environment. At right,
man in caisson monitors a feedlot like one at
bottom of page to safeguard ground water.

Youths camp, fish and canoe on once
polluted river. It was restored with government
help by farmers living along its banks.
Steer eats experimental ration that includes
ground up newspaper,
a potential for paper waste disposal.

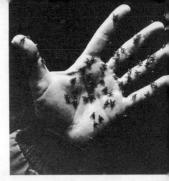

We can help control pests without harming the environment by using biological techniques, such as fruit flies sterilized by radiation, and a parasitic wasp that attacks the cabbage worm.

New processes will continue to improve natural
fibers. Left, inexpensive sculptured cotton lace.
Above, shearling jacket treated for washability.
New forms of food are emerging,
such as vegetable protein bits
that can be added to soup.

To meet the needs of a soaring population
as we head toward the 21st century,
usable water (top) may be reclaimed
by passing sewage through grass covered
basins, living filters. And the quality of life
will be enhanced by innovative new towns.

Foreword

CLIFFORD M. HARDIN

Secretary of Agriculture

THIS 1971 YEARBOOK OF AGRICULTURE—*A Good Life for More People*—is part of the U.S. Department of Agriculture's response to the new era of change in America, and to President Nixon's new policy of growth for the Nation.

The Administration's program is designed to encourage redistribution of the population of this Nation over the next 30 years to take some pressure off the metropolitan centers and create new growth centers around the smaller cities and towns of rural America.

Given that general policy, there are scores of issues that need attention, and many are highlighted in the following pages.

Although population forecasts are always uncertain, we could add millions of people to the American population by the turn of the century.

With this in mind, here are a couple of intriguing quotations from the 1971 Yearbook:

- "It seems to many that we need in the United States perhaps 400 or more new towns and cities—say of about 25,000 to 250,000 and with space to grow . . ."
- "Inevitably the next 30 years will bring an explosion of urban-type growth in areas that now consist of farm trading towns, placid villages, and the fields and woodlots of farmers."

In the years ahead we must make the changes necessary to make living *good* for the Americans of the year 2000 and beyond.

That is why we have devoted a substantial section of this book to articles concerned with Space for Living. We need the right kind of planning to provide space for people.

For instance, New Jersey is our most heavily populated State, and we tend to think of it as overcrowded, with its average of 941 persons per square mile. We forget that nearly two-thirds of New Jersey is in farms and forest.

What we need is the right kind of planning by smaller cities, towns, and rural communities to take the pressure off New Jersey's big cities and make a better life for everyone in the State. And New Jersey is but one example. Right now 74 percent of Americans live and work most of their time on 2 percent of our land. No wonder we feel crowded!

Yet there is ample room for economic expansion in rural areas. If the U.S. urban population did not exist, the vast land area comprising rural America would be large enough to be classified as the world's eighth largest country.

Part of the answer is to make new uses of land, build new communities, and rejuvenate old rural communities. The first priority is to provide productive work opportunity to the people who choose the new trend. It can be done. For example, in 1970 about 50 percent of capital expenditures by manufacturing industries was devoted to modern plants in rural areas.

After jobs, what next?

First of all, rural people need decent housing. Only a third of our population now live in rural areas, but half of our substandard housing is located there.

We must examine new methods of financing and planning housing for all the people, young and old. In rural areas, too, black families occupy almost a third of the substandard units, and this situation requires correction.

If we can achieve that, it still will not be enough unless we can retain, improve, and even create where necessary to make the quality of life all that Americans are entitled to expect.

People in nonmetropolitan America suffer from inadequate and unequal social services provided through Federal, State, and local programs.

We have made great strides—the Yearbook notes that a century ago only 2 percent of the Nation's 17-year-olds were high school graduates, and today 70 percent graduate—but we have further to go. Educational attainment of rural adults lags behind the rest of the Nation by almost three years.

We will need to offer many more services—in providing energy to the new population centers, better communications, transportation, and welfare. We at the U.S. Department of Agriculture have begun efforts to assist in improving our national water and land-use systems and more will be done through environmental assistance programs.

Farm production and forest production will give new emphasis to the protection and betterment of our environment. We must learn and practice recycling of agricultural and industrial wastes, and we are constantly devising new tools for this purpose.

Pest control becomes ever more important, particularly control that does not damage the environment. We are making significant progress and will achieve more.

By 2000, we may possibly need as much as 50 percent more agricultural production than we have today, and we feel we can meet such a goal. An increase in food and fiber, concurrent with dispersion of processing industries, should mean increased income for rural families. It will mean better, nearby markets for farmers. It will also bring more part-time work within reach of those farm families who wish to use it.

Today farming employs fewer than 5 million workers. Industries that process and distribute farm products employ 10 million. Some say that by 2000 we may have fewer than 2 million farmworkers on a million farms—but farming as a business will continue to be one of the Nation's largest. Our effort must be to deliver more income to rural areas.

There will be new stresses and strains from a high population density even if we make all the changes we can see needed.

Assuming that progress is accelerated, there may be relatively more change in the next 30 years than there has been in the past 70. Thus the year 2000 might be to 1971 as 1971 was to 1900—that can be the look of the future.

Our challenge is to evolve a new life style, with emphasis on quality environment. And that is the purpose of this book—to discuss the problems and the needed changes, and to offer some pathways to the future.

Preface

JACK HAYES

Yearbook Editor

OUR NATIONAL POPULATION is currently growing by about 2 million persons a year. While our future growth is not easily predictable, it seems reasonable to expect a major population increase between now and the first or second decade of Century 21.

We may even have 100 million more people by the year 2000, although recent trends in population increase would suggest it may not be that much.

In the 1971 Yearbook the authors examine how rural America, agriculture, and the rest of the Nation can deal with a big increase in the U.S. population.

This is a people-oriented book. And, in the editor's opinion, it is generally a hopeful book. There is an undercurrent of optimism among the authors, as they tackle the many problems ahead.

The general approach is to lay out the needs, describe what is now being done, and tell how much further we need to go. Plenty of shortfalls are indicated. No reader will come away satisfied that all is well.

Imprint on Living, a U.S. Department of Agriculture report published in 1970, sketched some of the problems that this Yearbook deals with:

"Each year we demand more from soil and water.

"Cities grow bigger, industrial plants more numerous, agriculture more intensified.

"Farmland is taken up by more suburbs and more super highways.

"Water in quantity is needed for work, for play, and for household uses unknown a generation ago. . . .

"The same amount of fresh water will fall from the skies" in the year 2000 as now, the report continues, "but we will use twice as much water. We will be fed from the same thin layer of top soil that feeds us today. . . ."

Rural area needs include a big increase in housing, better community facilities of all kinds, more industry and jobs, better planning and zoning, and improved education and vocational training.

As one of the Yearbook's authors says, "If we didn't have people, we wouldn't have these problems. . . . The trouble with the world is people. And the joy is, too." So let's roll up our sleeves. There's a lot of work to be done.

The scope of the 1971 Yearbook is long range, looking beyond the immediate horizon to another century.

It isn't always easy for authors who are accustomed to dealing with current fact and short-range forecasts to shift from binoculars to a telescope, to project beyond available studies. But that reserve leads to a certain solidity and authority in these pages. There is little of Jules Verne or science fiction.

As in most Yearbooks, the authors are mainly specialists from the Agriculture Department or the State land-grant colleges.

Turning back a hundred years to the 1871 *Report of the Commissioner of Agriculture*, forerunner of the current Yearbooks, you will find that more than 40 pages were devoted to the land-grant colleges.

The historic State-Federal ties are still there.

Chairman of the 1971 Yearbook Committee was Francis J. Kutish, Staff Economist Group. Committee members were:

James H. Copp, Economic Research Service
Melvin L. Cotner, Economic Research Service
Lloyd H. Davis, Science & Education Staff
Earl R. Glover, Agricultural Research Service
Elizabeth S. Hight, Food and Nutrition Service
Paul J. Jehlik, Cooperative State Research Service
F. Glennon Loyd, Soil Conservation Service
Charles W. McDougall, Extension Service
Robert E. Nipp, Farmers Home Administration
Nolan C. O'Neal, Forest Service
Thomas S. Ronningen, Cooperative State Research Service
Donald E. Runyon, Rural Electrification Administration

Contents

Space for Living

Services for Living

Production Resources for Living

Issues for the Future

space for living

100 Million
More People
Coming Up?

CALVIN L. BEALE

DEMOGRAPHERS should be a humble breed. They have been wrong in their predictions about some major trends in the population. Even after the baby boom of World War II, many population analysts failed to see how much growth the United States was about to get.

They continued to project low rates of future increase that would have led to no more than 166 million people in 1970 compared with the 204.7 million found in the 1970 census. Yet paradoxically, while underestimating total growth, they overestimated the future size of the farm population.

The demographic record is not all one of shortsightedness, however. In the 1940 Yearbook of Agriculture, two of the U.S. Department of Agriculture's demographers wrote of the need for a national policy on rural-urban migration. But the Nation's leaders in government, business, and civic life did not attempt to cope with the effects of the huge flow of people out of rural areas until after most of the potential flow had already taken place.

In any event, the well-publicized difficulty that demographers have had in projecting certain trends has not lost them their clientele. The questions continue to press in. How many births will we have? How large will our population get? Where will people live?

The questions are particularly important at a time when values and objectives of the young adult generation seem to be changing in ways that might affect family size, and when the technology and acceptance of birth control methods have also changed. So, the discussion that follows is directed to a consideration of the present and future size of the U.S. population and its location.

The Bureau of the Census estimates that there were 206 million people living in the United States on January 1, 1971, making this country the world's fourth most populous nation. After a period of rather rapid growth in the 1940's and 1950's, the rate of population change slowed in the 1960's as the birth rate went down. Even so, we are still currently adding 2 million people a year, through the combination of natural increase (excess of births over deaths) and immigration.

Arrival of the population at the 200 million mark has drawn attention to the probable timing of the addition of the next 100 million. We have also seen a rapid rise of interest in the zero population growth concept, with its insistence on the necessity to end population growth and to do so well before another 100 million has been added to our total.

What is the range of probabilities and alternatives before us? Wide, very wide. The critical fact before all nations today in which childbearing is largely deliberate, is that the death rate in such societies is low. Less than 4 percent of all infants born in modern societies die before reaching age 25, whereas in the most underdeveloped countries it is not uncommon for 20 percent to die before 1 year of age.

In the United States, each 100 women passing through the childbearing years need to have only about 210 children to fully replace their generation—100 for themselves, 100 for the fathers, and about 10 to allow for children who fail to survive to adulthood. Under these conditions, even an average of three children per family leads to fairly rapid population growth—about 40 percent in each 25-year generation.

*

CALVIN L. BEALE is Leader of the Population Studies Group, Economic Development Division, Economic Research Service.

2

Thus, fairly minor shifts in average family size can have considerable effect on the future size of the Nation's population. Women who are presently 35–39 years old will have borne about 320 children per 100 women by the time they fully complete their childbearing. If we perpetuate the family size preferences of this generation, the Nation would add its next 100 million people very quickly—by about 1997—and its next 200 million by 2015!

On the other hand, women who are presently 55–64 years old, and who thus lived much of their young adult life during the Depression, only bore 221 children per 100 women. This was a level barely sufficient to replace the parental population. If adopted by oncoming generations of young adults, it would bring the Nation to a nearly stationary—or zero growth—status without immigration by 2037. Even so, the population would be about 275 million by that time.

In short, within our recent history, we have had one generation motivated to have families large enough to provide a rapid population increase and another which restricted its family size to the replacement level, even without modern birth control methods. This is what makes accurate projection of future population size so difficult.

At present, the number of young people entering the marriage and childbearing ages is very large in relation to the number of people at advanced ages where most deaths occur. And the number of young adults will become ever larger throughout the 1970's, reflecting the coming of age of the huge numbers of children who were born in the 1950's. Thus, even if young adults marry late and form rather modest-sized families, they are so numerous that the births they have will greatly exceed deaths that occur from the much smaller numbers of older people.

Recent years do, in fact, show less early marriage and early childbearing. In the mid-1950's, 20 percent of all girls married before age 18. That figure has now fallen to 12 percent.

Furthermore, women who are presently under 25 years of age have borne only 70 percent as many children to date as had women of this age 10 years ago. Continuation of this relative level of childbearing would result in a completed average family size only slightly above replacement level.

Thus at the present point in time, the young generation seems to have different values and objectives concerning the family than their immediate predecessors did. But whether such changed behavior will persist through the remainder of their childbearing years no one can say with certainty.

It seems reasonable to conclude that in our past history families have rarely limited their family size from considerations of national welfare. Available family income or the family-size modes of one's social equals were more likely to be dominant factors.

Today, however, there is some evidence of couples consciously limiting their childbearing to a low level because of beliefs about the undesirability of further increasing the national population. Questions of future environmental quality seem to loom large in the thinking of such couples. In short, it is not at all impossible that childbearing may fall below generational replacement levels in the future.

A further element in the present and future growth of the U.S. population is immigration. Net migration into the country has grown to more than 400,000 per year, and presently contributes a fifth of our total population growth.

But should the birth rate decline further, and immigration remain at its present level, immigration would contribute an increasingly higher part of our total growth. Such a condition would almost certainly make the volume of immigration more of a national issue than it presently is.

Because many immigrants are young, they bear children after arriving here and thus make a further addition to population growth. Even if the immigrants have only enough

FUTURE U.S. POPULATION

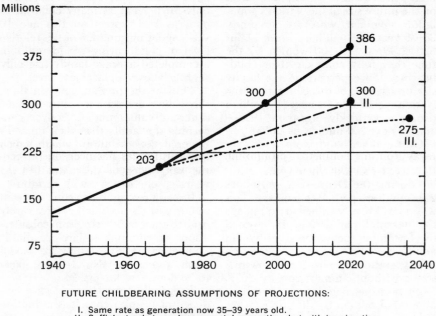

FUTURE CHILDBEARING ASSUMPTIONS OF PROJECTIONS:

   I. Same rate as generation now 35–39 years old.
  II. Sufficient only to replace parental generation, but with immigration.
 III. Same as II, but no immigration.

Source: Bureau of the Census.

children to replace themselves, current immigration levels will add about 5 million additional to our population size every 10 years.

To summarize the prospects for adding a hundred million more—if the present and oncoming generations bear children at the rate that people now 35–39 years old have, and if present immigration levels continue, we will have that next hundred million by 1997. If childbearing drops to the level needed only for generational replacement and immigration continues, we will not get it until the year 2020. If childbearing were to drop to this level or lower *and* if net immigration were stopped, we would not add another hundred million, but would still add many million people beyond our present level.

At present the interest of policy makers in population trends seems to focus as much on the distribution of people as on their number. Population distribution policy issues are discussed in another chapter, but the recent trends will be described here.

About 74 percent of our people now live in urban territory, that is, in places of 2,500 or more population or in the densely settled suburbs of large cities. The remaining 26 percent, or about 54 million, are rural, living in the open country or in towns of less than 2,500 population.

The rural proportion has declined in every census for 150 years. The number of rural people has changed very little at the national level in the last 40 years. All of our net growth has been urban.

We have been a predominantly urban people since 1920. It is not so much the fact of urbanization that is of interest these days, however, as it is the scale of urbanization. There are now 32 metropolitan areas in the United States that contain more than 1 million people each! And some of

4

these now link with smaller metro areas to form several massive metropolitan regions.

Between 1960 and 1970, the population in metropolitan areas grew more than twice as rapidly as that in the small city and rural territory that makes up the nonmetro areas (17 percent compared with 7 percent). Since both populations would grow at about the same rate in the absence of migration, the difference is a clear indication of the movement of many people away from the nonmetro and into the metro areas during the decade.

People move for many reasons, but the most common one is economic. Too often, the primarily agricultural or coal mining sections of the Nation have been areas of declining employment as mechanization displaced workers, and people sought better jobs—or even any job—in the larger cities. As a result, we have more than 18 million adults living in our urban places and suburbs who are of rural childhood origin, and they make up a fifth of the total urban adult population.

If one considers only nonfarm people, then the trends outside of metro areas look rather different. The nonfarm nonmetropolitan population grew somewhat more rapidly than the Nation as a whole did in the 1960's, reflecting a favorable growth rate of nonagricultural jobs.

The continued drop in farm employment offset so much of this gain that the public image of small city and rural areas has been one of economic stagnation or decline. But the agricultural job decline has about run its course. With the farm population now only a third as large, it just isn't possible for as many workers to be displaced in the future.

If the nonmetropolitan areas can continue their recent gains in nonagricultural jobs, more of these gains will be translated in the future into overall growth and a greater ability to retain population in the small city and rural areas.

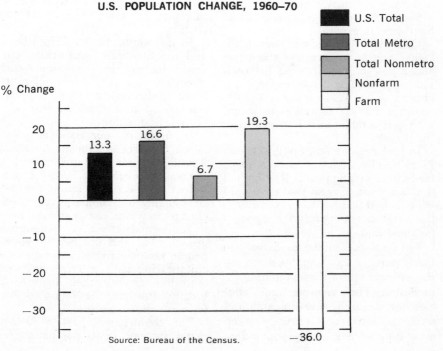

U.S. POPULATION CHANGE, 1960–70

Source: Bureau of the Census.

Construction of new homes near Largo, Md., a suburb of Washington.

It must be recognized, however, that as rural or nonmetropolitan areas grow, the larger ones are transformed by the growth into urban or metropolitan areas, and are reclassified as such. Thus there is very little prospect of increasing the total size of the rural and small city population.

The population has been shifting regionally as well as from small communities to large. Despite the jibes—serious or comic—that are made about southern California's smog, sprawl, and freeways, many people are still attracted to that area and to the whole Southwest in general.

California, Arizona, and Nevada together appear to have had about two and a half million increase in population in the last 10 years from migration alone. At the other end of the country, Florida continues to boom, with over a million net immigrants in the decade.

In both regions—the Southwest and Florida—climate seems to be a major factor in attracting people. The United States is short of areas that have mild winters, and it is hard to predict anything but increasing future congestion for those that do.

People also continue to move into many parts of the megalopolitan belt that stretches from Washington, D.C., to Boston. The extensive trade, educational, research, governmental, and service industries of this densely settled area support a growing population.

But most of the growth is now in outlying parts of the belt, with the central cities or older suburbs often being just as great exporters of people as any agricultural area.

On the other hand, large areas in the Great Plains and western Corn Belt are failing to retain their potential population growth. The States of Iowa, Kansas, Nebraska, North and South Dakota, Montana, and Wyoming grew in population by only 2 percent in the 1960's, including their metropolitan areas. They sent two-thirds of a million migrants to other regions of the country.

In the South, the Mississippi Delta and the Southern Appalachian coal fields declined in population, each giving up about 300,000 migrants. Many of them went directly to northern cities, if past trends are any judge of their destinations.

In summary, our national population is currently growing by about 2 million a year. Its future growth is not easily predictable, because attitudes toward desirable family size may be changing, and comparatively minor changes in typical family size can have a substantial effect on population growth. But the number of young people now coming of marriage and childbearing age is so large that even with low fertility their births will greatly outnumber the Nation's deaths for many years to come.

The country will have a further major increase in its population regardless of whether we attain another 100 million in this century or not. This increase will almost certainly be concentrated in the metropolitan-sized communities, just as the present population is. But with the diminishing loss of jobs from farming, the rural and small city areas seem much more likely than in the past to be able to develop enough nonagricultural employment to offset the further declines in farming. Many areas have shown this capacity in the 1960's.

Managing Space for All of Us

GENE WUNDERLICH and
WILLIAM DYER ANDERSON

FELLOWSHIP of man is fine, in moderate amounts. After a point, however, the presence of others may annoy—and even destroy us. The increase in human numbers presents us with a problem of managing diminishing average space.

A strategy for coping with this problem is to (1) promote the art and science of understanding space relationships; (2) design and engineer structures and population for effective use of space; and (3) design and develop organizations and procedures for regulating human interaction. Some of the ingredients of this strategy follow below in this and other chapters.

In this chapter we treat the space problem narrowly as a human problem. Viewing spaceship earth strictly as a human enterprise is subject to many dangers, as ecologists have made us painfully aware. Nevertheless, if our chapter is to focus on human relationships, we will simply have to acknowl-

edge that the earth contains many creatures and features and let it go at that. The message of this chapter is mostly about the distances among people.

But what is the meaning of space to an individual? North Americans, for example, feel intruded upon if a stranger invades the 4-foot-distance barrier. They are uncomfortable if even a friend converses closer than 2 feet. Yet 25 feet is a "public" distance and people do not care to do private business at such lengths even if they can be heard. Distance has important effects on human relationships in work, living, and recreation.

Within limits, perceptions of distance are a result of culture. It is known, for example, that the typical Latin American prefers to stand about six inches closer to his partner in conversation than the North American. Unless this cultural differential is understood by parties involved, the North American is "cold and standoffish" and the Latin American is "pushy and overbearing." Distance can be measured psychologically, socially, and culturally.

We can extend the idea of linear distance into a two-dimensional area or territory. Even further, we can say that man surrounds himself in a psychological "space bubble"—of variable dimensions for different functions. Intrusions into this space may be regarded as hostile or at least disagreeable.

In order to voluntarily yield a portion of this space, some compensation is required. For example, one will accept a crowded bus if it is cheaper or more convenient than riding one's own car. Or a person will accept a smaller residential lot because it is cheaper than a large one. When one's private space is invaded, one expects the compensation of a graceful "thank you" or "excuse me."

*

GENE WUNDERLICH is an economist in the Natural Resource Economics Division, Economic Research Service.
WILLIAM DYER ANDERSON is an attorney in the Division.

Space can be traded off against other desired ends. For some the value of space is high. For others, space can be foregone easily in favor of other ends. Because space can be traded off against other ends, and because space has a value, even if not always in money, it has an economic quality.

The need for space may have deep psychological roots. We are aware that overcrowding can result in pathological behavior. Animal experiments have revealed antisocial, cannibalistic, and suicidal behaviors which if projected into human populations would destroy the fabric of society. Yet, research is far from providing final answers to questions on man's need for space.

For the present, the uses of space for privacy, escape, reflection, esthetic interest, recreation, and other purposes must be assumed on the basis of personal feeling by our designers, land use planners, engineers, and social scientists.

These psychological relations of space to individuals are important in the planning and construction of better communities, transportation systems, and industries. Space is, therefore, an important factor in public policy.

Space can be taken into account in the way we build our houses, factories, parks, and roadways; where we locate our cities, industries, and agriculture; and how we develop our technology. Space also can be taken into account in our social and economic organization and the means by which we control our collective behavior.

A search for some absolute numbers of acres, square feet, miles, or cubic feet of space needed for 60 million to 100 million more persons expected around the turn of the century is not likely to be fruitful. Space is an idea. Each person has his own perception of space needs for different functions. These needs become absolutes only in the extreme, and they change over time.

Some space, like your home, you will occupy the whole year. Other space such as motels, hospitals, and barbershops you may occupy only a portion of their total available time. Recreation space may vary widely from a theatre seat to a hiking area.

Concentric model town built since 1962 at Urubupunga, in the Brazilian interior. A model farm takes up the core. The spiral growth protects the agricultural areas from urban sprawl.

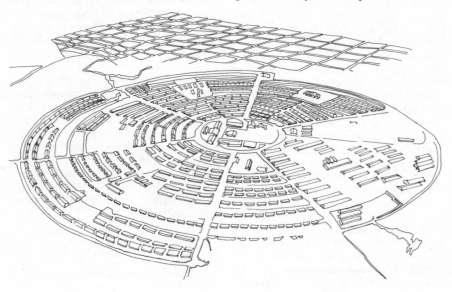

Some uses of space: Top, Minnesota farmland. Center, children in District of Columbia park (left) and two boys using "tree finder" along a trail in George Washington National Forest, Va. (right.) Bottom, heavy traffic at San Ysidro, Calif.

Space such as road right-of-way is made use of by you although you will not occupy it. Some areas, which you never see or experience directly, provide goods and services for you: manufacturing plants, public utilities, and farmland. These shared or reserved areas may enter into a community or national space budget but not directly into the space budget of an individual.

The space needs of an urban apartment dweller whose recreation is the theatre, and who uses public transportation to a compact office, will be much smaller than those of a suburbanite who prefers camping and commutes by car to his occupation as a park attendant. Both may require less space than the Wyoming rancher requires just for his homestead.

People make residential, occupational, and travel decisions according to their preferences and opportunities. These preferences change, often to accommodate the situations individuals find themselves in.

Besides an understanding of the psychological, social, and economic functions of space, we need to know how the environmental characteristics of space can be conserved and created.

Can space be created? The earth's surface area is fixed. For practical purposes, the geographic boundaries and general topographical features of the Nation are fixed. All 3.6 million square miles of the United States are habitable, but in some areas only at extreme cost. Industry can be placed anywhere but at what cost, and to whom will the cost accrue? Homes can be built anywhere but would people want to live in them?

Decreasing the population is probably the simplest, least expensive, and most direct way of "creating" space for people. The arithmetic of space for the nation with a fixed total area requires that average space for people can be created only by decreasing the population. In specific locations, however, space—or the sense of space—can be created in a number of ways.

Dispersal of population obviously

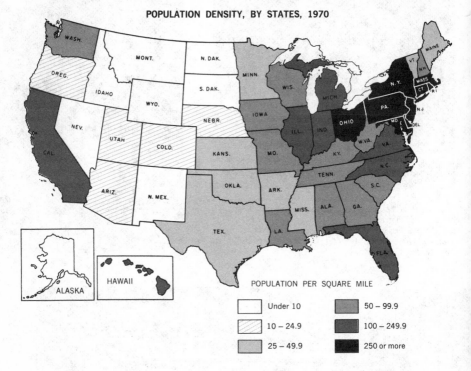

POPULATION DENSITY, BY STATES, 1970

POPULATION PER SQUARE MILE

	Under 10		50 – 99.9
	10 – 24.9		100 – 249.9
	25 – 49.9		250 or more

would expand per capita space of some densely settled areas. A uniform distribution of the 300 million people projected in the highest population forecast for the United States around the turn of the century would produce community densities of about 100 people per square mile. The State of North Carolina has an average density of 101 persons per square mile now.

An average density per State allows wide variation, however. Even the most densely populated State in the Union—New Jersey with 941 persons per square mile—has large areas of open countryside. Nearly two-thirds of New Jersey's land is in farms and forests.

How congested we feel will depend on how we design and use our space. Space per capita can be created by expanding the usable area. About 12 percent of the area of the United States is swamp, desert, mountains, and other areas unsuitable for use without radical alterations. However, nuclear energy, earth moving and excavation machinery, high-speed transportation and communication, water recycling, and other technologies make environmental alterations possible—whether desirable is another question.

New microclimates can be created within enclosed areas. Geodesic domes enclosing 2,000 acres can be constructed for $2 a square foot, at current prices. Such domes could have profound effects on the clustering of people and the means for meeting their space demands.

Floating cities have been designed and proposed to relieve congestion of urban areas. A British firm has developed plans for a city built on stilts for shallow portions of the ocean. The United States has over 800,000 square miles of continental shelf, much of it capable of supporting structures. Oil drilling platforms already have been erected in depths to 295 feet at a cost of $1 million per 98 feet.

Agriculture's traditional function of supplying food and fiber may be assumed by factories, either by produc-

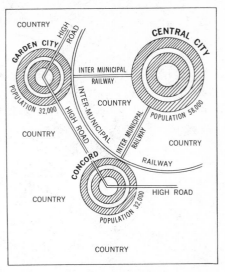

Ebenezer Howard's ideal concentric city (1898) had a glass-covered Crystal Palace in the form of a circular shopping street and a hierarchical core of culture and good government. The inviolate greenbelt separating it from its smaller satellite duplicates was to be filled with sheep, grain, and orchards, instead of factories and cluster housing.

ing substitutes such as synthetic fibers or by intensifying biological processes such as high-rise confinement feeding of livestock. Technologies for these changes already exist. If factories replace farms in producing food, then the space and environmental features of agriculture will take on a relatively greater importance. Today's farmers may become tomorrow's landscape architects.

Very rapid underground transportation travelling in deep tubes could permit dispersal of population without use of surface area for roadways or airports. New tunneling and subsurface construction techniques anticipate vast changes in transportation, hence population distribution.

Much of the apparent congestion of urban surface areas can be relieved by effective use of subsurface levels. By the year 2000, utilities, transportation, and the other services can be provided below ground so as not to obstruct visual enjoyment of surface

11

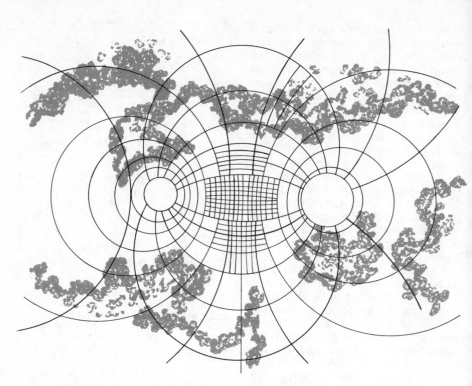

The city and its open land is a system. Open land is necessary for the system's survival.

space, or above ground to serve multiple purposes such as office buildings erected over highways.

Above-surface opportunities are expanding with new materials, designs, and construction techniques. Today's cities are a product of technological developments such as the elevator, automobile, telephone, and structural steel. Frank Lloyd Wright's dream of a mile-high building comes closer to reality each year. High buildings, more widely spaced, increase the number of planes of vision and the separation of buildings and people thus create the effect of more space in our urban areas.

But the creation of space is often expensive. Where the cost of congestion is most acute, in our cities, the use of below-surface and above-surface levels, the construction of cities in the sea, and the development of transportation may be necessary.

In most areas of the Nation, how-ever, space simply can be conserved or managed better or innovatively. Space, in other words, can be used to save our other valuable resources. The countryside—farmland, forests, open areas—can be managed so (1) it is accessible to more people and (2) its quality is maintained or enhanced.

A national system of highways has provided easy, inexpensive access to open areas for recreation. Limitations on access are due more to crowding of public facilities largely at peak loads, or the lack of means to mobilize privately controlled space, than to lack of physical mobility.

The more critical problems of open areas are in maintaining those qualities for which open areas are sought. Freedom, privacy, cleanliness, and tranquility are expected in the great open spaces. In the face of growing numbers, these qualities may be preserved only through organization, management, and control.

12

With increased mobility and inter-dependence of people, their statistical assignment to a unit of space becomes less and less meaningful in describing our space problems. Do 70 percent of the people live on 2 percent of the land? No. They "live" on all the space they use.

Such statistics are derived by conveniently assigning people's "living" to a statistical boundary such as a SMSA (Standard Metropolitan Statistical Area), county, or city. It takes no account of how this 70 percent uses the other 98 percent of the space. Neither does it describe extreme congestion occurring when 10 percent of the people attempt to use .00001 percent of the space at the same time.

The widening access to space is true even of our national boundaries. Ecumenopolis—the world community —is in our near future. A decade from now the travel time to the other side of the earth will be just a few hours. Furthermore, many of our present transportation needs will be replaced by 3-dimensional, all sensory systems which are now technologically available. These communication systems will provide electronic presence to long distance communications so natural that they will seem to be living presence. In three decades earth distances won't matter.

So perhaps the idea of average or per capita space is becoming more and more realistic. Technology is eliminating opportunities for natural monopolies of territory. One can no longer secure space by traversing un-peopled distance. Space will increasingly become a matter of coordinating activity, including presence, among people. The physical experience of space will depend upon timing. Timing requires organization and control.

How is organization and control to be brought about? What are the instruments of control, who will use them, and how? What policy guidelines are we to follow in using these instruments of control? Only recently have we thought in terms of a specific policy on population and its distribution.

One of the largest known population migrations in the world was made from rural to urban places in the United States, a nation committed to democratic principles and individual freedom, by people who, according to many polls, preferred to live in small towns and rural areas.

Thus we conclude that the policy of having no policy with respect to population distribution did not result in much freedom of choice as to where people live. Economic forces which determine the location of jobs shape our migration patterns. Government policies and programs have not been neutral. Social welfare legislation, expenditures for transportation, housing programs, even agricultural programs have tended to provide incentives for migration to urban areas.

Efforts to redirect growth must not only remove the incentives influencing present location but must also assign priorities for growth in areas where it is not likely to occur. The rationale for this action has been set out specifically in policy discussions in recent years. Typical of the arguments offered are the diseconomies associated with urban concentrations and the social burdens of congestion.

A variety of policy instruments are available to influence national population distribution. For example, public investments in power, communication, transportation, sewer and water supplies, health facilities, recreation facilities, and housing could carry assigned priorities for location and thereby induce private development in those areas. Direct Federal Government involvement in large scale urban developments and new communities is another possibility.

The problems of employment location could be attacked more directly by providing incentives for industrial or business location through the tax structure, direct payments, or low interest loans. Use and disposal of publicly-owned property may have significant effects in some areas. Direct relocation payments could be made to individuals. Job training and improved

13

employment information systems are other alternatives that have been offered.

Population distribution of the future will be influenced by the development of technology. While we recognize that present land settlement patterns are largely a product of past technological developments, few policymakers suggest intervention in the technology development and adoption process to positively influence future population location.

We could assume in the past that technology was spontaneous—almost an act of God. This is no longer the case. However, emphasis in the area of technology assessment seems to be largely on protecting society from adverse effects—an understandable bias in view of past experience.

The catalytic effect of major technological developments on population distribution could be used as a powerful policy instrument. For example, a new regional airport may attract support activities equal to a city of 80,000 people. We are relatively certain that these facilities will be placed somewhere. The decision will be made by relatively few individuals and groups, private and public, and thus could be simpler to implement as a population redistribution measure than, for instance, a tax incentive. It could be more target specific.

A complete population policy includes unpeopled places. In terms of irreparable damage to unique space, the wilderness and other natural areas probably stand to suffer most from 60 million to 100 million more people.

Approximately 10 million acres of land are now protected under the Wilderness Act of 1964 but as the President's Council on Environmental Quality notes, less than one percent is east of the Mississippi River. The potential for preservation of areas representative of our natural heritage rapidly diminish with the increase in population and mobility.

Natural areas marked for more in-

tensive use are likewise threatened. Overcrowding of park space in particular areas has reached the point of negating its purpose. Some effort at rationing the use of park space has been undertaken in the form of required advance reservations. Automobiles have been banned in certain places. These forms of control on use will become common.

Changes in the workweek over the next 30 years will also have major impact on use of this space. Will we eventually need different workweeks for different individuals in order to allocate the weekend use of such unique resources as seashores and recreation areas among increasing populations?

There is probably general agreement on the need for planning and controlling the use of some space on a subnational but greater-than-local basis. New concepts of regionalism, variously defined, have been advanced. The optimum organizational level will probably still be a subject of controversy in the year 2000.

What seems most likely to occur is a more active role by States. They are the units of government in our Federal system with the broadest range of inherent government authority. All land use will probably be subject to some form of regulatory control, and direct regulation by the States over areas of more than local concern seems almost inevitable.

Traditional local governments will be consolidated both in areas of population growth and relative decline, for different reasons. Primary decisions regarding the use of space where people live and work will continue to be made by territorially larger local governments. This trend, which tends to remove government from the people, will be countered by an increase in both formal and informal organizations within localities to represent smaller community interests.

The nature of local controls over the use of space will change considerably. Zoning, which has been the major space regulator of local governments, has traditionally dealt with height, use, setback, and area requirements. In the future, amenity controls dealing with noise, traffic pattern and volume, population density, water and air pollution, and open areas will be essential components.

One does not have to be an Einstein to accept the idea that space is not only a question of where but also a question of when. Timing use will become increasingly important in space management. Church buildings, for example, are now being used by different denominations at different times as an alternative to maintaining separate facilities which are essentially unoccupied a majority of the time. Changes in the education process may call for shorter formal class periods and thus give rise to "shifts" using school facilities at different times.

The same concept could apply in many areas including the management of office space. Peak load design is generally not conducive to an efficient use of space.

But providing for 60 million to 100 million more people is not just a question of technical capability or institutional strategy. The question is, if we effectively exercise physical and social controls, what will be the consequences on the individual? The problem has been stated as the conscious and purposeful control over the development of the physical and social environment while at the same time maintaining a relatively free society.

To maintain a democratic system of government, space must be planned to foster an environment conducive to democratic life styles, systems, and patterns of government and behavior.

Our past population increases have produced collective actions both private and public which tend to diminish the status of individual values. The possibility of future intrusions on individual values gives cause for concern. Some have suggested we should adopt a new Bill of Rights. Others believe an entirely new Constitution is necessary.

As a minimum in strategies for social control over space, we must consider the psychological impact of involuntarily changed life styles and behavior. Schemes using fine-tuned incentives for voluntary individual response must be coupled with selective applications of regulatory and coercive powers of government.

Individual privacy should be a major concern in space planning. Besides the issue of protecting rights, which is important, there is a need to assure conditions which make the exercise of the privilege possible.

Indirect effects of public action to control space must be anticipated and greater effort made to provide equal opportunity and equal treatment.

Notwithstanding the complexity of dealing with larger numbers of people in decision making, there will be an increasing need to involve those individuals who will be directly affected by the public decisions to be made. Short term efficiencies gained at the expense of participatory democracy may in the long run prove very costly.

Property will incur far more social obligations, such as restrictions on use and transfer, than we presently consider acceptable.

Efforts to maintain the integrity of our property system will call for many changes in ownership form; some are well underway.

In summary, the space needs for future man can be met by:

1. Controlling population increases.
2. Improving our understanding of the psychological, sociological, and economic meaning of space and designing preferred distributions of people.
3. Organizing and controlling the use of space to minimize competing demands.
4. Protecting the individual while the policies for 1, 2, and 3 are being implemented.

Population Distribution Issues

ALAN R. BIRD

N O AMERICAN family should have more than two children. That is the new life style many people and even some "experts" have prescribed for us. If Americans want this "duplet" living, the "pill" and changing social attitudes have made it possible. So have liberalized abortion laws.

"Populate or perish." That is the age-old dictum of man and beast. The switch to small families flies in the face of man's own heritage. So there must be some good reasons. There are.

Drugs! Sex! Crime! Poverty! Mental Illness! Moral Decay! How about those for starters?

Teenagers and young adults are "blowing their minds" with drugs. Robberies and shootings of taxi drivers, liquor store clerks, and others who handle cash are as routine as obituaries. So are rapes and killings of stray pedestrians and tourists. Often witnesses just stand by and watch. Otherwise, they run away or lock the door.

This is a familiar portrait of life today that many would paint. It is the portrait that causes others to cry "Will the real America please stand up?"

If we didn't have people we wouldn't have these problems. Let's forego the simplistic solution implied by this statement. There are enough heralds of doom who claim that man is destroying himself already.

Let's assume, instead, that people are here to stay. Then we can admit that piling too many people in too small a space makes problems. These people are the seeds of discontent. Add to this congestion a dose of poverty and you have a seedbed for crime. Add the impersonal services of a mass society, strong feelings about race and private property, and you add enough heat and sweat to germinate that seed. People don't like to be mutilated, folded, or stapled any more than computer cards.

Right now, 74 percent of all Americans live and work most of their time on 2 percent of our land.

Because of such problems as air and water pollution, too much noise, traffic congestion, and crime, strong voices have called for a national policy on population distribution. Equally vocal skeptics question whether more national programs and policies would actually improve upon present settlement patterns. Before we explore other options, let's assume for a minute that present settlement trends will continue.

If the future mirrors the recent past, we can look for further clustering of people around the shoreline of the United States, including both the ocean shores and the shores of the Great Lakes. And we can look for a continued outmigration of rural people, mainly blacks from the Southeast, whites from Southern Appalachia and small towns and open country in the Great Plains.

A few rural areas will build on recent turnarounds of population and gradually expand. Notable are the Ozarks where retirement and outdoor recreation are big, and parts of Colorado that will become another metropolitan corridor around Denver.

If we can't or won't play King Canute and attempt to turn this human tide, the next option is to try to slow it down. That leads to the two-child family—the "duplets." Those advocating such a national family planning program would say that people should only have as many children as they can afford. Couples

*

ALAN R. BIRD is Deputy Director, Economic Development Division, Economic Research Service.

should only have children if they can properly take care of them. By adopting such a policy, proponents might expect to face, say, only 70 million new Americans by the turn of the century instead of 90 or 100 million. Of course, this national family planning would allow exceptions. Otherwise, such a policy in the past would have denied us President Kennedy and Bobby, and many other leading citizens of our heritage.

That is part of the price for reducing the number of poor, relatively untrained members of society. Such a selective policy of population growth would, in effect, be an attempt to improve the "quality" of the population—if it could ever be determined who should set the standards.

In practice, standards of population quality have been set. Immigrants are now admitted to the United States on the basis of their ability to contribute to society. Healthy people with particular skills in short supply are admitted irrespective of country of origin. This policy contrasts with former selection methods on the basis of country-by-country quotas. These quotas were, in turn, established on the basis of historical rates of immigration from these countries.

Interestingly enough, immigrants tend to settle in metropolitan areas. They also comprised 16 percent of the net national population increase through the sixties. In the one year, 1968, over 450,000 immigrants entered the United States—more than enough to populate nine cities of over 50,000 each. In 1967 and 1969, annual immigration was about 360,000—about the size of Newark, Fort Worth, Oakland, or Portland, Oreg.

If we could just assure ourselves that all Americans had adequate incomes, education, training, and job and leisure opportunities, maybe the people themselves would improve their communities and overcome the problems of congestion and urban decay. The importance of adequate education and training for rural people is underlined by the fact that two-thirds of the population growth from the last generation by American women who have recently completed childbearing came from the 27 percent of all women who were rural.

Let's consider some related economic and social questions. None of us wants to pay more for the things we buy. But you and I, along with the butcher, the baker, and the cathode tube maker don't mind reasonable price increases for the things we sell. And these mild increases and not-so-mild increases for land prices and other prices actually help cities and suburbia to improve themselves.

Houses and businesses change hands more readily because "things are looking better." The house owner sells at a "profit" due to appreciation of values and invests this capital gain elsewhere to reduce his income tax burden and because he has to live somewhere. The new buyer "gains" because he can assume an old loan at less than the "going" interest rate. And besides, the house will gain in value to "pay for his rent" in a few years.

Both owners must keep the house in good repair and ready for sale. Servicemen, builders, realtors, bankers, and even the welcome wagon help.

Businesses expect more houses, more people, and more roads. They must expand to "meet competition." And the growing community puts a floor on their losses. The building may have many other uses. It may even be condemned for a freeway and earn a handsome compensation.

Now suppose our new couple decides, "I wouldn't bring kids into this world" or "It's dumb to have more than two kids when we could have a color TV, a stereo, and our own hairdryers instead." Suddenly we find that our soaring executive with the promotion in L. A. must take a loss to sell his three- or five-bedroom split-level in Fairmont Heights. Bigger homes are a glut on the market. And modern new apartments are not to be had at any price. "Man, they're outa this world."

17

Our budding Vice-President of Supercilious Inc. also has trouble trading cars. In a dealer's eyes, his ultra station wagon might as well be a hearse. The "in" things are "Jags" and other intimate forms of transportation with "four on the floor." Detroit and even the steel companies feel the pinch.

Others may raise questions about what kinds of people come from two-child families that have "everything" and who go to school with only other "duplets." The answers are not obvious. However, it's a reasonable guess that this new generation would have some questions of their own, like: Who ever thought suburbia was so great? Why should we live in these run-down cities?

At a 1970 National Biological Conference a geneticist claimed that "human biological evolution would virtually come to a standstill if every woman has only two children.

"New genes are worked into the population rapidly where there are large families," he said, "and it is new genes that make man more adaptable to his changing environment." So these "duplet" families would have a greater need to move to a favorable location—or to improve their own communities.

Such major changes in age structure and life styles could even produce further unexpected changes in settlement patterns. For example, a net emigration. There are those who predict the present trickle of skilled Americans to other countries will grow to a steady stream. Who can say? At least it would be dangerous to ignore such possibilities—especially in the face of the living precedents of the American people themselves.

Let's retreat to the safety of projecting that settlement patterns in the next three decades will be much the same as they are now. And let's assume (some may say "hope") that population increases will be much the same in numbers and by localities. The problems of congestion are still with us. So what?

Those who decry overcrowding would no doubt like to see more decentralizing of settlement. They would probably favor more rapid growth of smaller towns and cities. Let's say that more people settle in smaller towns and cities and not quite so many in larger cities and their suburbs.

Why hasn't this happened anyway? After all, Gallup Polls in 1966 and 1970 reported that most people prefer to live outside cities. Many more than those who live in small towns or on a farm report they would prefer to live in these places.

Many smaller towns and cities have added people and jobs in the 1960's. Percentagewise, these additions have often matched and even exceeded national averages.

To decentralize faster, still more people would need to move to smaller towns. That calls for many more jobs in these towns. Far and away the most of these jobs will be outside agriculture and outside agribusiness. In fact, they will tend to be like the jobs people now have in and near the bigger cities. In fact, these smaller towns will tend to be like the bigger cities as they add more jobs and more people.

So why would more people move and why would we want to help them move? A likely answer, in a word, is "money." Companies and even government bureaucracies could open branch plants or agencies and provide services "closer to the people." Promising employees could be promoted to bigger jobs away from home. Other city boys could fill the vacancies at home.

For all this to happen, new communities that develop around smaller cities would need to be better places to live and work than the new suburbs of big cities. Commuting, schools, health services, freedom from riots, other violence, and smog are some of the draw cards a smaller community might offer. Even if these smaller cities grew more like the larger ones—and became "successful" enough to have their own smog and riot problems—many people could benefit from a better life during this growing period.

Other payoffs may come from de-centralizing. Millions of rural people are beyond convenient commuting distance to a city of even 25,000. And experts tend to agree that a citizen needs ready access to such a city if his family is to have the modern services and facilities that go with the "good life." So this further decentralizing could provide a bonus payoff. The rural and small-town millions would be better read, better cared for, and even better fed.

What about new towns? The prospect of building new communities that really blend the best of town and country is an exciting one. It has particular appeal to those who would like to show what the latest American know-how can produce. Other groups can point to the billions spent on defense and plead for at least an occasional bold flourish on the domestic front. We can't afford to ignore the new town idea. But expert opinion suggests we can't afford to ignore the thousands of small towns already in being either.

From our earliest days, America has had her new towns. Witness, for example, Plymouth, Jamestown, and Washington, D.C. Long before the year 2000, new technology and pathbreaking discoveries could well result in many more. Economic desalinization processes, for example, could result in many new cities ringing our shoreline.

In the near future, the models for America's new towns are the Restons and Columbias—satellite communities within commuting distances of major cities. These towns have evolved largely through the efforts of private companies. America has not seen nearly as much government intervention and direction in fostering new towns as there has been in Europe. Should the government do more to encourage new towns? That question can produce a lively debate—and more questions.

We've explored decentralization possibilities and even found some that look promising. What about the con side? It's not obvious that people in the ghettoes have benefitted. And slower population gains in the suburbs could add to suburban problems—businesses with lower turnover, schools with empty classrooms, vacant houses, and the like. It is possible that a basic problem of cities and adjoining suburbs is underpopulation instead of overpopulation.

Let's explore that question. Mass transit is a commonly suggested answer to traffic congestion and air pollution. To pay, such a system needs many more people living on the same area of land—and perhaps high commuter taxes to help finance smog control and other services as well as encourage economical use of mass transit.

Technicians are already thinking of extending the idea of the Houston Astrodome to enclosing whole communities. In a way, some of our modern skyscrapers already are enclosed communities with homes, offices, shopping, and recreation all in the same building—yes, and even parking. These kinds of breakthroughs are feasible to service high-volume needs. They are even more feasible as average family incomes increase.

So it's within reason to expect still better living but different kinds of living, in large cities, smaller towns, and even open country. Individual citizens and families would have a wider range of choice of where to live and work and how to live.

Ironically enough, all of this might well come about faster if America's population grew more rapidly than it has in the past. Indeed, it may be difficult to achieve otherwise. Better training and higher incomes would help all to contribute to this better life. Even greater immigration of skilled people would help.

The trouble with the world is people. And the joy is, too. Further decentralizing of population in the United States could add to this joy or add to the trouble. T'aint what you do, it's the way that you do it! And if we don't do anything, why talk anyway?

19

Rural Growth— Critical Test for Local Government

JOSEPH C. DOHERTY

DESPITE ALL THE CLAMOR over pollution of the Nation's land, water, and air, not much is heard about what is happening in and around the smaller cities and towns that serve rural America. Yet, many of these nonmetropolitan growth centers and their satellite towns and villages stand today where the big city suburbs were 35 years ago—on the edge of a growth explosion.

Public officials and community leaders in hundreds of smaller cities, towns, and rural counties are working hard to build programs that will encourage development, yet preserve the amenities and attractions of the rural-small town environment.

• In Texas the Alamo Area Council of Governments, based in San Antonio but representative of a five-county urban and rural region, is sponsoring a program that will promote the growth of satellite towns while preserving good agricultural and recreational lands in the area between these towns and the city.

• Near Aspen, Colo., in the heart of the Rockies, a large new recreation complex of apartments, townhouses, and detached single family houses is creating a modern urban setting where there was wilderness a few years ago. The development has split the community. Some like it; others are bitterly opposed.

• Planners and civic leaders running the Georgia Mountains Planning and Development Commission program for 14 rural counties in the northeast part of the State hope to channel expanding industrial growth into concentrated areas, while helping

workers living in the small towns and farming communities find better ways to commute to work.

• In the five-county "upper tier" region of northeastern Pennsylvania, which is farming and recreation country, the rapid expansion of housing projects on farmland without zoning or other land use controls has local officials worrying about future pollution, tax, and service problems.

You can find dozens of similar examples in every State where a wide variety of developments are urbanizing rural America.

The 1970 Census appears to support the conventional view that expansion during the 1960's occurred principally in the urban regions and that rural America continued to decline.

Seven hundred mostly rural counties did show a population decline in the 1960's of 10 percent or more. However, these were concentrated in particular areas—the Great Plains, Southern Appalachian coal fields, the Mississippi Delta, south central Alabama—which lacked dynamic growth centers or where special developments, such as the expansion of a recreation industry or government installation, didn't occur. But, if you dig deeper, 1970 Census figures reveal some highly interesting and opposite trends:

—The proportion of people living outside SMSA's (standard metropolitan statistical areas) did *not* decline significantly. It remains about 30 percent of the total, with the remainder being divided between the large cities and their suburbs. However, only 18 percent of people in rural areas were classified as farm dwellers in 1970, compared with 29 percent in 1960.

—Small urban centers serving rural America, i.e., towns of 25,000 to 50,000 outside the SMSA's, were among the fastest growing places in the Nation during the decade.

*

JOSEPH C. DOHERTY is Assistant for District Planning Coordination in the Office of the Administrator, Farmers Home Administration.

—On a percentage basis, private nonfarm employment rose faster in rural counties than in metropolitan areas. New plants or the expansion of existing ones in rural America accounted for about 20 percent of the national gain in manufacturing employment during the decade of the 1960's. This was an impressive record since rural areas started with a comparatively small industrial base at the start of the decade.

These figures point to the continuing urbanization of large parts of rural America. And the trend is just getting of Americans for places to go and things to do.

• Finally, the attitude of people about where and how they want to live and to raise a family may be changing. The desirability of life in big city regions begins to pale as the conveniences and pleasures of the city disappear and the inconveniences and dangers grow.

The growth centers of nonmetropolitan America, in particular, appear to stand on the threshold of a major expansion. These are the smaller cities in the 10,000–50,000 population range

Two views of zoning.

underway. Inevitably the next 30 years will bring an explosion of urban-type growth in areas that now consist of farm trading towns, placid villages, and the fields and woodlots of farmers.

All the basic factors—technical, commercial, and psychological—are falling into place:

• New transportation and communication facilities and the growth of major markets in formerly agricultural areas make decentralization of industry not only practical but highly desirable.

• The need for space, water, raw materials, and a potentially productive labor supply will turn more and more manufacturers to the small cities and rural towns and their environs.

• New recreational facilities will be built and old ones expanded in rural areas to meet the insatiable demand serving a broad small town–farming region.

The future holds promise of a better life for people living in expanding rural areas. The rest of the nation will benefit too as resources and people flow back into less crowded areas.

Yet the prospect has its darker side. Explosive rural development can do serious and irreversible damage to large parts of the American countryside. Unplanned and uncontrolled growth will produce the same environmental blight and monotonous sprawl in the urbanizing countryside during the next 30 years that has scarred the landscape of the Nation's larger urban regions during the past three decades.

The issue is critical. Small town and countryside America is painfully unprepared to cope with the coming deluge. Both county and municipal

Skiers using recreational facilities. Recreation enterprises can be a major source of land pollution if they are uncontrolled and unplanned.

government is weak, understaffed, underfinanced.

The tools public officials elsewhere have available to gain some measure of control over land use are unavailable or unused. Zoning, subdivision controls, building codes, the use of eminent domain, and a real estate tax

policy attuned to needs of the total community are highly controversial in many small towns and rural counties.

Even where county and municipal officials understand the need to make use of these tools, have the authority from the State, and are supported by a majority of the public, they may not

22

have sufficient personnel with enough training and skill to do the job.

A root cause of the problem is, of course, the small population base that still characterizes the overwhelming majority of rural jurisdictions. A total of 1,673 counties have a population of less than 20,000. Of the nearly 900 counties with 10,000 or less people, 703 do not have a town of 2,500 or more within their borders.

Problems of public financing and administration arising from such a small population base are compounded by the huge number of general purpose governments and special district authorities whose actions and programs directly affect land use and physical development.

Besides the 3,140 county governments, there are some 18,000 incorporated municipal governments, 17,000 townships, 25,000 school districts, and 18,000 other special districts. An estimated 50,000 unincorporated towns also must be counted in. Half or more of all these units are outside standard metropolitan statistical areas.

Local governments administer public and special services. They acquire land. They apply land use controls and related ordinances. They raise revenue. They direct capital investments. They are the critical factor in determining the environment in which Americans live out their lives.

Where there is little coordination among local governments within an area, as happens all too often, the policies they pursue and the actions they take may be contradictory, wasteful, and not in the interest of the majority.

This is especially debilitating in nonmetropolitan areas, where the resource and revenue base is small and already hard-pressed public agencies simply cannot afford the additional cost of overlapping and contradictory policies or projects.

One county may adopt enlightened land use control measures while the adjoining county doesn't even accept the idea of a simple zoning ordinance. Too bad for the progressive county when open pit trash dumps or sprawling honky tonks spread along its border.

A town is willing to extend its sewage system to the growing unincorporated area nearby if the latter agrees to annexation. People in the

NUMBER OF LOCAL GOVERNMENTS BY TYPE AND METROPOLITAN STATUS

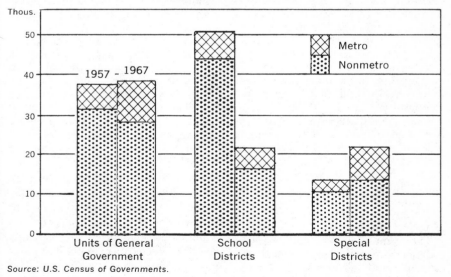

Source: U.S. Census of Governments.

Highway sprawl in an urbanizing rural area.

area turn it down. They create their own sewer district instead, at great expense.

A rural growth center obtains land for industrial expansion in the center of a nearby commercial farming area. More suitable land was available, but no one in the county ever considered establishing agricultural and industrial zones that would have channeled industrial development to the suitable areas while preserving prime agricultural land.

Those acquainted with local government operations can recall dozens of similar cases.

Land pollution occurs when the emerging small city and the countryside are degraded by a jumble of ill-designed buildings, unsuitable uses, sprawling and poorly constructed development, and ill-planned industrial or other installations that may be not only eyesores but also positive hazards to the health and well-being of the community.

If land pollution in rural-small town America is to be controlled, public officials and community leaders in these areas must be willing to use the fundamental tools available to shape and influence growth in the interest of a more attractive and humane rural environment. This is just another way of saying "in the public interest."

There must first of all be close collaboration among general local governments and soil and water conservation districts. The latter are among

the few agencies consistently working to preserve and protect rural environmental values. The districts, in turn, and cooperating government agencies, such as the Soil Conservation Service, need to provide greatly increased technical help to local officials in planning community land use control programs.

Many land-grant universities recently have established "community resource development" (CRD) extension programs to assist elected officials and other leaders in smaller cities, towns, and communities to solve governmental problems, including those of land use planning and control. Where available, the CRD extension agents, working with county extension staffs, can be an invaluable resource for hard-pressed local officials.

However, no outside technical assistance or counseling, regardless of how skilled or knowledgeable, can substitute for a determined effort by local elected officials. These officials must be willing to develop and support an effective and continuing program of comprehensive planning, to follow up with intelligent use of zoning and other land use controls and measures that can guide and influence development, and to make cooperative arrangements with other jurisdictions that will solve environmental problems which cross boundaries.

To be effective, a community's planning program must be conducted as an integral part of local government administration and be supported and implemented by governmental action.

State legislatures recognize the fact that planning is a local government responsibility by conferring planning powers on subjurisdictions.

State laws that authorize planning also describe the functions and purpose and the manner of setting up the programs authorized. Laws differ among the States. Local authorities must base their planning operations on what the statutes of their State allow.

Nevertheless, the spirit in which the authorized planning programs are conducted is just as important as the letter of the law: Is the planning program of the small city or town or rural county carried out simply as a matter of form and to meet certain State and Federal requirements? Or is it an organic part of the administration of public business, influencing policy decisions of public officials and the operation of local government? The answer makes all the difference.

Planning as a local government function has gone through something of a reawakening in recent years, after a period of dormancy during and immediately following World War II. States refurbished older planning legislation and adopted new statutes, with increasing emphasis on cooperative planning among jurisdictions.

The urban planning assistance program of the Federal Government established by Section 701 of the Housing Act of 1954 greatly accelerated the trend by offering financial help to States and localities for planning. (By fiscal year 1970 the amount of money appropriated for this assistance totaled $50 million.)

Planning requirements connected with the large number of Federal grant and loan programs created in recent years also stimulated local planning.

Unfortunately, the flurry of activity has not always been productive of real benefits, particularly in the smaller counties and rural towns and cities. The Department of Housing and Urban Development reported in 1969, on the basis of four studies:

"Planning supported by the '701' program has been only moderately effective as a tool for guiding and implementing public policies in small communities.

"The comprehensive plans have become stereotyped and are often not designed to deal with the important problems of the community. They are often too rigid and long range to serve current or developing needs of the community or to be related to the community's planning and fiscal capabilities.

"Too much emphasis has been placed on the production of planning documents and not enough on the process of planning."

If planning programs in smaller communities have had only limited success, follow up actions by local government to put plans into effect have run an even rougher course. In rural counties, especially, basic measures for carrying out land use plans—such as subdivision regulations, sanitary codes, building codes and zoning ordinances—often generate intense opposition.

In too many communities, the lesson has not yet been learned that an ounce of zoning today will prevent a pound of fiscal, administrative, and legal headaches tomorrow. The table on p. 26, from data prepared for the National Commission on Urban Problems, is an indication of how smaller rural counties and towns are lagging.

Particularly serious is the fact that rural counties and smaller townships lag so far behind in making use of basic land use control techniques. For it is in the open country areas of rural counties that many of the battles to preserve a humane environment will be waged in the 1970's. Although 80 percent of counties in the United States are authorized to adopt zoning ordinances, it appears that only about 20 percent of rural counties had done so as of 1968.

A zoning ordinance establishes zoning districts, and sets forth the uses

Group	Number of governments	Planning board	Zoning ordinance	Subdivision regulation	Building code	Housing code
Counties_____	2,645	48	19	24	10	5
Cities[1]_____	1,352	92	91	82	74	54
Towns[2]_____	3,675	57	53	31	51	28
New England-type townships						
4,999+ population____	333	79	74	73	53	16
1,000 to 4,999 population____	2,399	38	20	19	15	8

[1] 5,000 to 49,999 population
[2] 1,000 to 4,999 population

Source: National Commission on Urban Problems, Washington, D. C. Research Report No. 6, 1968

permitted in each. Most county ordinances establish agricultural, residential, business and industrial zones, although rapidly urbanizing communities may need additional types of zones.

Zoning protects residential areas, preserves prime agricultural land for its best use, diverts industrial development to those concentrated areas where services can be provided and the nuisance factor kept to a minimum, and sets aside recreation facilities and open spaces for public and private use. A community, in short, uses zoning to maintain itself as a viable, convenient and attractive place to live, work, and do business.

The zoning ordinance is no more effective than its enforcement and administration. Machinery for adjusting the codes to keep them flexible and responsive to changes in conditions facing the community and an appeals procedure must be established. These and other requirements are generally set forth in the State enabling act permitting jurisdictions to adopt and enforce zoning ordinances.

Of critical importance is the continuing effort by officials to relate the zoning program to other key measures for controlling land use in the public interest: to subdivision regulations, building codes, a capital improvements program, sanitary codes, and the use of condemnation powers. Inter-

relations between zoning programs and objectives and taxing policies followed by the community are particularly critical.

Zoning, of course, directly affects one of the most cherished individual rights we have, the property right, and code adoption and enforcement are neither administratively simple nor readily acceptable to often important sectors of the public.

But there is simply no practical alternative in our free society to the difficult and controversial process of zoning administration as a way for reconciling the long-term interests of the community and the immediate rights of the individual to use his property as he sees fit.

In undertaking an effective planning and zoning effort, the major operational problem facing rural counties and the smaller cities and towns is a lack of resources to do the job.

A recent development of great importance to smaller rural counties and municipalities, therefore, is the establishment by States of multicounty agencies to assist these communities with planning, zoning, and other governmental functions. These agencies may also have the job of preparing regional plans in those fields, such as transportation, public facilities, and pollution control, that cross county and city boundaries.

By June of 1970, 15 States had in

operation or were organizing officially designated regional agencies. In approximately 20 additional States, regional program areas were designated, although agencies had not yet been set up for most of them.

Recent Federal policies are accelerating the move to intercounty cooperation. The Demonstration Cities and Metropolitan Development Act of 1966 and the Intergovernmental Cooperation Act of 1968 encouraged establishment of a network of regional review agencies to help coordinate capital improvement projects receiving Federal aid in an area.

The Housing and Urban Development Act of 1968 called for improved local planning programs on an areawide basis and authorized the Secretaries of HUD and of Agriculture to support planning in "nonmetropolitan districts" that cut across rural county and town boundaries.

Various functional planning programs assisted by Federal grants, such as HUD regulations for water and sewer facilities and open space land program planning issued in July 1970, also call for an areawide approach that crosses county and city boundaries. Wherever possible, HUD is using the State-designated multicounty planning agencies for this purpose.

Several Federal programs, such as those of the Economic Development Administration and the Soil Conservation Service (in the case of Resource Conservation and Development project areas), also require a local board or agency that represents a number of local jurisdictions.

Intercounty regional agencies being established by the States are generally operated by a board consisting of a majority of local elected officials in the area. The staff may be made up of specialists in economic development

Subdivision development on formerly agricultural land.

planning, and public administration. They are financed through State and local funds and also various planning assistance programs of the Federal Government, such as the HUD 701 program referred to before.

Enabling statutes authorizing regional programs generally provide for voluntary association. Local governments may "opt out" any time they desire.

Once a regional agency program goes into operation, few member governments take this option. It soon becomes clear to local elected officials that the regional agency can relieve them of many problems.

Depending on the resources available, a regional agency may perform all or some of the following for member governments:

—Prepare a comprehensive plan.

—Draw up a model zoning ordinance.

—Advise on fiscal administration.

—Assist in setting up a joint purchasing program or other cooperative administrative arrangement among governments.

—Organize special projects, such as an areawide solid waste disposal or air pollution control program.

—Perform review functions required for various Federally assisted projects.

—Prepare regional development plans covering many different jurisdictions.

The foregoing is by no means a complete list.

As rural America urbanizes, the regional agency can give officials of the smaller cities, towns, and counties the tools they need but now do not have to grapple with the problems— and take advantage of the opportunities—that urbanization brings.

Regional agencies give recognition to the still little known fact that in rural America, an "extended community" made up of a small city, rural towns, and open country farming communities is the real administrative, economic development, and social unit.

Local government officials and citizen leaders in rural America are now on the firing line in a battle to save a big part of the Nation's environment. Standing alone, the institutions they represent most certainly will be rolled under by the massive changes coming. Standing together in a regional grouping, they at least have a fighting chance to preserve their communities while promoting sound development. They may thus be able to teach the big cities that a degraded environment isn't necessarily the price we have to pay for progress.

Town—Country Planning

CHARLES E. KELLOGG

THOUGHTFUL PEOPLE have a new concern about their future environment in our country. Yet in thinking about the physical and biological environment we must also be mindful of our other goals and values, not the least of which are economic opportunities, jobs, and cultural environment.

For too long we have thought of our rural environment as separate from the urban environment. The well-being of rural people and that of urban people are inevitably tied together; they share many of the same environmental, cultural, and economic opportunities and problems. Thus we must think and work together for sustained and efficient use of our resources for all people.

Most of our large cities are overcrowded. Most of them lack living

*

CHARLES E. KELLOGG retired in 1971 as Deputy Administrator for Soil Survey, Soil Conservation Service.

space for growing children, especially places for them to play near their homes. Problems (and costs) of crime and traffic have increased, especially as buildings were made higher.

Since all heavy transport for many years was by boat, the old cities were located near oceans or navigable streams and lakes. The levels of water fluctuated greatly during the glacial periods of the past 3 million years.

When ice piled up on the land, the oceans were low. As the ice melted, violent streams rushed to the sea and the oceans rose. In such areas are soil of many combinations of sand, silt, gravel, clay, and muck within short distances. They vary widely in their suitability for structures. Yet people built their homes, factories, and highways there.

The industrial revolution began with steam power. Steam could not be transported far, nor could the workers. So we had the beginning of the huddling of factories and workers. Homes had little open space around them and few useful nearby playgrounds and nature study areas.

Such huddling is no longer needed. We now have excellent highways, electric lines, telephone cables, radio and television stations, and the like. Perhaps we cannot get rid of all the crowding inherited from the past, but certainly we should not add to it. Yet some new suburbs still have few provisions for children.

The industrial revolution also changed agriculture. In the early days farmers produced on the farm most of their tools and fertilizers. They processed most of what they grew on their farms. In colonial times the words "farming" and "agriculture" had about the same meaning.

Today these words have quite different meanings. Agriculture is a very large economic enterprise in the United States. Probably only about 15 to 20 percent of the people employed full time in agriculture live and work on farms.

Fertilizers and machines of all kinds have resulted in the substitution of onfarm labor by city labor. For fuel and power farmers rely largely on oil and electric companies. Modern agriculture has large industrial sectors for manufacturing tools and chemicals and for processing farm products. Other service sectors of agriculture include finance, marketing, research, education, and so on.

At the beginning of World War I most people in the United States lived in the country. At the end of it most people lived in the cities. As city labor took over jobs formerly done on farms, young rural people migrated to the cities for jobs.

Actually there is no need to maintain excessive concentrations of people in cities, let alone add to them. The people of the United States have abundant soils for all their foreseeable uses. These include soils for farming, forestry, recreation, houses, factories, highways, and airports.

Every commercial farmer needs an efficient town nearby. He needs the services of mechanics, electricians, and all the rest. He must be able to market his products and to buy what he needs for his farm and home. These services amount to a great deal in any farming area. In addition to farming, many rural areas have resources for forestry, mining, and other economic activities that require services from a town.

Also, a thriving town needs a good resource base within its trade area. These resources should be efficiently used to have good incomes within the trade areas—money to spend—and to have good environments. For example, soil erosion leads to sedimentation. Sediment or other pollutants in the air or streams affect the environment and the economy of both country and city people.

It seems to many that we need in the United States perhaps 400 or more new towns and cities—say of about 25,000 to 250,000 population and with space to grow—in addition to the rural people living in the trade area. Some existing sites of small towns and villages may be suitable provided they have, or will have, excellent transport with

Above, crowded homes in one of old eastern cities. Below, room to live and play in a new town. Right, fifth graders use nature study area in Stow, Mass.

Ozone damage, called weather fleck, on tobacco plant. Air pollutants cause considerable plant damage each year.

interstate highways, railways, and an airport.

Such cities should be planned to have adequate open space for both parks and playgrounds, and for later expansion. All children should have the advantages of playgrounds and nature study areas near their homes. Areas for recreation outside the city are useful but they have nothing like the importance of interesting places for young people between the time school is out and bedtime. Eager youngsters will find something to do. Lacking opportunities for normal play, they make trouble.

The open space left in a new town should exceed that needed for recreation and playgrounds, in order to provide for changes within the city. In town and town-and-country planning, full use should be made of estimated trends in population, the economy, and everything else that can be predicted. Yet experience tells us that a first principle of planning is

that not all changes can be predicted. None of us knows what will be invented in the next generation.

Unless some land suitable for building is left open, the hands of all future planning boards are tied. To get something new, they must first destroy what has been built.

A good soil survey is an essential part of the base for deciding what to put where. A soil survey shows which soils are suitable for various crops, trees, and grasses. It shows which soils have few, moderate, or severe limitations for houses and other structures. It shows the limits of the flood plains.

Soil surveys started in the United States in 1899 in cooperation with the experiment stations of the land-grant universities. Now other Federal, State, and local agencies also cooperate in the entire effort, called the National Cooperative Soil Survey.

In the beginning the main emphasis was to help farmers select uses and management systems suitable for the kinds of soil on their farms and to select kinds of soil for specific crops. Soil surveys serve as the base for conservation assistance to landowners in the work of the Soil Conservation Service and the conservation work of many other public and private agencies.

With continued research and use, soil surveys were greatly improved. In the late 1920's it was found they could be equally useful for planning highway location and design. Later use of soil surveys for planning houses and other structures has greatly accelerated since 1950.

Some kinds of soil cannot support normal houses. One could put up a $10,000,000 building almost anywhere if he can afford a million or two for the foundation. Certainly, no one can afford such a foundation for a $30,000 to $60,000 house.

Some soils are occasionally flooded or seasonally wet. Although poor for housing, these may be excellent for certain kinds of recreation during most of the year. Yet if such a soil is mistakenly used for housing, it will be extremely costly to restore the land to its natural shape and vegetation after the houses fall.

A kind of soil in its natural landscape is an "ecosystem," as that term is used in recent writing on ecology and environment. Each kind of soil has a unique set of characteristics resulting from a unique combination of the five factors that produce it. These are the active factors of (1) climate and (2) the combination of living creatures—plants, animals, and microorganisms—acting on (3) the parent material as (4) conditioned by relief (slope and drainage of the landscape) and (5) the age of the landform.

Soils are natural objects. Land is a place within which production takes place. The definition of land includes the concept of "soil" and other factors as well, such as size of the area, its relationship to other kinds of land, and its distance from markets and other community and cultural services. Land is real estate. Land units of equal size and with similar soils could have enormously different potentials and values because of these other characteristics of land.

A viable town needs a planned area for industries related to the local resources, including those from farming. A good farming area produces many resources for industry. Increasingly livestock is being processed locally, not in a distant city. Nor is it done on farms much any more. Near some towns, sites must be found for manufacturing wood pulp or paper. Sites are needed for the manufacture of bricks, cement blocks, or other building materials.

For such a town to serve its own needs and those of a normal trade area, marketers, processors of farm and forest products, suppliers of chemicals and machines, department stores, and many other businesses are needed. So are hospitals, schools, at least one college, libraries, theaters, and other cultural institutions. A dependable water supply must be developed.

In other words, with the essential

Soil survey underway in Carrboro, N. C. Soils information is being recorded on an aerial photo.

32

transport and many other services required by efficient farming in the area, a considerable infrastructure will be developed. Obviously, such an infrastructure can also serve other industries requiring skilled workers but little heavy transport for great distances.

Each of the businesses, including farms, should have good outputs for the investments and operating costs. Further, as a producing factory, farm, or other business is successful, it employs people. People spend money, and this employs more people.

Thus the income from a producing enterprïse may be increased several times within the trade area. This is known as the multiplier effect, as suggested by Lord Keynes. In planning new businesses, such multiplier effects are important and should be evaluated. They can be very large.

To have success in any trade area, there must be employment at reasonably good wages. The town-and-country plan should account for all the local unemployed or underemployed people who are able to take jobs. It also should attract many young people from the old cities who are looking for good opportunities and pleasant places to live.

Our aim should be to have these new cities as culturally attractive as the old ones and with good income prospects for a wide range of skills. A rural city should also have all these attributes of a good environment and open space that make for pleasant living. This means good opportunities for youth, better health, and much lower crime rates.

Town-and-country planning must be done mainly within the authorities of States and counties. People with many different skills are needed. Soil scientists have an important role, but so do geologists, hydrologists, geographers, economists, architects, businessmen, lawyers, educators, and many others.

We want to see the kind of town where many sorts of people should like to live. For those interested in art and literature, this means libraries and other cultural facilities. For businessmen to see a future for themselves it means a brokerage office with a ticker tape. And so we might go through a long list.

Some present rural areas are as lacking in cultural facilities as crowded parts of big cities are lacking in clean air and space. We want trade areas where all children and young people can enjoy living and learning. All sorts of cultural clubs are possible. Young people need many choices.

Growing With Nature

ROBERT H. TWISS and
LOUISE PARKER

IN THE MARIN COUNTY HILLS just 25 miles north of San Francisco, Calif., the small town of Nicasio looks much like it did a century ago ... a quiet community of some 500 people, surrounded by rolling grass-covered hills and wooded canyons.

To local residents, Nicasio represents a special way of life. Some families have lived in the valley for several generations, gaining their living mainly from dairying. Others, although relative newcomers, also cherish its rural village character.

It probably won't be that way forever. Like many other parts of scenic rural America, Nicasio is on the threshold of more intensive use and development. Highways proposed to provide access to Point Reyes National Seashore would merge at Nicasio, putting the valley within easy commuting distance of San Francisco. Even without the highways, the valley is close enough to other major population centers that growth is likely.

If land speculation and development proceed in typical fashion, the almost certain result is that Nicasio will be covered with roads, small lots and houses, and the valley's key scenic areas and its natural vegetation destroyed.

Landowners face a difficult dilemma. On the one hand, they want to keep the beauty of the landscape and the rural character of the town. But it is virtually impossible for dairying and ranching to compete in today's urban land market. Land values go up. Taxes go up. Owners have to do something, and the usual answer is sell . . . in small parcels without regard for preserving environmental and social values.

But for Nicasio, there may be a better way out. In 1962, landowners faced up to the problem and took the first positive steps to protect the countryside from uncontrolled growth. They organized the Nicasio Landowners Association with the specific purpose of working to preserve the natural beauty of the valley and promote well-planned development.

In 1967, they went to the Marin County Planning Department and asked that a master plan be drawn up for the valley. County planners Paul Zucker and Al Solnit felt that saving Nicasio would be a real challenge, but that something more than the typical master plan would be needed.

In an unusual first step, the County Planning Department sought help from the Department of Landscape Architecture at the University of California

*

ROBERT H. TWISS is Associate Professor of Environmental Planning, Department of Landscape Architecture, College of Environmental Design, University of California, Berkeley.

LOUISE PARKER is an Information Specialist, U.S. Forest Service, Pacific Southwest Forest and Range Experiment Station, Berkeley.

fornia and from the U.S. Forest Service's Pacific Southwest Forest and Range Experiment Station. They put together a study team, including landscape architects, an engineering geologist, and a research forester to conduct a complete analysis of the Nicasio landscape.

The result was two years of study and a 50-page report, "Nicasio: Hidden Valley in Transition." This study was financed principally by the Forest Service, U.S. Department of Agriculture, by a grant from the America the Beautiful Fund, and the County Planning Department's contributed services. Many others, including the Soil Conservation Service, cooperated and contributed their time and effort.

The study is based on the premise that development should proceed with respect for the existing character of the landscape and the natural ecological patterns—a rather new approach to land use planning. Researchers believe they have developed an approach which will allow Nicasio to grow, not in rampant disregard for the land, but in harmony with nature.

Essentially the study is a "landscape analysis" with much emphasis on the area's scenic values. But the research group also studied the archaeology and cultural history of the valley, its topographic patterns, geology and soil, vegetation, wildlife, climate . . . everything that would affect, or be affected by, land use.

As a first step, team members walked and drove over much of the valley's 36 square miles. Landscape features were noted and "seen area" maps drawn up. These special maps pinpoint areas visible from a given set of viewpoints, and will help planners with the location and design of highways, high-rise buildings, or other prominent features which may some day be part of the landscape.

"Nicasio is a kind of pioneering effort," according to County Planner Al Solnit. "We couldn't look to the next valley over for solutions."

Similar studies have been undertaken by the University of California for its Santa Cruz campus, by landscape planner Ian McHarg in Pennsylvania, and in a few other areas of the country. Yet such a detailed study has never been attempted before as a part of county master planning on such a large scale in an area having many landowners.

But perhaps the most significant thing about Nicasio is that for the very first time in the Western United States, a landscape analysis has been prepared for an area before development begins. Credit must go to the landowners for their foresight, and for their concern with the land and the quality of their own environment.

It is one thing to promote the preservation of open space and parks in forest or mountain regions far from home; it is altogether another to submit voluntarily to the self-discipline of community planning in your own backyard.

For communities that want to follow a similar approach, the Nicasio study is a practical guide through the various steps of environmental planning. These include inventorying the natural environment, interpreting visual and esthetic characteristics, anticipating the impact of land development and the competition for limited natural environments, and developing suitable conservation programs.

The Nicasio study points up the potential problems and suggests the consequences of various planning and development activities.

The study found that the visual

EXAMPLES OF SITE COMPETITION

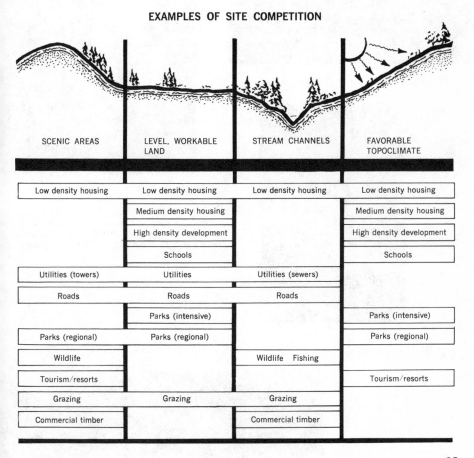

SCENIC AREAS	LEVEL, WORKABLE LAND	STREAM CHANNELS	FAVORABLE TOPOCLIMATE
Low density housing	Low density housing	Low density housing	Low density housing
	Medium density housing		Medium density housing
	High density development		High density development
	Schools		Schools
Utilities (towers)	Utilities	Utilities (sewers)	
Roads	Roads	Roads	
	Parks (intensive)		Parks (intensive)
Parks (regional)	Parks (regional)		Parks (regional)
Wildlife		Wildlife Fishing	
Tourism/resorts			Tourism/resorts
Grazing	Grazing	Grazing	
Commercial timber		Commercial timber	

Nicasio's beauty depends on its oak-studded grassy hills, redwood forest, wooded streambanks, and wind-sculpted trees. Residents have acted to preserve valley's distinctive qualities during anticipated development.

quality of Nicasio valley is due not to a few unique scenic attractions like mountain peaks, waterfalls, or rugged cliffs. Rather, it comes from the total effect of the natural environment—the topography, the central Nicasio square, the rich and varied plant life, and the charm of farm houses in a rural setting.

The golden expanse of summer grasslands, the deep shade of the redwood groves, the tangle of streamside trees and vines, and the wind-sculpted bay trees—all contribute to the "early California" character of Nicasio.

Nicasio's grasslands are especially important and care must be taken to preserve them. If grazing and fire are curtailed, the natural plant succession is for the low grasses to be replaced by dense shrubs and low trees. Moderate grazing, burning, or mowing will be required to maintain the grassland.

The valley has a varied geographic base, but much of the area is subject to extreme erosion or landslide hazard. Maps prepared especially for the study indicate where buildings can be located so as to avoid existing landslides and particularly earthquake-sensitive rock and soil formations. The town is just five miles east of one of the world's most active earthquake faults, the San Andreas. Landslides and uneven settling can be expected if a major quake occurs.

Thirteen soil types were identified, mapped, and classed according to their ability to hold up under various kinds of use.

Land managers and developers can consult the agricultural land capability report prepared by the Soil Conservation Service of USDA, working through the local Marin County Soil Conservation District. The report rates soils primarily on their potential for agriculture, but observations are also made about their suitability for other uses such as for septic tank fields, grading, landscaping, or for tree planting or forestation.

Nicasio reservoir is a central feature in the landscape, and serves as an alternate source of water for the Marin Municipal Water District. It is also vulnerable to siltation, pollution, and other abuses which might arise from development in the watershed.

The valley is noted for a moderate climate, but the report tempers this conclusion with a certain caution, pointing out that there is a rather persistent temperature inversion which would trap and hold air pollutants in the valley. Fog is a frequent visitor during the summer and should be considered in locating homes, schools, parks, or playgrounds.

Black-tailed deer are common and benefit from the natural conditions that encourage grass and shrubby vegetation. Many other forms of wildlife, including birds, fish, and small mammals, are abundant and depend upon native plant cover for survival.

Indian mounds—the remnant of old campgrounds of the Coastal Mi-Wok Indians who once frequented the valley—were located. Along with other features of the area's natural and cultural history, they can be included in an open space and park system.

Land trusts or other property agreements may be desirable so that owners can pool their holdings. In that way, owners could share the profits of development as well as the cost of preserving land quality.

"When development occurs . . . does Nicasio have to become a future addition to Noplace, U.S.A.?" the report asks. The future of Nicasio depends now on how well the study's recommendations are carried out, and whether or not landowners can overcome the usual economic pressures that influence land development. Landowners, and others who have been involved in this study, believe they have a good chance of preventing haphazard growth.

Raymond H. Shone, an attorney and president of the Landowners Association, believes that cooperation has been a strong factor in success of the effort so far.

"One thing I've always been impressed with is the sort of open feeling among the landowners . . . a feeling that all of us, regardless of whether we own small or large amounts of land, can pull together. We all have a stake in the future of Nicasio," Shone says.

For Nicasio, planning is just beginning. Following the environmental analysis, a general planning study was to be conducted during the fall and winter of 1970–71, and finally a master plan was to be drawn up. Landowners have organized a committee to work

The forces of growth which are propelling us headlong into the 21st century will undoubtedly bring increased mechanization, noise, hurry, and crowding—all of which tend to diminish the quality of human life.

We need open space. We need forest and wildlife at the back door. We need streams and green things. We need a sense of country . . . a land to belong to. And we need this as much in urban areas, where 70 percent of

The report on the study asks: "When development occurs. . .does Nicasio have to become a future addition to Noplace, U.S.A.?"

with Marin County and the University of California in the continued planning effort and to solve mutual local problems as they arise.

Nicasio is not alone. For other rural areas all around the country, it may already be too late to prevent the haphazard advance of suburbia . . . or it may be a good time to begin planning for the future.

There is probably no question that we can feed and house up to 100 million more Americans by the turn of the century.

But what kind of existence will we have? Will our living environment be as good as it is now? Or will the thousands of small, rural communities at the edge of major metropolitan centers be gobbled up in unplanned city and suburb?

the population lives, as we do in the country.

Concrete, asphalt, and highrise buildings indiscriminately covering the land will not give us that.

It is essential to anticipate the consequences of development and to use specialists in the natural and social sciences to help determine the impacts on the land and its resources. Residential development creates a particularly big impact on the land and is a major consideration in our new National Environmental Policy.

Studies, like that undertaken for Nicasio Valley, can help point the way toward a 21st century that will not only provide housing, food, and fiber for more people, but will also give us an environment with which we can live in harmony.

Rural Towns, Cores for New Communities

LOUIS D. MALOTKY and
DONALD E. RUNYON

OVER ONE CENTURY AGO the Homestead Act was landmark legislation designed to develop the land resources of this country.

The attraction was free land, and results were twofold. Land resources were developed, and our population dispersed throughout the West. Settlers responded to the opportunity to find new homes and jobs.

A farm-dominated economy resulted. But things have changed. Today we have an industrialized nation with only 5 percent of our population engaged in farming. The homestead is not what it used to be. It is a larger and far more complex operation. As farm size and technology grew, people migrated from the small farms to the cities in search of employment opportunities.

This migration of small-farm owners, tenants, and farmworkers began just after World War I. Since 1920, 40 million people have migrated from rural areas. This exodus remained at a steady 5 percent through the 1960's and has resulted in the decline and weakening of many rural communities.

Another factor contributed to small town ills. Good roads made shopping in larger towns easier and cheaper, with wider selections. Main Street merchants suffered, shops closed, people moved away, trade dwindled, and tax receipts dropped, adversely affecting local services and facilities.

With almost a third of the people, rural America has half of the Nation's poverty, half of its poor housing, half of its old age dependents, and half of those receiving child dependent care. Meanwhile, many of the rural millions crowding into cities are not prepared for urban life or urban jobs.

If we are to provide viable alternatives to these ills, and at the same time find living space by the year 2000 for perhaps 100 million more people, we must develop job opportunities, community services, and housing outside today's big cities and across the land.

To do this we need to consider three kinds of rural communities:

• The new satellite community, near and oriented to a larger city, based upon the premise of providing alternatives to innercity or suburban living and depending on a mix of local and city jobs for an economic base.

• Rural towns within convenient commuting distance of city jobs that can become cores for new communities, primarily residential in nature. The economic base is largely the paychecks the new residents bring to the town.

• And the rural town removed from reasonable commuting distance of a metropolitan center, but steered toward becoming a growth center by utilizing underemployed populations and undeveloped resources.

These communities may grow from the core of an existing town or be planned and built to specifications. Reston, Va., and Columbia, Md., are examples of "planned" satellite towns. Lenoir, N.C., is an existing rural town which has enjoyed an unprecedented growth due to planned community development.

Whether we're talking about homes, jobs and opportunities in existing rural towns, or in projected new satellite communities, we must start from the blueprint stage in almost every case. This is wiser after all, because trial

*

LOUIS D. MALOTKY is Deputy Assistant Administrator, Rural Housing, Farmers Home Administration.

DONALD E. RUNYON is Chief of Current Information in the Rural Electrification Administration.

New industry and the development of natural resources have created hundreds of service jobs in Kentucky near Mammoth Cave National Park. This waitress is one of 64 employees in one restaurant.

and error has proved there is no blanket plan which will fit all areas. Each community must consider its own potentials.

While no one plan will fit every community, there are various ways to rebuild a rural area, all of them proved successful in widely varied rural regions of the Nation.

Towns have become "growth centers" for many reasons. The growth center idea is based on the multiplier effect which means that establishment of a business, industry, or commercial recreational facility in a rural community multiplies growth in many directions.

Allied businesses and services are drawn in by the initial enterprise. The local economy expands, improving the tax base, and setting off more community and industrial development. Thus, through the multiplier effect, total area jobs and additional wages will exceed those directly connected with the actual original project.

Where a growth center has really caught on, and has healthy expansion, rural communities within a 40-mile radius may well profit by becoming satellites to the growth centers.

With good highways, people no longer need live in the town or city where they work. Satellite communities may be built around recreational facilities, like a lake or river, around a subdivision of good homes in open areas, near parks and schools, or around an attractive shopping center or mall.

Agri-industry and new businesses can be based in rural small towns because of improved highway, bus, air and water transportation, modern communications, and plenty of electric power.

Combined with progress on interstate highways, improvements in processing and marketing techniques help make once remote and isolated rural towns possible growth centers. The same highway system which can disable the small town is helping to make possible the rebuilding of rural America.

New communities, whether they are

satellite developments or rural towns that become the core for the new community, may be profitably planned around many resources. These might include: the resort and recreation industry, small private colleges, farm service or marketing cooperatives, commercial laboratories, data processing centers, and business consulting services. Increased hiring may result from dispersal of Federal installations in coming years.

Industry expansion has and will contribute to the creation of more core communities.

For instance, expansion within the Great Lakes Industrial Belt, and in parts of the Southeast, have opened rural job markets. Wearing apparel, building material, furniture and furnishings are being produced in these rural community factories.

New businesses are being established every day in rural towns. From them come consumer items including household fixtures and appliances, radio and TV sets, mobile homes, automobile trailers, pleasure boats, fertilizers, farm machinery, garden and power tools, costume jewelry, and watches and clocks. These are just some of the industries rejuvenating rural areas.

Gretna, Nebr., about 20 miles from downtown Omaha, is a rural town that has become the core for a bustling satellite community. Growth came about because of local drive and ambition, and local basic ingredients conducive to successful development.

In 1960, Gretna was totally a rural town. Ten years later, the old town was still there, but its character had changed. Homes are well maintained, yards are neat, the main street looks prosperous, a new high school has been built. There is also a "new" town, consisting of several hundred modest, well-designed homes.

While remaining essentially rural, surrounded by farms, Gretna has become a residential community—for people who work in the town, for retired farmers, and for commuters who drive to a major industrial plant

Plywood plant in Louisiana which was financed by tax from local people. Plant employs 200.

4 miles away, or on good highways into Omaha.

Most important, Gretna's citizens wanted improvement and growth. Local leadership provided the facilities and services that new citizens expect of a town—schools, water, sewers. Jobs were available in the community and within commuting distance. Transportation was reasonably convenient.

The area offered recreational facilities, natural beauty, good climate. Adequate housing and long term credit were available. The town reflected its civic pride.

Where such factors as these exist, rural towns offer growth potential as satellite communities. But local initiative and desire for growth are prerequisites for community development.

Each community must consider the people it wishes to attract, or to keep. Recently, 60 percent of persons polled said they'd prefer to live in rural areas if job or career opportunities and good living facilities existed there.

Citizens must consider that providing these jobs and essential services may well disturb and perhaps forever alter the face, character, and way of life of a community. Not everybody is willing to pay this price, and some fears aren't unfounded.

Accidental progress can create problems in an unprepared community. Unplanned suburban sprawl can replace beauty with ugliness. Development that results in traffic jams, unsightly building, and higher taxes to people who feel they are losing a good way of life and receiving little or no benefits to offset these costs, can paralyze their will to get involved in community and industrial development.

But growth can be orderly if the citizens want it that way. Careful advance planning can maximize the benefits and minimize the destructive forces of change. When they consider their local needs, problems, and resources, they have taken an essential but necessary first long step forward.

Local resources plus local initiative and desire equal growth potential. It is almost a geometric equation.

Once local initiative has started the program of community development moving, aid is available from many sources.

Private industry, private and publicly assisted financial institutions, local, State, and Federal agencies are equipped to work cooperatively on plans bearing the stamp of local leadership and local direction.

Local planning assures built-in safeguards for clean water, clean air, preservation of natural beauty, and low frequency of noise and objectionable odors.

Development is unlikely to occur unless a community provides essential services—schools, water and waste systems, electricity, communications, transportation, hospitals, paving—which make a town attractive.

Despite the need for these facilities and services to the development and rejuvenation of rural communities, they are often difficult to secure.

There are reasons for this. For one thing, some people in government and business are convinced that megalopolis growth is the only logical outcome of our national trends. To them, rural areas are doomed by change and progress.

Other groups and organizations compete for urban renewal funds to the detriment of rural renewal funds. Most new homes are being built in and near metropolitan centers. This is where population growth has been most rapid. It is also where the private loan funds and large-scale builders are, both of which are scarce in rural areas.

There must be increased rural building if families are to be attracted to rural areas. Rural substandard housing must be replaced. Rural families want to continue to live in rural areas, while families moving from cities to rural areas will need housing.

This need is not going unnoticed. The rural housing program of the Farmers Home Administration, a credit agency in USDA, has in the past few years greatly broadened the opportunities available to rural families and to those who want to move to rural areas to have a decent home.

In fiscal year 1961, the Farmers Home Administration made about 5,000 rural housing loans. In fiscal 1969, the number had increased to 50,000. In fiscal 1970, nearly 80,000 loans had been made. And in fiscal 1971, the loan figure was expected to reach 118,000.

In terms of dollars, the Farmers Home Administration made loans totaling $500 million in 1969, $800 million in 1970, and in fiscal 1971 loans are expected to amount to almost $1.5 billion. Of this amount, 98 percent is insured funds.

Through its insured loan program, the Farmers Home Administration is able to bring housing credit from retirement, pension and trust funds, and similar sources of investments in cities, to the farms, the open country, and small rural towns. Loans are made to families out of a rural housing revolving fund and then sold in the private market. At the time of sale they are fully insured by the Government as to both interest and principal.

The housing program is moving forward with other agency support. Rural electric and telephone systems financed by the Rural Electrification Administration encourage the Farmers Home Administration loan applications in many rural communities. REA borrowers are leaders in all phases of community development.

Bardstown, Ky., is an excellent example. The Salt River Rural Electric Cooperative Corporation, an REA-financed system serving the area, led in forming an Industrial Development Corporation (IDC). This has helped the town overcome problems of underemployment and economic instability.

Using funds solicited from businessmen, the IDC optioned a 47-acre tract for projected industrial development. The land is well situated for rail and highway transportation.

The city installed water and sewer mains to the property. Electric power for the entire development is provided by the Salt River Electric Co-op.

The first industry to avail itself of park facilities was a $5 million plastics building materials plant. A $7 million paper products company followed, employing 300 local people.

Other improvements include an airport, a water district, recreation projects, hospital expansion, a new vocational school, and a consolidated senior high school.

As community development continues, local employment increases. Related businesses and services are attracted, tax bases expanded. The entire area benefits.

In some rural areas, local planners have begun community development programs with the first step of cultivating a sense of community pride.

One of the most successful industrial and community developments of the past 20 years began in a depressed Appalachian foothills region with a local campaign, inspired by an REA borrower, to paint, clean up, and repair.

Inspired from this modest beginning, desire for growth and renewal caught fire throughout the area. The region now has good homes, recreation and tourist attractions, businesses, expanding industries, and many facilities for better living.

Civic pride, bolstered by first-step community-wide facelifting, make the next steps upward easier.

A rural community which hopes to grow must recognize that it cannot reach toward goals remaining from an outmoded way of life. Its preplanning must inventory its human, natural, and economic resources, and then develop new directions, new reasons for existence, new tools for accomplishing these aims.

Many rural towns have realized their growth potential in just this way. Community leaders of Pratt, Kans., converted unused portions of a World War II airbase into cattle feedlots. Forming the Pratt Industrial

43

Development, Inc., they obtained $1.5 million in financing from local people, local banks, and the Small Business Administration. They effected at least four positive improvements upon the local economy. They:

—utilized land lying idle;
—increased local employment;
—broadened the local tax base;
—and created a market for feed grain beyond the capacity of local growers.

The feedlots, initially built to handle 10,000 cattle, soon expanded to 35,000 head and are growing. Financing for planned expansion projects in the area is in the hands of 15 banks.

What other towns are doing should be carefully studied by community planners. It takes only one good idea to spark a worthwhile development project. Keep the idea simple.

These towns we have cited are moving forward aggressively. None had resources which made them special. Each had the will to work and grow and develop. What they have done, you, too, may be able to do in your community as the need exists.

Helping Shape the Future of Chicagoland

F. GLENNON LOYD

Planners for the northeast Illinois area, including Chicago, forecast a doubled suburban population by the year 2000. Soil and water conservation districts in the area are helping with plans to provide the coming residents a clean and green environment.

The Northeastern Illinois Planning Commission predicts that within 30 years 6.8 million people will live in the suburbs around Chicago. Then the suburban census alone would equal the 1960 population of the entire metropolitan area, including Chicago.

The dramatic demand for agricultural land for urban development and industry is reflected already in outlying rural and suburban communities. More than 1,700 units of government now serve the metropolitan area. Their officials daily make decisions that one way or another affect the pattern of the rural to urban land use change.

Northeast Illinois soil and water conservation districts are not standing idly by, contemplating the day the suburbs will accommodate half of the area's anticipated 10 million plus residents. The districts, with decades of experience in land and water management, are helping bring about an orderly change for a better living environment through two avenues.

In matters that are largely county problems, the SWCD directors work with township, village, city, and county governments, as well as with their planning, zoning, and highway people.

For dealing with soil and water problems of a multicounty nature, the districts—in cooperation with 16 county, State, and Federal resource agencies—have formed the Northeast Illinois Natural Resource Service Center.

First suggestion for the multicounty service center came from John Quay, who has a long and stimulating relationship with soil and water conservation districts and the U.S. Department of Agriculture's Soil Conservation Service.

Quay, an architect turned planner, has interests in both detailed and regional planning. He is executive secretary of the McHenry County Regional Planning Commission. Previously he had been a commissioner of the Northeastern Illinois Planning Commission.

Action on Quay's proposal came in 1968 when the Lake, McHenry, North Cook, Kane-DuPage, and Will-South Cook SWCD's incorporated the Northeast Illinois Natural Resource Service Center. Several months later the Kendall SWCD joined in the venture. The Kankakee district signed up in 1970.

Now the seven SWCD's in the eight counties were united in a group effort. With their cooperating agencies they began seeking solutions to planning problems involving natural resources in the block of counties of the expanding metropolis.

To head up the service center, the district directors chose as executive director one of their own, Kenneth V. Fiske, chairman of the McHenry SWCD, and secretary of the Association of Illinois SWCD's.

Offices for the resource service center are provided by cooperative arrangement with the famous Morton Arboretum, located near the suburb of Lisle, Ill., in the geographic center of the eight-county area being served.

Office space is also provided for cooperating agencies.

Fiske looks upon the center as a "merchandiser" of the natural resource expertise and coordinated technical data that will help solve the metropolitan area's multicounty land, air, water, and people problems.

The active center has long-range objectives to:

• Provide the general public, municipal and county governments, and all public and private agencies with natural resource information which will lead to orderly development of the area.

• Work toward consideration of the natural resource facts at all levels of planning decision.

*

F. GLENNON LOYD is deputy director of the Information Division, Soil Conservation Service.

• Aid in developing a sound natural resources educational program at the graduate level for all teachers in the eight counties.

• Help study watershed areas whose boundaries or benefits cross county lines, regardless of their size or potential for project help under Public Law 566.

• Help establish sound organizational structures in the Fox and Des Plaines River watersheds.

• Assist public and private organizations in developing areas for recreation and nature preserves that will result in the least possible environmental damage.

The center's board of directors has pursued a policy of making sure the center works only on truly multicounty natural resource concerns—"and we insist that individual conservation districts, municipalities and counties take full responsibility for their own individual programs."

The center in 1970 channeled more than 350 requests for specific service to the appropriate local or county agency for action. The inquiries involved proper land use, pollution, recreation potential, and technical resource data assistance to municipal building and zoning boards.

The director, assisted by a small office staff, is involved in a variety of actions.

For example, the center has been a focal point in planning future use of the Fox River basin. Coming out of Wisconsin, the Fox traverses Lake, McHenry, Kane, Kendall, and La Salle Counties.

The center's aim has been to get the resource development proposals of all Fox River watershed interests evaluated, coordinated, and translated into action. It cosponsored the first meeting of a Citizens Advisory Council for the Chain of Lakes-Fox River with the Northern Illinois Water Resource and Conservation Commission.

The Illinois Water Pollution and Water Resource Commission is looking toward a suitable organizational

45

structure for an intercommunity, interstate, interagency action program for the cleanup and natural resource development of the Fox. A cooperative land use study of the Fox Valley and graphic presentation of the findings are available.

A novel study in which the center is involved is the 20,000-acre watershed of the east branch of the Kishwaukee River in McHenry County. This project is one of the first in the Nation to make a determination as to whether application of natural resource data is a sound means of determining the "people-carrying capacity."

It was designed to demonstrate to municipalities, counties, and the State, the multiagency approach to solve the problems of a watershed too small to be eligible for direct Federal aid under the Public Law 566 small watershed protection and flood prevention program.

Through the center's efforts, some 20 agencies coordinated activities and provided factual resource data.

Other studies the center is involved in are highway corridor natural resource inventories, soil survey, water impoundment inventories, and the unique Natural Resources Information System (NARIS).

Perhaps NARIS is the center's most ambitious undertaking—a uniform system of recording and storing resource data by electric computer. The NARIS system contains a wide range of natural resource data for an area on a consistent basis. It is designed to present understandable, orderly resource facts to decision-makers, be they village officials or technical planning or zoning people.

When fully operative, NARIS will yield for decision-makers a natural resource inventory for every 40-acre parcel of land within the eight counties. Inputs come mainly from five State agencies, two Federal agencies, and three local agencies. Among the inputs are data on:

—Geology and ground water, from the Illinois State Geological Survey

—Surface water and climatology from the State Water Survey

—Vegetation from the State Conservation Department's Division of Forestry

—Surface water impoundments, fish life and wildlife from the Conservation Department's Divisions of Game and Fisheries

—Soil and geophysical information from the Soil Conservation Service

—Flood and geophysical information from the U.S. Department of the Interior's Geological Survey

—Information from the Northeastern Illinois Planning Commission, the Metropolitan Sanitary District of Greater Chicago, and the Chicago Area Transportation Study.

NARIS is a cooperative product of the Center for Advanced Computations of the University of Illinois and the resources center. The resources center proposed the idea of a computerized natural resources system to the university. A Ford Foundation grant for NARIS helped get the project under way.

Given the location of a 40-acre tract, NARIS will be able to (1) indicate what soil and water problems would be faced in building on the tract; (2) predict the impact of the proposed building on other natural resources in the area; and (3) forecast the economic price or benefit for both the short and long run.

After considering all the natural resources together, decision makers might determine that the private or social costs involved in overcoming site limitations would be too great. For such a situation, NARIS could search its "memory" to find any suitable alternate areas that would meet given criteria. A positive response like this offers decision makers a creative tool to achieve their specific goals while having the means to consider the environment and local resource base.

When programmed fully, NARIS will be able to respond to such puzzlers as "Suggest possible routes for an interstate highway between X and Y that will minimize both engineering costs and ecological damage."

Pilot of the system was Marengo Township in McHenry County. The NARIS time schedule calls for the data base for all of McHenry and Lake counties to be operative in 1971, and the other counties by 1972.

Fiske and the NARIS people point out that once the system is developed, it could be expanded to other counties and States by collecting and modifying existing data to machine-readable form.

The NARIS project recognizes that not all the variables for each resource in the eight counties will be available in the next few years. But more than enough data already are available to give immediate benefits to county users.

The center looks forward to the day when each of the 1,700 units of government as well as private developers can be given helpful and comprehensive resource guidance from the system more quickly than by means presently available.

Wilderness Lands for Learning

NOLAN O'NEAL

WILDERNESS is a concept that is relative. The earth under my footstep may be a wilderness to the micro-organisms living there. To the early settlers of North America, the entire continent presented a vast wild, harsh, challenging land ruled by natural actions and interactions. To one raised in a metropolis today, any clump of trees some distance from the city may have the appearance of wilderness.

In the ancient wilderness that encompassed the world, man fought for his survival with all other creatures. And the contest was not too lopsided in his favor. Yet though man's physical endowments were not too impressive, he outsmarted all competitors.

Some fear man may have outsmarted himself, but few would offer to swap places with the other less dominant creatures. Accepting our membership in human society, however, carries with it the growing alarm and concern about the environmental melange we have fashioned.

Perhaps we should take modest pride in the incredible adaptability that allows us to inhabit and thrive in deserts, tropics, arctic ice fields, oceans, manmade wonders, slums, or suburban monotony.

Man has learned to eat an amazing variety of food and he survives amidst the waters and the air—rank with his own pollutants. His procreation boggles the mind while he extends his life cycle. Despite a thousand hazards born of his mechanical genius, he looks forward with jittery confidence to outliving the balance of terror that science has contributed to warfare.

Yet in the midst of all our "progress," we are creatures of an eonic evolution. In every cell, I suspect, there is a magnetic pull back to our beginnings—to the natural world of water and woods, where the feel, the smells, the sounds, the interactions with other organisms are shared experience in a balanced biological community.

Whether from this magnetic pull or an instinctive urge to escape the delirium of cities, mounting millions of people sally forth in mobile re-

*

NOLAN O'NEAL is Assistant Director of Information and Education for Programs, Forest Service.

minders of home to plunge into the out of doors. Among these frenzied visitors are a steadily increasing number who seek solitude in open spaces, who realize what John Muir meant when he said: "In God's wilderness lies the hope of the world—the great fresh, unblighted, unredeemed wilderness. The galling harness of civilization drops off, and the wounds heal ere we are aware."

All this has something to do with a law enacted by Congress that describes wilderness and designates certain remote areas fitting this description to be forever shielded from some of the more apparent intrusions of man. This action is part of a growing recognition that nature must be at least partially protected from her most aggressive child. It, too, may be part of the magnetic pull, expressed collectively.

The U.S. Department of Agriculture's Forest Service long ago became aware of the need to protect millions of acres of remote, mountainous country and decided to act on it. The criteria for "Wilderness" were severe; in the Eastern United States, only a few places measured up. Even the once glorious woodlands around the great web of lakes traveled by the French voyageur fur traders in Minnesota have been largely reclaimed from areas logged and burned.

The inaccessible western mountains, however, presented a great opportunity to hold vast areas free from man's disruptions. Forest Service leaders like Aldo Leopold and Robert Marshall, no doubt influenced by such earlier apostles of the wild as Ralph Waldo Emerson, Henry Thoreau, and John Muir, pushed for restrictive designations; and the protected wilderness areas—"where man himself is a visitor who does not remain"—were born.

Opposite page, above, tropical rain forest in Puerto Rico. Below, a forest officer points out land snail to two visitors.

In 1924, under authority of the Organic Act of 1897, the Gila Wilderness in New Mexico became the first official Wilderness in the National Forest System. Since then, a total of 88 areas on 75 National Forests in 14 States, and covering over 14 million acres, are being given wilderness protection.

The Wilderness Act of 1964—a legislative landmark in conservation —gave congressional sanction to existing Wilderness Areas and set the pattern for those to come.

Important management guides have been developed to protect these rugged appearing, but actually fragile, eco-systems.

Although the search for solitude in the out of doors is reason enough to protect remnants of the American wilderness, many suggest it is even more urgent that "islands" of undisturbed natural areas be established close to our urban centers.

Since few can retreat to the expansive National Forest wilderness country, it is obvious that the need must be served by thousands of such small *islands* — diverse, scattered, accessible—"Eco-islands" where man can observe, study, and enjoy the natural world.

Many believe our whole educational system becomes more meaningful when tied to the environment— even if it only demonstrates the tragic consequence of disregarding the interdependent web of life surrounding us.

The ecology of environment can be presented from a blacktop parking lot, a school lawn, or a 1-acre manmade park. But for comparison and broad understanding, we also need areas where natural interactions are not impeded. For how can we gage the impact of man on his surroundings without some concept of a world without his intrusions?

We must make certain that children born in a drastically altered America have an opportunity to seek understanding of the processes of life—to respond to the tug of

49

natural things linked to the life of the seas, rivers, swamps, the plains, and the forests.

But these natural spots are as fragile and delicate as living lace. We can only continue to enjoy them and let their lessons sustain and enrich our lives if we have the wisdom and compassion to enter as visitors,

Above, tree's growth rings take you back in history. Right, students learn about box turtle in George Washington National Forest, Va. Below, environmental specialist "Ernie" McDonald shares in discovery process.

leaving without visible trace, our presence there "as fish through the water—as birds through the air."

We are very recent arrivals on the planet Earth and have occupied our Nation for just an instant in time. But, even now, we must search diligently for a trace of what was originally here. Surely the genius and energy that transformed a wilderness continent can protect and expand a few remnants. Our population projections only add urgency to our search for and protection of the bits and pieces of natural areas close to our cities and along our transportation routes. These thousands of diverse biotic communities can be the learning satellites to the great wilderness areas within our National Forests.

Aldo Leopold said: "The richest values of wilderness lie not in the days of Daniel Boone, nor even in the present, but rather in the future." We must reflect and act on his wisdom; our children will be grateful.

White Collar, Blue Collar: Job Trends

JAMES G. MADDOX

THOUSANDS of Americans switch jobs every year. Some workers stay with the same employers but change occupations. Others move from one industry to another, for example—from farming to a job in manufacturing or construction.

Many of these job changes have resulted in large numbers of people moving from the open country to small towns and cities or large urban centers. They have also had important impacts on the scope and type of educational and training programs needed to qualify workers for new jobs, the number of people receiving public welfare assistance, and on many other aspects of society.

In order to understand past changes, and to gain insights into probable future developments, we need answers to such questions as these: In what industries, occupations, and geographic regions have jobs been increasing or decreasing? What are the major factors that have brought about these changes? To what extent are the changes of the past likely to be of significance in the future?

Knowledge about the nature and extent of future job opportunities is particularly relevant to young people who are preparing themselves to choose careers and enter the labor force in the years ahead.

One of the most important past trends has been a pronounced upward shift in the share of total employment in service-producing industries, and a downward shift in the proportion of employees in goods-producing industries.

The principal goods-producing industries are agriculture, mining, manufacturing, and construction. In 1950, employment in these four industries was 47 percent of the total of almost 60 million civilian workers in all industries. By 1968, total employment had risen to 76 million, but the share of the total in these four industries had declined to 37 percent.

In contrast, the share of employees in the five major service-producing industries—wholesale and retail trade; transportation, communications, and public utilities; personal, professional, and business services; Federal, State, and local governments; and finance, insurance, and real estate—rose from

*

JAMES G. MADDOX is Professor of Economics in the School of Agriculture and Life Sciences at North Carolina State University, Raleigh.

53 to 63 percent of our total civilian employment.

There are several striking examples of this pattern of change. In 1950, almost 8 million persons—hired workers, self-employed, and unpaid family workers—had jobs in agriculture, forestry, and fisheries. They represented 13 percent of total employment.

By 1968, their number had declined to slightly less than 4 million. Thus, there had been a decrease of more than 50 percent in agricultural employment in 18 years, and the proportion of total employment that was in agriculture had declined to 5 percent.

Conversely, the number of employees in wholesale and retail trade increased from 11 million in 1950 to 16 million in 1968—a gain of 45 percent—and their share of total employment rose from 19 to 22 percent. Similarly, civilian employment in Federal, State, and local governments increased by 210 percent—from under 3 million workers in 1950 to over 8 million in 1968. Their share of total employment rose from 4 to 11 percent in this 18-year period.

What is the explanation for this shift of workers from goods-related to service-related industries? Two factors were of major importance.

• Technological improvements and the substitution of machinery for manpower have proceeded much more rapidly in farming, mining, and many types of manufacturing than they have in most of the service-producing industries. It has been both easier and more profitable to mechanize the production of commodities than the production of services.

• As personal incomes and leisure time have risen, consumers have greatly increased their demands for many types of services, such as education, medical care, and recreation. Likewise, an increasing proportion of income is being spent for repairs to automobiles, radios, television sets, and other household items; and for advertising, entertainment, and numerous types of activities.

All this has increased the demand for workers in the service-producing industries.

The changes which have resulted in an increasing share of the total work force being employed in service-related industries, together with new production processes in many goods-producing industries, have had repercussions on the distribution of employees among different occupations. The service industries have a high proportion of white collar employees, such as professional and technical workers, managers, officials and proprietors of business firms, and clerical and salesworkers.

It is not surprising, therefore, that the number of white collar workers rose from approximately 22 million in 1950 to 35 million in 1968—a gain of almost 59 percent. In contrast, the number of blue collar workers—craftsmen and foremen, operators of machines and equipment, and lower-skilled nonfarm laborers—increased from 23 million to 27 million, or only 18 percent.

As a result of these differential rates of change, the proportion of white collar employees rose from 38 to 47 percent of the total number of employees between 1950 and 1968 while the proportion of blue collar workers declined from 39 to 36 percent. The proportion of farm laborers and household servants also declined.

Within the white collar group, the most rapid rates of increase were among professional and technical workers, whose number rose from less than 5 million in 1950 to over 10 million in 1968, and among clerical workers, whose number increased from under 8 million to almost 13 million. The share of employment represented by the total of professional, technical, and clerical workers rose from 20 to 30 percent of all employees between 1950 and 1968.

The pronounced upward shift in the number and proportion of white collar workers, especially those in professional and technical occupations, not only reflects changes in the kinds of workers being demanded in our increasingly service-oriented society, but also indicates that the educational level of the workforce is rising.

Emphasis the Nation has put on education and training has qualified an increasing number of people for white collar occupations, raised the productivity and earnings of blue collar workers, and put a premium on brainpower as contrasted with musclepower in many types of jobs.

This points to the importance of a good education and adaptable skills, if young people who are entering the labor force for the first time and older workers who are shifting from one industry to another are to succeed in getting and holding good-paying jobs.

In addition to job trends among different kinds of industries and occupations, there have been important geographic shifts in employment. To a large extent, persons of working age migrate in response to changes in the location of job opportunities.

The 1968 *Manpower Report of the President* pointed out that: "There are two types of relationships between migration and economic development. First, migration acts as a key factor in an adjustment process whereby labor moves from where it is redundant to where it is needed; second, and more significant for the long run, the movement of labor attracts business to areas which are growing, because the right skills and qualities of labor are available and because purchases by the workers and their families increase market opportunities.

"In other words, areas which tend initially to attract people reinforce this attraction through the process of migration."

Largely as a result of these two types of forces, long-term job trends have been from rural to urban areas. Today, most jobs in the United States are in and around cities.

Historically, the heaviest concentrations of both industry and population were in New England, the Middle Atlantic, and the East North Central regions of the country. However, these patterns are changing.

For the past three decades, employment and population have expanded quite rapidly in the Southwest and the Pacific regions, and nonfarm employment has grown more rapidly in the South than in the older industrial areas of the North.

While these regional shifts in employment have provided large numbers of jobs outside of the older industrialized areas of the country, there has been some tendency in the 1960's for jobs to be less concentrated in large cities.

Among the important factors influencing location of industries in recent years are: local pools of trainable workers; low-cost real estate on which to locate manufacturing plants, warehouses, and parking lots for workers; ready access to new interstate highways; and availability of numerous types of public facilities and business services that are particularly important to relatively small manufacturing firms.

Consequently, there appears to be a tendency for an increasing proportion of the new plants of expanding manufacturing industries to locate in medium-sized and small cities, rather than in large, congested, urban centers. Likewise, there are numerous examples of both service-producing and manufacturing firms that have moved out of the older, congested, central areas of the large cities and located in the suburbs.

As we look toward the future, it is reasonable to believe that most of the past trends will continue. However, much depends on public policies in the years ahead. If fiscal and monetary measures succeed in keeping national unemployment rates low, an increasing proportion of the future work force is likely to be employed in service-related jobs and in those kinds of goods-producing industries

53

which require rising levels of education and skill on the part of workers. This will result from increasing specialization in production processes and from rising per capita incomes of consumers.

Employment in agriculture is expected to continue to decline during the decade of the 1970's. It is quite probable that the rate of increase in manufacturing jobs will not be as rapid as in trade, government, and many types of professional and business services. Thus, past directions of change in the number and proportion of employees among groups of industries and occupations are likely to continue into the future.

Some geographic dispersal of employment will also probably continue. This will flow from growing public concern over problems of congestion and pollution, and rising public and private costs associated with the heavy concentration of population in metropolitan areas. It will also result from the emergence of new industries related to improving the quality of the environment and to producing low-cost housing, and from new and faster forms of transportation.

The underlying factors which have brought about past job trends among industries, occupations, and geographic areas have raised the general level of productivity of the economy. At the same time they increased the levels of living of most workers, and enlarged the opportunities of many members of the labor force.

However, shifting job patterns have not occurred without sizable private and public costs. Because of a lack of information about job vacancies and because of inadequate education and skills, many workers in rural areas have been stranded in dead-end situations.

At the same time, large numbers of Negroes, Puerto Ricans, and a few other minority groups who have moved into overcrowded slum areas of central cities are handicapped in many respects, including accessibility to suburban areas where jobs around urban centers have been increasing most rapidly.

Partly as a result of these factors, welfare rolls have risen, and public costs for training workers to acquire new skills have increased. Many rural areas have lost large numbers of people, thousands of businesses in hundreds of small towns have disappeared, and many local governments are hard pressed to finance their activities.

Probably the most serious economic and social conditions exist in the older sections of our large cities, where the combination of employment and housing discrimination against Negroes and other minorities have created deplorable living conditions and explosive racial situations.

Clearly, the shifts in employment patterns which result from economic growth and development do not affect all groups equally. Most of us receive significant benefits. Others suffer real costs. Public policies need to take account of both types of effects.

Rural Areas And the People-Jobs Cycle

JOHN R. FERNSTROM and
RONALD E. KAMPE

PEOPLE go where the jobs are and jobs develop where people are. The people-job phenomenon is circular in nature and once started tends to continue from its own momentum—without regard to the interest of the individual or the nation.

Thus left to evolve by itself, the cycle continues and in many cities creates complex problems for city, State, and Federal governments to cope with. Congestion, clogged highways, smog, pollution of all types, crime, and other problems of a large metropolis beset them.

The bigger the city the more complicated it becomes to solve the social and economic problems. New York City spends for other-than-school costs half again as much per capita as the other cities over 1,000,000, nearly twice as much per capita as cities between 500,000 and 1,000,000, nearly three times as much as the cities under 500,000. But many of the other large cities are in trouble, too, with limited taxable resources and more than their share of poverty problems, school problems, sprawl problems, pollution problems.

Yet the cycle continues on, with more and more people moving to the cities. Many do not necessarily want to go but individually they are unable to change their fate, for they must go where jobs are.

In a recent study of 35 northeastern counties in North Carolina, employed residents in the region are projected to increase by 78,995 or 20 percent from 1960 to 1975, which is about seven times more than the increase from 1950 to 1960. Despite this projected increase in employment, the net emigration for the region from 1960 to 1975 will need to be about 46,000 to maintain the 1960 population-employment ratio in 1975.

The people left behind in rural areas suffer since migrations have weakened the local communities through loss of population that provides the local tax base, supports civic endeavors, provides the membership for local organizations, and makes up the local merchants' cus-

*

JOHN R. FERNSTROM is Program Leader, Economic Development, Community Resource Development Staff, Extension Service.
RONALD E. KAMPE is Assistant Chief, Area Analysis Branch, Economic Development Division, Economic Research Service.

tomers. A recent report summarizes the problem:

"The Nation's smaller communities outside of metropolitan areas will be increasingly bypassed by the economic mainstream and will also find it difficult to offer enough jobs for all their residents and those of surrounding rural areas. Many rural areas will suffer from a further siphoning off of the young and able work force with a resultant greater concentration of older and unskilled among those remaining, and a continuing decline in the capacity of rural communities to support basic public services."

In regard to the cities, the same report was equally pessimistic. The continuation of current trends, it was said, would bring about such consequences as the following:

• While the evidence is not conclusive, increased size and congestion may take a social and psychological toll in urban living conditions.

• Advantages of suburban areas in attracting new industry will continue to widen the gap between the economies of cities and their surrounding neighbors, deepening the problems of many cities. A most serious aspect of these problems will be the growing inability of cities to provide jobs for their residents.

• Continued concentration of urban growth in suburban and outlying areas foreshadows a prolongation of development practices creating "urban sprawl"—the disorderly and wasteful use of land at the growing edge of urban areas.

This vision of the future has become widely accepted among experts studying the problem. Some people believe these developments are probably inevitable; that they are the consequences of the industrial revolution or of natural social evolutionary forces, as well as the collective manifestation of individual preferences. The fact is, however, that if these developments materialize, it will be largely because of policy decisions or the lack of them.

55

But there are signs of change. Industry once located in large cities in order to enjoy a large labor force, local access to materials and services, and intercity transportation facilities. Now it is responding to new opportunities created by improved transportation facilities and the increasing ability of rural areas to support new economic growth.

Industry and other forms of business no longer need to locate in the heart of a densely populated urban area in order to obtain services and labor. For example, in 1970 at least eight major U.S. corporations moved their corporate headquarters from New York City to locations in nearby Connecticut.

The modern highway system makes it feasible to attract workers from a much larger geographic area. Thus areas that earlier might have been bypassed are now attracting industry.

Manufacturing industries spent more than $31 billion in 1970 in capital expenditures. Of this, approximately 50 percent was devoted to modern plants in rural areas where municipal facilities were provided and where labor was available.

We as a nation face some important policy decisions. Should we have public policies and programs that encourage or speed up this rural industrialization process, or should we support continued migration? Is it in the national interest to have industrial growth in all areas of the country or should growth be encouraged in just certain areas and discouraged in others?

Should we bring jobs to the people or people to the jobs? Should industry of a certain type be encouraged to locate in rural areas while others are discouraged? And if we decide on a

Right, besides horses and blue grass, rural Kentucky has a new crop—industry. Below, refinery on the Mississippi in St. James Parish, La.

certain policy, what about the people who may be adversely affected by the policy action? These are only a few of many complex and interwoven policy questions that we must face.

There appears to be a national consensus that recognizes our Nation must act upon these problems of unbalanced growth and population distribution which arise from our laissez-faire economic policies. Commissions appointed by two Presidents as well as a Senate Committee have all drawn such conclusions from their studies. But to arrive at what a national policy should be and what programs would best implement such a policy is difficult.

In considering the position of rural areas, let's first look at what's going on in rural America that is counter to popular ideas in both rural and urban America. The things going on today can be an aid in formulating national policy and point to successful programs for rural development stressing the use of rural space for jobs which can stop the cycle of job centralization.

For several decades now, the people who live in the open spaces and the towns and villages of rural America have been establishing new community identities. The boundaries are not marked by arbitrary political lines, but are established by the reach of modern communications and by the automobile and all-weather roads.

Commuting time by car sets the feasible limits on the choice of job opportunities, on access to health care and to education, on the participation in cultural events, and on the dimensions of the marketplace for the buyer and seller of consumer goods and services.

In reverse fashion, these same elements have made the streams and fields, the woods and lakes of the countryside into a potential source for greatly expanded outdoor recreation facilities for the town family.

Thus, an area that can support new growth has evolved by a process of voluntary choices of both town and rural people.

A past weakness of our rural economy has been lack of an adequate structure of social and economic organizations, which in turn has resulted in little incentive for leadership development that is required to provide an adequate level of public service.

Nor has it been economical for every town or small city to attempt to provide a wide range of social, cultural, and economic services which are commonly associated with larger urban centers.

Yet the larger economic area, comprised of rural and town people together, provides a population base which can support a full range of well developed public services. The related interests of both town and rural areas establish the essential design and vitality of the area.

The mere existence or recognition of these functional communities has not solved all the social and economic problems of those who live within their boundaries. But people working together on an area-wide basis are providing a dramatic new dimension to the rural economy.

Using the area-wide organizational concept, most areas have a labor force large enough to provide workers for new plants locating in the area.

Further, many rural workers display certain attitudes which are beneficial to industry. Most rural workers maintain a stance of rugged individualism. They will commute long distances before accepting unemployment.

Rural people identify strongly with their employer for they are now, or were recently, closely associated with the management of a farming operation or a small rural business. They know of struggles to make a profit and tend to be sympathetic to the problems of the manager.

Many industries that migrated from traditional centers of production to areas possessing no "developed skills" show a net increase in productivity.

Although special skills may not always be found in rural area workers, most can be developed. Also, "skills" can be broken down into a group of related "semi-skills." Many highly integrated products can be reengineered to simplify and reduce specialized labor requirements.

The rural area, then, offers a highly productive labor force for a new industrial plant. Cost savings, as a result, are being achieved for each unit produced.

Many of the national corporations already understand the economic advantages of a rural location. Because of the competition in urban centers for workers and the rapidly increasing wages that result, industries frequently are selecting rural areas for plant locations.

Location of plants in areas with little competition for labor also minimizes the inflationary spiral caused by competition for workmen in the areas where labor shortages exist.

It is also important to realize that providing higher incomes in the rural areas broadens the base for consumer goods. Therefore, industries will have more prosperous customers if they locate their plants and provide the wages where the wages are really needed.

Providing jobs only in large urban centers will offer a temporary cure for one of the problems created by population migration but will create others. But providing jobs in or near the hometowns of the workers will help change the pattern of migration, strengthen the local communities, improve their tax base, and revitalize the economic life within these communities. This will help in balancing the economy of the Nation.

Because Chrysler Corp. placed a factory in Bowling Green, Ky., Windle Harmon, a resident of the area, was able to stay home, and learn skills that will earn money for him in the Chrysler plant.

Quality of education need not suffer from the rural environment. Again, the use of the larger community is the key. Rural school systems regularly graduate students who perform exceptionally well in institutions of higher learning, and many can provide local industries with vocationally-trained labor.

Post secondary vocational education is increasingly being provided in rural regions. Such programs upgrade and diversify the labor forces of rural areas continually. Clearly, then, non-urban areas are not necessarily educationally deprived.

Available industrial land abounds in many rural areas. Often the land is available in the form of community-sponsored industrial sites or parks, thus insuring its sound development.

This land is universally available at rates below the prices of urban areas—decreasing the fixed real estate investment by a manufacturer, and at the same time increasing funds available for working capital. On the basis of demand in the recent past, planning for industry locating outside metropolitan areas should provide at least 15,000 to 20,000 acres of new plant sites every year.

Many rural communities extend municipal water systems to industrial tracts, while others erect water towers. Communities also extend municipal sewerage to these industrial sites.

Railroad lines and waterways traverse a surprisingly large number of the tracts—insuring complete transportation services to industries locating there. Consequently, more desirable industrial land frequently may be obtained for less money by locating in a rural area.

The Interstate Highway System links rural and metropolitan in a way that was never possible before. Many States construct limited access, high-speed secondary roads to complement the Interstate System along with development of more and more regional or local airports.

The P. R. Mallory Company, Inc.,

of Indianapolis, Ind., provides an example of how well a rural location works. The firm makes products for a wide variety of consumer, industrial, and government markets. The company announced plans in 1970 to establish a 35,000-square-foot plant at Camden, Tenn., to be used for manufacture of electronic parts and assemblies.

The Camden plant is Mallory's fourth manufacturing facility in Tennessee. One at Cleveland produces primary batteries, the Waynesboro operation makes AC oil capacitors, and the Sparta plant manufactures sequence timing devices.

At almost the same time another manufacturer of timing devices, the Scott & Fetzer Company of Cleveland, Ohio, announced a new plant in Smithville, Tenn., to make timing controls.

Illustrations of this kind of trend toward decentralization of industry into nonmetropolitan America can be cited from across the Nation.

Rural areas are becoming less isolated and need not be considered culturally deprived. The same expressways that support rural industries bring businesses, services, shopping, sports, and cultural facilities nearer the smaller communities. Recreational facilities are located in even the smallest community. Cooperation among civic leaders has led to community sports programs, swimming pools, golf courses, ski lifts, public parks with tennis courts, badminton courts and equipment for juvenile play.

Personal amenities are not always manmade and found within the big city. More and more of our affluent society is learning to appreciate the pleasures of the wide open spaces. The rash of campers on our highways, the growing fleet of pleasure boats on our waterways, and the sale of camping and hiking equipment confirm that rural areas have much to offer our pleasure-seeking society.

Communities actively seeking new industry recognize that making the family of the employee contented leads to happier employees and higher productivity. Personal amenities of all types, then, are more and more considered vital by smaller communities.

The basic solution to the problem of air pollution is simply not permitting excessive quantities to accumulate in the air. How can this be done?

Not allowing pollutants to be expelled into the atmosphere would be one way. Dispersing pollutants to a low level of accumulation would be another. And the latter can be accomplished more readily in rural areas.

Managers seeking new plant sites must consider the special relationship between the problems of air pollution and the climate, topography, and industrial density of an area.

Putting plants where the climate and topography of the area is conducive to a natural air flow will aid in dispersing pollutants. Building tall stacks to vent the emissions at high atmospheric levels will also help. And locating in a less dense industrial area where pollutants are not already at a dangerous level will do much to lessen the national problem of hazardous accumulation of polluted air.

The same principles apply to water pollution. Pollution problems are compounded when several industries, even with highly treated effluent, attempt to concentrate their discharges into limited receiving waters. The environmental health of the nation will demand the decentralization of pollution sources to avoid toxic concentrations.

There are rivers in the rural areas of America that can accept adequately treated effluents and recover with minimum disturbance to the existing aquatic life. There are open spaces where adequately controlled industrial emissions can be absorbed into the atmosphere without danger to the environment.

As industries seeking new plant sites begin to recognize the need for increased dispersion of their plants, there will be more opportunities for smaller communities seeking industry. New plants can constitute an opportunity, if the community knows its environmental capacity to tolerate the impact of these plants. Understanding and wise planning can minimize and limit the pollution potential of new industry and at the same time produce desirable job opportunities for rural Americans.

We have discussed features of rural areas that should attract industry. But is it in the national interest for rural areas to grow, and if so should all areas grow or only selected ones? If we assume a national policy to provide adequate social services to all citizens, then it may be in our interest to encourage industry to locate where the economy must be strengthened.

Forestry and mining industries are dependent upon available resources. Farming is a seasonal industry and an industry where, as the result of modern technology, the number of farmers has declined and will continue to decline. There will be one million fewer farmers by 1980. Industries in rural areas can complement agriculture by providing employment, and perhaps more importantly provide the means for a more orderly adjustment of personnel in the agriculture sector.

But some areas may lack the resources, both physical and human, to develop into a larger functional economic area necessary to sustain economic growth. It may still be in the Nation's interest to encourage outmigration from these areas and subsidize the social needs of those who wish to remain.

The question of people and jobs is not easy to resolve. If left unchecked, densely populated areas gain in population while sparsely populated areas thin out, and the results are problems specific to both. We as a nation must look at the space available and our responsibility towards our citizens and adopt a population policy that will put this space to its best use.

There is no doubt the urban planners can provide for larger cities, that the highway engineers can provide for more complex highway systems, that the architects can build taller buildings, and that modern science and technology can solve the problems of the cities. But there is considerable doubt that the money will be provided to pay for the complex solutions required if the problems are allowed to escalate and compound much further.

Some urban planners tend to feel that in order to provide urban services at reasonable tax rates, the ideal size of a city is one with less than a million people. They view pyramiding taxes in rapidly growing States such as California or in New York City as proof that social and economic costs rise out of proportion to population increases. Breaking the people-jobs cycle through decentralization may now be necessary for economic, environmental, and human survival.

How a Town Can Attract Industry

G. W. F. (DUTCH) CAVENDER and
RICHARD G. SCHMITT, JR.

INDUSTRIALIZATION continues at a rapid rate in the United States but with little planning to encourage balanced population growth. Industry and jobs in rural areas are basic to population dispersion. Efforts toward this end should materially influence the pattern of living for the additional 100 million Americans or so expected by the turn of the century.

This chapter discusses what we have learned about mobilizing resources to attract industry, some techniques that

have been used successfully, and some reasons for failure.

Rural industrialization is the placing of job-producing enterprises in small cities, towns, and rural communities. It requires the cooperation of local citizens, businesses, industry and government at all levels. Communities successful in rural industrialization are likely to change their citizens' attitudes from doubt and apathy to progress and hope.

Much rural industrialization in the past occurred through development of agribusiness. Such development came about because of the interdependence of agriculture and industry. Our effort now is to demonstrate that rural areas are good places for industry regardless of the product.

The economics of plant location probably had the greatest influence on the initial location of many rural industries in our country. Industries that depended on natural resources like timber, coal, water, minerals, or agricultural products were started when the economics of processing pointed to a plant location close to the source of raw materials.

As processing and marketing became more specialized, many industries found it to their advantage to locate close to the consumer, and as our country grew in population, more and more close to, or in, the cities. At that time, cities could more ably provide the skilled labor and services industry needed.

By 1917, a Nation that had been rural and agriculturally oriented since its birth had more people living in urban areas than in the countryside.

Over time, advancement in agricultural technology caused large pockets of rural unemployment. This has resulted in a continuing outmigration to the cities in search of job opportunities.

*

G. W. F. (DUTCH) CAVENDER is Assistant Administrator, Special Projects, Farmers Home Administration.

RICHARD G. SCHMITT, JR., is Assistant to the Administrator, Farmers Home Administration.

Iron and steel company plant in South Carolina has provided jobs for 400 farmworkers from area. Mill was started with government loan, loan from Tri-County Electric Cooperative, and money raised locally by employees themselves. USDA has made loans to finance new homes for mill employees.

Industry does much to improve a community's economic and social condition. Among the benefits are jobs, income, increased revenue to support schools and other governmental facilities, and an overall upgrading of the level of living for local citizens. A primary industry carries another advantage, since it's estimated that 100 new industrial jobs will create the equivalent of 70 additional service jobs.

A community whose economy depends on agriculture has difficulty financing adequate governmental services. Industry and business strengthen the tax base. They also support social and cultural projects essential to a more complete life for local citizens. Much outmigration is caused by lack of economic opportunities; some is due to a search for cultural and social advantages.

There are distinct advantages to industry when it locates in a rural area. These advantages are becoming more apparent as State and local governments act to attract plants to their areas. Among the advantages are improved community facilities, adequate space at less cost, lower tax rate, nearness to some markets, nearness to raw materials, wholesome environment, room for expansion, available trainable labor, and greater appreciation on the part of local citizens and government.

Another important advantage to industry is a satisfied employee. Increasingly, rural communities are making possible better housing at less cost, easy access to and from the plant, more recreational facilities, a greater chance to participate in local community affairs, and reduced living expenses.

Elected officials and local business and community leaders usually take the initiative to launch an industrialization program. The community that eventually attracts a plant is the one that supports a representative who relentlessly pushes for it.

Many rural communities can't afford a hired representative to look for capital, technical assistance, and other things needed to attract a client. This is one reason why many rural communities fail in their industrialization efforts.

Before a community starts seeking industry, it must make some concrete decisions. Among them are: Is it willing to provide what's needed to attract and hold industry? If so can it get the necessary financing, and is it willing to obligate itself for such facilities and services? What kind of industry does it want; and if it already has industry, does it want more? How much more? The community should organize local interested citizens to outline objectives, and inventory assets and needs.

These objectives should be documented in an attractive manner to catch industry eyes. The overall economic plan as required by the Economic Development Administration is a good way to start. Such a plan provides basic materials for brochures that may be used to inform the prospective client.

Many communities build their recruiting campaign on bringing in industry from outside. However, they should never overlook the possibility of expanding present industry or establishing new industries from within. This is why making a thorough study of resources and needs is so important.

Let's make clear that when we talk about placing industry in rural areas, we are not thinking of pirating—or relocating—plants but instead bringing in subsidiary plants and plants developing new products.

Competition for industry and business to locate in rural areas sometimes makes it necessary for individual communities to provide plants with a combination of attractions that may offset advantages to the community. While industries will not often make undue demands on a community, those that do should be scrutinized very closely. However, the more attractive proposition helps influence plant location. After all, industry must make money to survive.

Many communities have lost good industries because of adverse local attitudes. Industry likes to operate where it is wanted. Management is interested in good schools and a friendly climate. It appreciates a community that looks and acts progressively. This is reflected by things like civic clubs, health facilities, churches, good race relations, and a well-kept community.

The Farmers Home Administration, through its basic authorities, can help fill many industry needs. At the same time, this can lead to second and third level jobs that will help hold income within the area. FHA programs include financial assistance for water and waste disposal systems, housing, and cooperatives, and small business loans for low-income rural people.

Often a local community fails to land a job-producing industry because of inability to meet the needs of the company. In some cases it may be desirable for several communities to combine efforts and resources to satisfy these requirements. Each local community in an area need not have a plant to achieve economic and community development. An industrial park, centrally located in a growth area within an hour's commuting distance, can benefit several communities. Leaders should be alert to the multi-county planning that is taking place so they may determine how their area can fit into an overall plan.

Some communities are geared to accommodate the needs of industry and have been successful in their plant location efforts without outside assistance. But many are less fortunate, and depend to varying degrees on outside help. Private, nonprofit groups including local chambers of commerce and other service organizations can assist.

States, through their departments of economic development, help communities prepare for the industry that is seeking new sites. The Federal Government aids by providing both technical and financial assistance. It also supplies information to companies seeking to locate in rural areas.

In the mid-1960's, one such plant location was being sought. The Air Preheater Company, Inc., a subsidiary of Combustion Engineering, Inc., had successfully operated in Wellsville, N.Y. The company wanted to expand operations by locating a branch plant in the Southeast to serve an identified area market. W. R. McKee, then company president, approached the Federal Government to obtain background information.

After a thorough review of the facts, Marion, N.C., a town of about 4,000 people, was chosen. Recently, McKee stated in a letter: "Our branch plant at Marion, N.C., has worked out very satisfactorily. Our present employment at that location is approximately 230 people.

"The whole operation has progressed so nicely that we are now in the process of approximately doubling the size of the plant. We have been most pleased with the caliber of employee and their demonstrated ability to learn through our training programs."

President Nixon and Secretary of Agriculture Hardin have continually pointed to the need for a more uniform population distribution over the Nation. They are encouraging private industry and State and local government to become involved in a program that will make the countryside a more attractive place to live.

The U.S. Department of Agriculture has taken specific steps to reorient some of its resources to assist rural areas in community and industrial development. It has field offices in nearly every rural county. USDA has organized personnel at both State and county levels into Rural Development Committees. Many of these committees have invited other appropriate State and county officials to serve with them.

Function of the Rural Development Committee is to provide coordinated technical assistance and information to local governments and development groups to carry out plans to improve their communities economically, socially, and culturally.

USDA has several basic programs that can be used to attract industry. Among them are credit for power and communications; soil, water, and forestry information; loans and grants to install water and waste disposal systems; credit for housing; information; and technical assistance.

Other sources of Federal assistance are: Economic Development Administration, Regional Commissions, Department of Housing and Urban Development, grants for sewage treatment (under Environmental Protection Agency), Small Business Administration, and technical training by the Department of Labor.

A community that sets out on an industrialization program should be prepared for failures as well as successes. Today the competition for new plants is great. For one acquired, many may be lost. However, the better organized a community, the more dedicated it is, the more willing to fill industry's needs, the more likely will be its successes.

Let us say here that tax advantages and other monetary considerations are not always the most important to industry. Often, attitude, cooperation, a look of progressiveness can be more important than tax breaks.

The community that fails to land a first or second industrial client should review its approach, and see where mistakes were made. If possible, it should correct these mistakes before going after other companies.

Hundreds of communities have undertaken industrialization. Some have failed; many have been successful. For others, it is too early to tell. Those who

64

would doubt that rural industrialization is possible should look at the following examples:

The Waccamaw Clay Products Company of Horry County, S.C., was established by residents with the support of local leaders. The area has depended on agriculture and seasonal tourist trade for an economic base. Unique deposits of clay which give certain shades of brown that cannot be obtained elsewhere provided the attraction for the plant.

Of the firm's 70 employees, most were unemployed, having been farm laborers. The company received much of its financing locally and was supported by the State and an Economic Development Administration loan. The company continues to provide a quality product and has an expanding market.

Stillwell, Okla., a town of approximately 2,000 people in Adair County, sorely needed additional water in the early 1960's. For one thing the Stillwell Canning Plant, largest industry in the county, wanted to expand. It provided employment for over 1,100 full-time and seasonal workers.

The plant's success depended on production of fruits and vegetables. Therefore, local farmers were helped by its existence. Canning and freezing were carried on year round.

Several agencies of the Federal Government, including the Soil Conservation Service, the Farmers Home Administration, and the U.S. Department of Commerce, provided technical and financial assistance to build a multi-purpose reservoir. As a result, the town was able to get adequate water and the canning plant expanded operations. The entire community has shown new life. Results include more recreation opportunities, better conservation of land and water, and a healthier economy.

Monticello, Miss., is a town of 1,790 people. It is in Lawrence County (total population 11,137) near large acreages of forest land. The St. Regis Paper Company, looking to expand operations, chose Monticello because of abundant water, good transportation, and plentiful raw material.

The final decision was not made, however, until after considerable effort by local citizens, business, and government at all levels. This effort provided access roads, water, waste disposal, housing, power, recreation, and other services.

In 1968, the $110 million plant went into operation, using 800,000 to 900,000 cords of wood annually. It provided 2,000 jobs while under construction. There are now 528 permanent employees with a payroll of $7 million annually. Ten chip mills, five tie and pulp yards, and a box factory employ another 220 in other parts of rural Mississippi.

The plant provides a wood market for farmers. In addition, it has stimulated new and expanded businesses, creating numerous service jobs. This one plant releases an estimated $50 million into the State's economy annually.

E. M. Graham, Monticello Mayor, said recently: "This plant has been a tremendous boost to the entire area. It has caused new and expanded businesses, a general upgrading of living conditions and more interest in community life by local citizens."

Plant Comptroller Boyd F. Jordan said: "We are pleased with our location. We have been made to feel a part of the community; attitudes are excellent. Everyone that could has pitched in to help."

The town of New Madrid, population 2,682, located on the Mississippi River in southeastern Missouri, has landed an $80 million plant that will employ 650 full-time persons and produce a $4.5 million annual payroll. The plant will produce aluminum products and begin operations in late 1972. This success was due to the initiative of local people who followed up on information that the company planned to expand.

Although told they could not qualify, the local people put together facts with documentation. The State Division of Commerce initiated an

St. Regis Paper Company plant in Monticello, Miss.

application for a grant from the Economic Development Administration for an industrial park. The city government approved industrial development bonds for the plant and a new municipal electric plant. The electric plant will involve investment of an additional $90 million.

Major reasons why the company chose this location were the ideal water site location and a favorable power rate.

Since construction started, other developments include three new medical doctors, a new technical vocational school, and renewed outlook for existing industries—including auto parts, garments, feed, and lumber.

Warren County, Tenn., had made some progress in industrialization by 1960, but many of its people were still leaving in search of jobs. Porter Henegar, then Executive Secretary of the Warren County Chamber of Commerce, said recently: "We realized a new approach was needed, so we started using a rifle instead of a shotgun. We began inventorying our resources and needs and established goals."

In 1960, the county seat of McMinnville undertook development of a water supply that could serve the entire county for domestic and industrial purposes. Now 68 percent of all Warren County citizens use the system, and there is ample capacity for expansion. The Farmers Home Administration provided financial assistance for five of the six rural water districts.

The area's first industrial park was acquired in 1965. There are now 400 acres fully accessible to utilities, plus a mile of rail frontage.

McMinnville and Warren County have furnished facilities and services for business and industry. They have also provided economic, social, and cultural opportunities for their citizens. They did this by taking advantage of available programs of both the private and public sector and making full use of local assets.

This has resulted in successful in-

Water tower in Warren County, Tenn.

dustrialization. There are 10 plants that employ from 250 to 1,050 persons, several others with 50 to 250 employees, and some that employ fewer than 50. Many of the plants have been established since 1960. The county has not neglected its long-established industries or its agriculture and nursery stock enterprise.

There are now 7,500 industrial jobs in the county. Clarence Redmon, of the Caney Fork Electric Cooperative (REA), said: "Warren County's industry has also provided an economic boost to adjoining counties where the lumber and coal business had declined."

Why did the Carrier Corporation come to Warren County? Personnel Manager Clyde Briggs replied: "One reason was the climate; another was the availability of low cost electricity and third was central location for the distribution of our product." He added that several places within a radius of 100 miles would have been acceptable, but Warren County was chosen because of progressive attitudes of the people, and community services and programs available for employees.

What have been the results? With outmigration stemmed, population in the county increased from 23,102 in 1960 to 26,972 in 1970. The tax base rose from $7.3 million to $42 million, retail sales shot up 94 percent, and assets of financial institutions went from $22 million to more than $62 million in the same period. Broadscale results included hundreds more gainfully employed, new housing, and a general upgrading of living conditions.

A recent USDA survey revealed that half the industrial jobs created in the last decade were in the countryside. But the change in composition of our total population, which shows a continual decline of people living in rural areas, reminds us that past efforts have not been adequate to hold and attract people in rural areas. More can and should be done.

National Goals for Housing

ROBERT E. FREEMAN and
KENT D. MILLER

*H*ouston. *Tranquility Base here. The Eagle has landed.* July 20, 1969. Man was on the moon. A national goal of the 1960's had been achieved.

A less dramatic but more substantial national goal is to provide 26.2 million new or rehabilitated housing units by 1978.

This goal is contained in the Hous-

ing and Urban Development Act of 1968. It is very unusual for social legislation to contain so definite a target, especially where the private sector does nearly all the construction and rehabilitation. Thus, the origin of the goal, accomplishments to date, and prospects for completion are of special interest.

Congressional support for housing goes back to the 1939 legislation. A more current contribution was made by the Department of Housing and Urban Development (HUD) in the form of specific projections of the number of units required to provide every American family with decent housing. The HUD projections were corroborated by similar but independent research. Finally, the urban unrest of the mid-1960's gave urgency to the cause of decent housing.

HUD's projections start with the Bureau of the Census forecast that 13.1 million new households will be formed from 1968 to 1978. This alone accounts for half of the national goals.

Echoes from the "baby boom" after World War II are being heard in the housing market. The ever increasing number of new young families, plus a developing trend toward more households consisting of just one person, has created added pressure on housing facilities.

The 1950's saw new households develop at the rate of 9 million per decade. In the 1960's it was 10 million. A generally larger population in the seventies will add 13.1 million.

The rural increase in households through 1978 may be held to only 2 million above the 1960 census figure. The total number of rural households has been growing quite slowly for some years. Decline in the farm portion of

*

ROBERT E. FREEMAN retired in February 1971 as Group Leader of the Housing and Facilities Group, Community Facilities Branch, Economic Development Division, Economic Research Service.
KENT D. MILLER is Chief, Research and Statistical Information, Division of Information, Office of Management Services.

the rural population—from 7.6 million households in 1940 to 3 million in 1970—was partially offset by growth in the rural nonfarm sector. At the last available census count in 1960, there were 14.7 million rural households counting open country residents and those in communities below 2,500 people. This group was equal to 28 percent of the 53 million total households in the United States.

The current trend in establishing new households can be upset by any number of circumstances. If a war, economic crisis, or other things interfere seriously with residential construction, fewer new households may be formed. Conversely, an unexpectedly large building expansion could result in comparatively lower prices and encourage the formation of more new households than now appears likely.

As indicated earlier, about half of the official 10-year goal is for new households. The other half of the projected housing construction is needed for a variety of reasons. Much is needed to help solve the search for decent living facilities for the rural and urban poor. Housing will also be needed to replace worn out and destroyed dwellings.

There are always some vacant houses and apartments and as the total number of living units rises, the vacancy rate advances. HUD says 4.4 million units will be required by 1978 to allow for the greater number of vacancies. It is estimated that a fourth of the vacancies will be in rural America because of the upswing in leisure and desires for second homes in vacation areas.

Eliminating unusable structures will mean building 4 million replacements. The Bureau of the Census says dilapidated housing "does not provide safe and adequate shelter, and in its present condition endangers the health, safety or well being of the occupants."

When the housing goal was set in 1968, it was felt that most dilapidated facilities would require replacement rather than repair. It was estimated that there were about 2 million dilapidated structures in 1968 and about 2 million more would fall into this category by 1978. About half of the replacements needed for these dilapidated units are expected to be located in rural areas.

Two million more units will have to be built because of expected losses to fire, demolition, and similar causes. Because of migration, an additional 1 million new residences will be needed in towns and cities by 1978. The rural share of these 3 million units is estimated to be about 1 million units.

A 1966 Census survey found 4.2 million occupied units were substandard because they lacked some basic item of plumbing or had minor structural defects. Some of these living accommodations are expected to slip from simply deteriorating to a dilapidated condition. Others can be repaired. The estimate was for some 1.7 million to be rehabilitated through private funds and another 2 million with public funds.

In total, the rural portion of the

Mexican-Americans in front of home in Southwest.

1978 National Housing Goal is about 7 million units or a quarter of the 26 million units to be added.

The data Census of Housing and related 1970 from the population census is providing a vital new benchmark for the housing projections and goals. It is yielding the first complete count since 1960 of the numbers and locations of housing units with and without complete plumbing, the extent of changes during the past decade, and the current household incomes of those living in standard and substandard housing. These will provide a base for revised projections of the need for new and rehabilitated units and the prospective needs for public aid.

For the fiscal year ended June 20, 1969, conventional housing starts plus subsidized rehabilitations were only 2 percent below the target established a year earlier. By mid-1970, progress toward this goal had sagged 30 percent. Even so the reduction in new housing starts during 1969–70 was less severe than during the 1966 credit crunch. The new emphasis on housing has provided much more Federal support to the mortgage market.

Despite increased Federal support for residential purchases and the initiation of interest-supplement loans to low-income borrowers, construction of conventional housing has not matched demand. Vacancy numbers have shrunk, rents have increased, and new house prices have advanced several notches. Some recovery is anticipated in 1971 similar to that which followed the 1966 monetary pinch. Public assisted starts will play a major role in the resurgence of conventional housing construction.

The situation may not be as dire as indicated. Increased production of mobile homes has more than made up for the decline in building of conventional homes and apartments. When HUD first offered its housing projections, mobile homes were not considered a substantial part of the scene. This view is no longer held.

In earlier years, mobile homes had made only a marginal contribution to the total housing supply. The units

All electric mobile home replaces old farm home in background, in North Carolina.

were considered necessary mainly to answer transient needs, and a sizable portion of the new units were thought to be replacements for older mobile homes. But the mobile home output of 1968 was 412,700 units, nearly double the 217,300 that rolled out of factories in 1966. By 1968, they represented about 22 percent of total housing starts.

The U.S. Department of Agriculture has a prominent role in aiding the private sector in achieving the goal of decent housing for all citizens by 1978. Major direct action is the mortgage loan program of the Farmers Home Administration, which aids the rural portion of the 6 million households who require public assistance to achieve adequate housing. Farmers Home also makes loans for water and sewer systems, which are needed in many rural towns and villages.

During the 1950's, Farmers Home averaged only 3,300 loans per year, involving $21.4 million. In fiscal year 1966, following congressional authority to make insured loans, the volume reached 32,029 loans for $258 million, and by fiscal 1970 there were 73,982 housing loans made for $794 million.

One reason for this growth record is that mortgage loans are now available to rural nonfarm residents as well as farmers. Farmers Home can lend in places up to 10,000 population. In recent years, the great majority of their home loans have been to rural nonfarm families living in open country or in small towns.

The permanent staff of the Farmers Home Administration at the county level, backed by a local advisory committee, is a main source of strength in the program. The staff actually consults with the prospective borrowers, supervises construction, receives the monthly payments, and checks on any financial, structural, or upkeep problems that may arise. Even with a comparatively low-income group of borrowers, this close contact has resulted in an exceptionally good repayment rate.

Farmers Home loans are expressly designed not to compete with private lending agencies. Loans are made only to those borrowers who are unable to obtain adequate credit from other sources. This provides a larger clientele than one might expect, because of a "credit gap" in rural areas.

Savings and loan associations and the other traditional mortgage lenders have tended to serve first the larger communities. The Federal Housing Administration and Veterans Administration mortgage guarantees also have not reached rural America in appreciable volume, because these loans are originally made by private lenders, with backing by the Federal agencies. Country banks exist in the small towns and serve many needs within the community, but often have not had many resources available for long-term mortgage lending. Thus, Farmers Home helps fill a real gap in mortgage credit.

Farmers Home housing loans have been concentrated in the South Central and Southeastern States, where a majority of the substandard rural housing and low income households are located. Based on household numbers, black households have obtained a more than proportionate share of loans.

Interest-supplement loans first authorized in the 1968 Housing and Development Act created an area of close cooperation between USDA's Farmers Home and HUD.

The Act provides that lenders receive market rates of interest. However, for low-income households the government pays most of the interest charge, which often amounts to half the monthly payment. The Act specified that Farmers Home service these loans in rural areas. Thus, where borrowers cannot obtain mortgage financing from regular lenders, Farmers Home processes the HUD forms and arranges the interest-supplement payments.

Farmers Home field staff has provided a more effective means of extending these loans to rural areas than would otherwise have been available through HUD.

National forest timber is a significant

factor affecting lumber for housing. The sudden and spectacular 1969 rise in the price of softwood lumber and plywood centered attention on the basic sources of lumber. Even though prices soon reverted to 1968 levels, the Forest Service pointed out that an accelerated program of protection and management, on both public and private holdings, would be needed during the 1970's to maintain adequate timber supplies for increasing demands at reasonable prices.

The National Forests will require expanded efforts in timber planting and harvesting, constructing forest roads, and protecting forests from fire and pests. And these programs must be kept in balance with recreation, wildlife, and other multiple use values of the forest. Increased assistance to State and private forests will be needed to promote sound management.

There are active programs of research in several Federal agencies directed at long run housing goal achievements. HUD is providing large-scale testing of factory manufactured housing components and units. USDA's housing technology researchers in the Forest Service and Agricultural Research Service were called upon to help frame the program and review proposals submitted by industry.

Engineers in the Agricultural Research Service test housing materials, structures, and building methods and develop house plans. In recent years, they have emphasized low-cost housing, and have worked closely with the Farmers Home Administration.

Home economists of USDA and the Experiment Stations have long been active in checking the livability of house plans, and in interior design and home management. The Economic Research Service has recently established a housing research unit, with particular responsibility for analyzing rural housing trends and the impact of governmental programs in rural areas.

The Cooperative State Research Service helps coordinate housing research at State Experiment Stations. Extension Service has carried many of these findings to the people. The Rural Electrification Administration has led in electrifying nearly all homes in rural America and has a program for providing modern telephone service.

Achievement of the national housing goal of over 26 million new and rehabilitated units by 1978 faltered as a result of monetary stringencies during 1969–70, but the final goal is not beyond reach with a healthy national economy.

Poor Housing Blights Our Countryside

RONALD BIRD and
NOLAN KEGLEY

MUCH OF THE HOUSING in rural America is bad.

Surveys indicate that in 1968 one in every six rural homes was substandard. About one million rural homes were dilapidated—literally falling down—and another two million were classified substandard, mostly because of inadequate plumbing.

It is doubtful that conditions have changed much since then because of the low incomes of most people who live in this poor housing.

Bad housing is much more prevalent in rural areas than in urban areas. City slums and ghettos are easy to recognize because they are all packed together. They make a striking impression at a glance. Poverty—and the poor housing and living conditions that go with it—is more subtle in rural areas. You see a home that is rundown or dilapidated, then down the road you see another, and somewhere else you see another. Because you see them separately and one at a time the magnitude of the problem doesn't hit you so squarely.

It is estimated that about five million of the 63 million housing units in the United States in 1970 were substandard. About three million of these were located in rural areas and in small towns of less than 5,500 persons, compared with two million located in cities and towns with larger populations. In 1970, rural America had about 27 percent of the population, but it also had about 60 percent of the substandard housing.

Housing improved more rapidly in the rural areas than in urban areas in 1968. Rural people lived in three million substandard units compared with 5.4 million in 1960. In urban areas in 1968, two million occupied units were substandard compared with 3.1 million in 1960.

Unfortunately, the very worst housing remains. The number of dilapidated structures that were occupied in rural and urban areas was about 2 million units in 1960 and in 1970. The numbers were about equally divided between urban and rural areas.

Bad housing is a regional phenomenon. In 1960, about 60 percent of substandard rural housing was located in the South. There were more substandard homes in North Carolina or in Kentucky, than in all the 13 Western States. These differences have probably expanded rather than contracted since then because income disparities have widened.

We commonly assume that the cost of constructing new housing and remodeling older homes is less in low-income rural areas than in urban areas.

*

RONALD BIRD is Assistant Branch Chief, Community Facilities Branch, Economic Development Division, Economic Research Service.

NOLAN KEGLEY is an Information Specialist, Farmers Home Administration.

However, a study recently made in Ohio does not support this assumption. The study showed that new house construction costs did not vary substantially among economic or geographic regions. Building costs were practically the same in the central part of the State in and around the cities of Dayton and Columbus as they were in the southeastern part of the State, in the mostly rural farming areas above the Ohio River. Costs of remodeling a kitchen and bathroom also were similar in all areas, as were installation charges for various heating facilities.

Most improvements in occupied units during the 1960's consisted of adding plumbing to structurally sound units. And more plumbing was installed in rural areas than in urban areas. The number of structurally sound dwellings without plumbing decreased from 3.5 million to two million in rural areas compared with a decrease of two million to one million in urban areas.

The most important factor influencing the quality of rural housing is family income. Poor people live in poor housing. In 1960, rural families with incomes less than $3,000 a year occupied almost two-thirds of the substandard housing. In 1970 it was the same thing all over again: Families with incomes less than $3,000 still occupied two-thirds of the substandard housing.

Poor quality housing in rural areas has been going down at about the same rate that the number of families with incomes below $3,000 has decreased. In 1960, about 6.7 million families in rural areas had incomes less than $3,000 and they lived in 4.4 million substandard units. By 1970, the number of rural families with incomes less than $3,000 decreased to about 3.4 million—half the 1960 total. The number of substandard homes they occupied also decreased by one-half to 2.2 million. Most of the other substandard housing was occupied by families with incomes from $3,000 to $6,000.

While the cost of homes and the availability of financing are important factors in housing, they are not the only considerations. A study of rural housing showed that in even the most affluent families, 9 percent of the housing was substandard.

Studies indicate that owned rural housing improved far more rapidly from 1960 to 1970 than did rented housing. It is estimated that the number of owned substandard units decreased from about 2.8 million units in 1960 to 1.2 million units in 1970. But the number of rented substandard units declined considerably less, from two million units to 1.8 million.

This lack of progress in improvement in rented housing is partially related to the fact that half the substandard rented housing is occupied by tenants who pay no cash rent.

Most of the no-cash-rent houses are left over from the plantation and sharecropper systems. The houses provide shelter and little else. In the old days the landlord housed his farm labor, but because of mechanization, the workers are no longer needed.

They stay in the houses eking out an existence through whatever part-time jobs they can find. Residents of these ramshackle hovels cannot afford to repair them, and probably wouldn't if they could, since they don't own them and don't have the chance to buy them. The owners no longer need the employees and certainly don't need the houses they live in. When the tenants move on, the shacks are pushed down and that land added to the production of the farm.

These shelters have proven remarkably durable as they have stood in their dilapidated condition for several decades. Also, they continue to be occupied.

Another of our most serious rural housing problems is the persistently bad condition of rural housing occupied by our black population. Today, about 75 percent of housing they occupy is substandard compared to about 85 percent in 1960.

In rural areas, black families occupy

Mother and children in 12- by 20-foot one-room home in Tennessee.

almost a third of the substandard units. Most of the housing they live in is rented. We've already discussed how bad rural rental housing is in general, and to make matters worse, black families made up four-fifths of the no-cash-rent occupants. Almost all those shelters are substandard.

More than two-thirds of the homes owned by black families are substandard compared to less than ten percent of those owned by white families.

Part of the difference in the quality of housing occupied by black and white occupants is due to disparity in income levels. But most of the difference probably relates to the availability of decent housing. It appears that the vast gulf between the quality of housing occupied by black and white occupants in all income levels widened rather than narrowed during the 1960's.

The poor condition of housing occupied by rural aged is another serious rural housing problem. In 1960 about 25 percent of substandard rural housing was occupied by elderly families. This is nearly 50 percent higher than their representation in the total population.

This situation has probably grown worse since 1960 as the aged represent a far higher percentage of the total population today. And a higher percentage of the poor are aged.

74

While a high percentage of aged live in poor housing, most are adequately housed. Apparently their past incomes made it possible for them to buy adequate homes before their incomes decreased. In 1960, 57 percent of people over 65 years old who owned their homes had adequate housing, even though their income was less than $3,000.

But although many rural aged live in adequate homes that are paid for, they still face the problem of paying an ever bigger share of their incomes for taxes based upon the value of the homes. For many aged this currently may amount to more than 25 percent of their incomes.

When they were young and had high incomes they were able to deduct part of these taxes from their income taxes. Now they are old, their incomes have decreased, yet the property tax continues to grow. The better the home, the higher the tax.

A Man's Home Must Give More Than Shelter

PAUL J. JEHLIK

IN RECENT YEARS a fresh concept of man-in-environment has emerged. The architect, the engineer, the mason, and the carpenter alone no longer are considered adequately equipped for locating and building our homes. Those with special knowledge of human behavior also need to be involved in designing, adapting, and locating housing to meet man's basic physical needs and his social and psychological needs as well.

This rethinking of human needs and satisfactions can be expected to accelerate a change, not only in housing (its design, quality, and location), but in many other aspects of human living. It no longer is enough to appraise housing solely in terms of space, sanitary facilities, running water, sewage disposal, electric lights, central heating, and other facilities that promote physical comfort.

Among man's earliest needs was a form of shelter to protect him from the elements, animals, and human enemies. Man still needs this protection.

A home constructed and located to avoid the discomforts of wind, floods, or power failure, and designed to minimize home accidents, provides a substantial degree of psychological security. For modern man, however, this is not enough.

A satisfying home, in a satisfying social environment, develops a strong emotional attachment on the part of the family, both for the home and for the community where it is located. Every person, young or old, wants to feel that he belongs and that he is not imposing himself upon the freedom of others. Psychiatrists and social scientists have observed that in order to become a person, every individual needs a place where he can become rooted.

If an individual does not identify closely with a place, including the house where he lives, he tends to lack memories or a sense of stability, a "we" feeling. With a rapidly increasing and mobile population, the challenge of assisting people to identify with a place and with a satisfying housing environment becomes increasingly important.

A good deal of information now available tells us that the kind of house a person lives in and the respect he has in the community strongly affect the image he has of himself.

Housing for many people represents status, suggesting achievement and

*

PAUL J. JEHLIK is Director of the Social Sciences Research Program, Cooperative State Research Service.

Using poor land and diversified housing to meet man's physical, social, and psychological needs, in Hawaii.

social acceptance. Emotion-laden feelings are transmitted readily and become crucial, especially in the lives of growing children.

Some children and youth succeed despite their housing or environment, but a much larger proportion probably could make the adjustment into adulthood and good citizenship if they did not have to overcome the drawbacks of inadequate housing and poor environment.

Social science researchers and others raise questions like these: What can be done to improve the image many people living in substandard houses and declining neighborhoods have of themselves? What happens to the aging and the elderly as they see their homes deteriorating? How can homes be better designed and located to uphold a wholesome concept of family and of the family members one to another?

Scientists point to a clear relationship between zest for living and mental health. Poor housing, crowding, un-

tidy neighborhoods, and depressing interiors leave little room for stimulating, wholesome, satisfying experience, but rather contribute to social and psychological deprivation.

Man as a social being needs to relate to others. The language a child hears determines what he will speak and to a large extent how he thinks and acts. His home and social environment may be expected to influence the way he thinks, the quality of his health, and his choice of work, as well as his attitudes.

For example, the lower one's socio-economic status, of which poor housing is often a major component, the more likely will that person experience limited social contacts so that he will live and move about in a rather limited geographic and social world.

Housing for the elderly poses some rather significant problems. Individuals at all age levels like to relate to their peers, to persons roughly of their own age and interests. What can those who plan housing and development communities do to take into consideration the elderly?

What are the best mixes of people, anyway? Should the elderly live among families in the productive ages and with children? What is the best socio-economic range? Should families and individuals living in modest homes be located side by side with the more affluent and wealthy? Would such mixes make people feel better or worse about their housing and themselves? Research findings are not too clear on these points.

Generally, everyone prefers to live in situations likely to conform to his own values and aspirations. These values may include the desire for privacy and beauty, the opportunity to relate to others, the exercise of individuality, family centeredness, and an otherwise psychologically satisfying social environment. Indeed, we may call this a frame of reference.

One of our great American traditions has been the freedom to choose our housing and its environment, even though compromises at times may need to be made. After completing a day's activity, the man, woman, or child who looks forward to returning home and enjoying the stay there most likely will continue as a socially and mentally healthy individual.

As never before the opportunity is here for initiating and encouraging housing programs which will be highly satisfying to those who occupy homes and reside in communities designed for all aspects of human living. Physical space is not enough. Social and psychological space also are important.

All this is said in the face of what one reads in the newspapers of heated controversies raging between firms desiring to develop cluster housing consisting of houses standing eave-to-eave, townhouses with tiny yards, tower apartments in the open country, and single-family homes on big lots. The arguments largely center around the economies of high density building on high priced land, not on concern for preference of the potential residents.

Now, let us examine some specifics of housing and the characteristics of occupants that relate to our discussion thus far.

Traveling about the United States one may find in various locations individual houses or clusters of dilapidated houses dotting areas of poor soil, in areas of insufficient opportunity, and occupied by residents with limited acquaintance with the outside world. Or, one may find rundown housing even in good soil and farming areas in sharp contrast with other areas of neatly painted houses, adequate employment, and many cultural opportunities and social advantages.

One may see efforts to "make do," but many of the houses look timeworn and, even though occupied, may appear to have been abandoned.

Interiors may be unkempt, the furnishings sparse, and decorations few. Frequently, such housing is crowded by too many occupants, with privacy a scarce commodity.

The style and quality of life among most inhabitants of this housing may be looked upon as substandard. The people have little or no capital; their skills are of limited economic value; and their employment is marked by irregularity and uncertainty. Often they are considered poor credit risks.

Strong motivations are frequently absent, and to take the initiative means a long, hard, uphill pull. Good work and management habits are often scarce. Broken families and irregular family life may be evident. Chronic anxiety and depression are commonplace.

These residents have little or no involvement in local politics, or measurable interest in local school or organized community efforts. They tend to defer such interests and actions to those more active or aggressive in public affairs.

Children and youth living in poor housing often are ashamed to invite more fortunate associates to visit their homes.

The discouraged feeling a child may develop about his own home and home

A beginning in housing and community improvement near Mountain City, Tenn.

environment frequently carries into adulthood. Some may think of themselves as "no good" irrespective of whether it is their housing or family life situation which contributed to this attitude. Such youths frequently find it very hard even to try to make a place for themselves.

People reared under these circumstances often are reluctant to take responsibility for such a feeling. For them, this is a way of life. It is easier to think of the rest of society as hostile, unfriendly, unsympathetic, and preventing their getting ahead.

With the foregoing in mind, let us discuss some of the statistics of housing.

Poor housing is regarded as one of the major economic and social disadvantages being experienced by *millions* of American families. Nearly half the poor housing in the Nation is in rural areas. About one million of the houses are considered unfit for human habitation. Yet, less than a third of the U.S. population resides in rural areas.

The Housing Act of 1949 called for a "decent home and a suitable living environment for every American family." The Housing and Urban Development Act of 1968 reaffirmed this goal.

In support of adequate housing for all who live in rural areas, the U.S. Department of Agriculture policy is to expand existing housing programs which reduce housing costs for low-income families by some form of cost sharing; to spur experimentation in construction methods to reduce costs; to help people make use of the housing programs of other Federal, State, and local agencies; and to work with private groups in developing housing in rural areas.

Census information shows that about a fifth of the U.S. population changes residence each year. About half of those who move do so within the same county. The other half move greater distances across county and State lines.

This means one out of every five families or individuals is either compelled or chooses to move for one reason or another each year.

Many, of course, move to obtain more satisfying housing in more satisfying communities. Then too, it is not unusual that the family of today expects more of its house and the environment it is located in than did families of earlier times.

Along with a frequent change in residence as a family goes through the life cycle, its requirements for housing change. The family's requirements are greatest during the productive years and while children are at home, and in later years tend to become more modest, particularly in regard to space. Adapting housing to the social and psychological needs of families as they go through the life cycle generates a problem of no small proportions.

Our concern about quality housing and its location in a quality environment becomes even more acute as we look forward to a rapid population increase between now and the turn of the century. The predicted population increase by the year 2000, according to the experts, is upwards of 60 to 100 million people.

To build homes for this number undoubtedly means going into some form of mass assembly line production like that for automobiles. But regardless of the way houses are produced—on a custom or a mass production basis—the important question for planners, architects, builders, and social scientists is whether the houses are designed and located in the best interest of those who will occupy them. Considerable innovation is called for in building homes and in developing the types of communities where they are located.

This means building new towns and cities and renovating the old. This means, also, planning and developing new types of open country areas. In sum, it means housing all Americans in a social environment that provides the best of the physical, social, and psychological worlds.

Housing Loans Lead to New Communities

ROBERT F. DUGAN and
ALLEN HOFFARD

M OST of our American rural communities "just happened." They grew up around a convenient country crossroad, or along a river that would provide power for a mill, or by a newly laid railroad siding. Rayburn Hills in Polk County,

Tex., is a new breed of rural community. It was deliberately created. The site was literally hacked out of the piney forest region of eastern Texas.

But Rayburn Hills is not to be confused with such other "new" towns as Reston, Va., and Columbia, Md., which were designed for future populations of 50,000 to 100,000 people with homes selling from $30,000 to $150,000.

Nor is Rayburn Hills the brainchild of a social engineer or a bigtime real estate developer.

Rayburn Hills is a modest little community of about 150 low-income families and their homes averaged less than $10,000. It is the creation of the rural credit service of the U.S. Department of Agriculture in cooperation with one of the Nation's largest corporations.

This is the story of that creation.

In July of 1968, U.S. Plywood-Champion Papers Inc. purchased a 200,000-acre timber stand in Polk County, Tex. The deal included a "company" town called Camden of some 600 inhabitants, with 300 homes—many of them dilapidated and vacant. Negro and white families lived in segregated areas and most of the black families had no indoor plumbing.

U.S. Plywood-Champion wanted to get out of the "company town" business, but the company needed these families to work in its large modern sawmill and it wanted the families to have decent, modern homes, at a cost they could afford.

In their search to find an answer to the problem, company officials were told about the Farmers Home Administration, which had a rural housing loan program for low and moderate income families.

They visited with George Dean, county supervisor for Farmers Home at Groveton, Tex.

*

ROBERT F. DUGAN and ALLEN HOFFARD are Public Information Specialists with the Farmers Home Administration.

The idea of Rayburn Hills was born in his office that day.

U.S. Plywood-Champion executives agreed to develop a 117-acre tract of its timberland just south of the town of Corrigan, Tex., about 8 miles from the company town of Camden. The tract was laid out in four blocks of half-acre lots, with water and sewer facilities, asphalt streets and street lights.

The company also agreed to deed these lots to the new residents over a 3-year period. In all, U.S. Plywood-Champion invested more than $800,000 in development of the Rayburn Hills site.

For its part, the Farmers Home Administration agreed to provide credit financing for construction of new homes for those families with reasonable repayment ability.

By the time the community is completed, Farmers Home will have provided housing loans for around 100 families. Most of these will be individual homes costing between $8,000 and $10,000 each with monthly payments ranging from $55 to $70. In addition, FHA financed a 36-family rental housing unit with a loan of $252,750.

Rayburn Hills is now a subdivision of the town of Corrigan, a community of some 1,500 population. Both communities profit from the annexation because it increases the tax base and eases the per capita burden of providing the basic community services that modern communities must have.

Creation of Rayburn Hills and its annexation to Corrigan produced an unexpected plus for the entire community. It attracted the attention of a second large corporation—Georgia-Pacific— which is constructing a large paper product plant and will provide employment for another 150 families.

Rayburn Hills is not an isolated, atypical case of the Federal Government working effectively with private enterprise to expand the employment opportunities and upgrade the quality of living of rural families.

Since fiscal 1970, when the rural housing loan program of the Farmers Home Administration was greatly expanded, the agency has pursued a persistent policy of working with hundreds of private companies in the home building trades, developers, realtors, and industries interested in locating in rural areas.

For example, in Alcolu, S.C., the Georgia-Pacific Co. was planning to close down its big Clarendon County sawmill operation because of lack of adequate, decent housing. Closing the plant would have cost 160 workers their jobs.

A concerned citizens committee came to the Farmers Home Administration and the agency proceeded to process loans for low-income housing for the workers. The committee found a local contractor willing to invest in land set aside for the housing project by the lumber corporation. Because housing in great numbers was needed, the contractor worked out a deal with a private firm in Alabama which manufactured prefabricated housing.

As a result of this rural housing project in Alcolu, Georgia-Pacific not only kept the sawmill open but expanded its operations.

Similar rural housing projects under the rural housing loan program have been arranged with companies such as Weyerhaeuser. Some are large projects involving as many as 250 homes. But others are more modest local programs of a dozen family units which are constructed under the USDA agency's new "conditional commitment" authorization.

Conditional commitment enables a builder to plan an enclave of up to 15 new homes, with reasonable assurance that the Farmers Home Administration will be willing to finance their purchase, when completed, by eligible rural families who apply.

Under this plan, builders are able to advertise their homes for sale, and to encourage prospects by indicating that financing may be available. With the use of another concept,

80

Top, prefab house is assembled in Alcolu, S.C. Above, section of all-electric paneled kitchen. Right, these youngsters can forget leaky roof, drafty bedroom, and smokey wood-stove when they move into modern, brick-veneer home (below).

builders also may "package" applications for rural housing loans. They assist potential borrowers in filling out all necessary forms and accompany the families to the local Farmers Home Administration office to file applications.

These new tools are designed to smooth the way for expansion of the rural housing program, the most rapidly growing phase of USDA's rural credit service.

With the national goal of a decent home for every American family still far from attainment, this expansion of the rural housing effort will be a key element in housing progress in the years just ahead.

The concern of private industry, and the close cooperation between the public and private sectors, as symbolized by the community of Rayburn Hills, provides optimistic evidence that the decade of the seventies will see important new breakthroughs toward attaining that vital national goal.

Helping People Buy Homes

ROBERT E. NIPP and
ELBERT BUZ PRUETT

It's 1980, and John, age 45, is looking for a four-bedroom home for his wife and three children. It's 1990, and Harry, just out of college and recently married, needs an apartment. It's the year 2000—the turn of the century—and Joe, age 40 and the head of a six-member household, must be able to rent a large house at modest cost.

If our Nation is to meet their needs and provide the millions of other American families with decent shelter, we must produce one new housing unit every 15 seconds and rehabilitate an outmoded housing unit every 210 seconds, day and night, 365 days a year, over the next 30 years. In 1970, we provided housing at 90 percent of this pace.

Our population, rural and urban, may rise by 100 million, to a total of 300 million by the year 2000. Thus, some 33 million new families will need a place to live. But we already face a housing crisis without population increase. A census survey in 1968 showed that nationally, 5 million occupied housing units were substandard. Some lacked plumbing, others were so dilapidated they endangered the health, safety, or well-being of the families living in them.

As required by the Housing and Urban Development Act of 1968, Federal agencies have extensively analyzed our nation's housing needs and goals and the prospects for meeting them. In light of their findings, HUD Secretary George Romney suggests that the construction and rehabilitation of some 26 million housing units over the next 10 years—including 6 million publicly subsidized for families with low and moderate income—is the minimum level acceptable as national policy.

Louis D. Malotky, housing director of the Farmers Home Administration of the U.S. Department of Agriculture, estimates that if we are to adequately house the 100 million population increase expected by the year 2000—and at the same time, upgrade existing substandard dwellings, replace the houses that would be lost, destroyed, worn out, or abandoned during this 30-year period—we will need as many houses as were occupied in 1970: about 63 million units.

About 1.4 million conventionally built homes and 400,000 mobile homes were built in 1970, some 7 percent fewer housing units than in

*

ROBERT E. NIPP is an Information Specialist with the Farmers Home Administration.
ELBERT BUZ PRUETT is a rural housing loan officer with Farmers Home.

Fiscal year	Unsubsidized new units	Subsidized new and rehabilitated units	Total
1971	1,535,000	505,000	2,040,000
1972	1,680,000	650,000	2,330,000
1973	1,955,000	695,000	2,650,000
1974	2,200,0C0	730,000	2,930,000
1975	2,355,000	730,000	3,085,0C0
1976	2,330,000	730,000	3,060,000
1977	2,330,C00	730,000	3,060,000
1978	2,272,000	722,000	2,994,000
Cumulative totals	16,657,000	5,492,000	22,149,000

Figures were provided by the Department of Housing and Urban Development. Fiscal years are from July 1 through June 30. Subsidized units are for families of low and moderate income.

the previous year. Because of this downswing in production, vacancy rates declined to the lowest levels since the immediate postwar period, and the large underlying demand for dwelling space drove up home prices and apartment rents at an accelerated rate.

Huge amounts of capital including mortgage credit will be required to bring housing production even with overall housing need. Hopefully, some 40 percent of this investment will be funneled into the countryside, beyond the confines of our 233 largest cities, to finance housing development in a rural environment.

More than money is required, of course, to charge-up a sharply accelerated housing program of the scale needed to provide 63 million units by the year 2000. Carpenters, bricklayers, cement finishers, electricians, painters, plumbers and pipefitters plus unskilled workers will be needed to fill the huge manpower requirement.

There will be demands on our national forests for large supplies of softwood lumber. Additionally, lumber substitutes and other types of building materials will be pressed into use. Innovative building materials and production methods also will undoubtedly come on the scene, offering ways to reduce construction costs and put the building of houses

on a volume basis similar to the way cars are made today.

Land use policies will also be germane to our national housing program so that every American has a full opportunity to live in housing featuring a pleasant environment and yet be within a reasonable distance of his job and daily activities.

The median price of all new conventionally built homes offered for sale is about $27,000. From $250 to $300 a month is needed to meet the interest, taxes, insurance, and related expenses on such a home carrying a conventional 30-year mortgage bearing 8-½ to 9 percent interest. These are exceptionally high costs for many prospective homeowners.

Although home mortgage interest rates were unusually high on new homes purchased in 1970, there are several safety valves that protect the home buyer or can be used to bail him out from his 20–30 year commitment if rates drop sharply.

First, most homes turn over every 5 to 8 years—therefore new mortgages are written that reflect prevailing interest rates. Second, mortgages can be refinanced if interest rates go down drastically, even though a small penalty may have to be paid. Third, creeping inflation of 5 percent annually tends to favor the home buyer as opposed to the family that rents. Fourth, the home buyer can deduct

83

GROWTH OF MOBILE HOMES
IN THE OVERALL HOUSING MARKET

NUMBER (THOUSANDS)   PERCENT

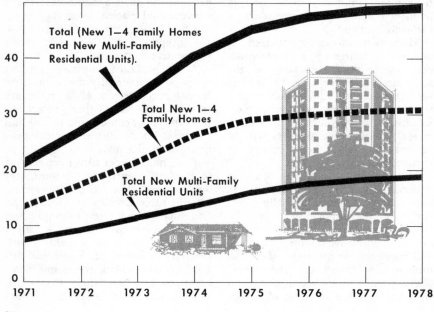

Number of Mobile Homes

Percentage of
All Conventional
Housing Starts

400 — 40
300 — 30
200 — 20
100 — 10
0 — 0

1960 1961 1962 1963 1964 1965 1966 1967 1968 1969 1970

MORTGAGE LOAN REQUIREMENTS
FOR NEW FARM AND NONFARM HOUSING

DOLLARS (BILLION)

Total (New 1—4 Family Homes
and New Multi-Family
Residential Units).

Total New 1—4
Family Homes

Total New Multi-Family
Residential Units

40
30
20
10
0

1971 1972 1973 1974 1975 1976 1977 1978

84

the interest on his home loan from his income tax.

Many American families feel they have a real problem paying more than $15,000 for a home, and there are few new houses in this price range. Exceptions are mobile homes, and this type of housing in 1970 accounted for 90 percent of all sales below $15,000. Overall, mobile homes secured more than a fifth of the new house market for single structure dwellings. The relatively low initial cost of mobile homes was a strong factor in their popularity.

Middle America's enthusiastic acceptance of the mobile home is revealed in this comment contained in a letter back to friends in the Washington, D.C., area from a family that moved during the fall of 1970 to Chico, Calif.

"Helen has been real busy with our new mobile home. It is huge; 24 x 64 feet and the master bath is 8 x 14 feet! We are now all settled inside but are just getting well started outside. Come and see us!"

"Yes, Bob and I are living in a 'mobile home,' (double wide)—but don't ever ask me about moving it, though it is possible! It is by far the most beautiful home we have ever lived in! For the first time in a long time I have great urges to create mosaics, paintings—artwork for the walls. Bob and I did tile the front entry floor."

The past several years has seen a remarkable change in thinking on who should be financing house construction. These days, more and more dependence is placed upon government financing or partial financing, as compared with 5, 10, and 20 years ago. Much more Federal aid is available also for construction of public housing and for subsidizing housing costs such as through interest supplements and other programs.

Federally-aided housing starts totaled some 27,000 in 1950 and 1960, grew to 306,000 by 1970, and are projected to total about 20 percent of all new housing by 1980.

The home ownership program in America is unique, compared with other countries. Here, families seek to own individual single-unit housing. A young couple gets married, moves out from under the roof of their parents, rents for a few years, then takes the giant step toward home ownership.

In Europe, Asia, and other countries, financing is not so readily available. New housing is not being built in the volume carried out in this country. And there is much more tendency for families, and spinster or widowed persons related by marriage or blood lines, to share shelter.

Average age of conventional homeowners in America was 33 years in 1969. About 50 percent were age 29 or less. Incomes of new owners average $12,500 with only 5 percent having incomes of less than $6,000.

Some one-third of the new homeowners in 1970 began with mobile homes with the balance buying conventional housing.

About one out of four of the housing units purchased were new in 1970. Some 5 percent of the housing purchased was on farms, 15 percent in open country, 8 percent in towns of up to 5,500 population; the balance was in larger cities and metropolitan areas.

As we move ahead through the years, toward the turn of the century, most of the funds needed to meet our housing capital requirements are expected to be raised with government support in the mortgage loan market through which privately-owned housing is traditionally financed.

In addition, significant portions of the new overall housing starts will be in the form of publicly owned housing. This housing ordinarily is financed in the tax-exempt municipal securities market.

Mobile homes will continue to be largely financed by consumer installment loans.

Thirteen principal lender groups provide most of the housing mortgage funds. Twelve of them are savings and loan associations, mutual savings banks, commercial banks, life insurance companies, noninsured pension funds, public retirement funds, fraternal societies, State-chartered credit unions, State and local government credit agencies, and mortgage investment trusts. The 13th group consists of individuals and others including fire and casualty insurance companies, savings bank life insurance companies, college endowment funds, personal trusts and estates.

The first four groups of lending institutions—savings and loan associations, mutual savings banks, commercial banks, and life insurance companies—held 86 percent of the total residential mortgage loans at the beginning of 1970. However, only 25 percent of their lending was in towns under 5,500 and rural areas.

Savings and loans are by far the single largest lender specializing in loans for single-family homes. They held $130 billion in residential mortgage loans at the beginning of 1970. S & L's obtain most of their funds through saving deposits. Some 91 percent of their loans at the beginning of 1970 were on one to four family structures. This is expected to decline to around 85 percent by 1980, as S & L's respond to the rising demand, and the sometimes higher yield opportunities for loans on multi-family structures. Savings and loans originate most of their own loans rather than purchase loans.

Mutual savings banks rank second in importance in total volume of holdings of residential mortgages. Three-fourths of their $48 billion in loans was on one to four family home loans. They purchase more than half of their home mortgage loans, the majority of which have been FHA-insured or VA-guaranteed. Money for loans comes from deposits.

Commercial banks ranked third, holding a total of $45 billion in residential mortgage loans at the beginning of 1970. Nearly all was in loans on one to four family homes. Commercial banks originate most of their own loans and purchase comparatively few loans. Money for loans comes from savings deposits.

Life insurance companies rank fourth, holding about $42 billion in residential mortgage loans at the beginning of 1970. They are the only nondeposit-type group of financial institutions which have traditionally supplied large amounts of funds for residential mortgage lending. Two-thirds of their investment is in one to four family home loans, one-third in multi-family loans.

Life insurance companies are rapidly increasing their share of multi-family loan holdings and they expect to have about half of their loans in this area within 10 years. Companies obtain most of their loans through purchases, typically from mortgage companies which originate the loans and later handle the servicing.

Mortgage companies act as middlemen, originating and selling mortgage loans and handling loan servicing contracts. Because they are so dependent on loan purchasing allocations from institutional lenders and commitments from the Federal National Mortgage Association (FNMA), their business generally shrinks considerably when credit tightens and picks up when credit eases.

Gross business by mortgage companies has ranged from $7.4 billion to $11.3 billion annually during the past few years and is expected to more than double within the next 10 years.

Private, noninsured pension funds held $4 billion in housing mortgages at the beginning of 1970 and expect to more than quadruple that amount over the next 10 years.

State and local government retirement funds held about $2.8 billion in home mortgage loans in the beginning of 1970. Their holdings are expected to increase to more than $10 billion over the next 10 years.

Fraternal societies and State-chartered credit unions, considered here together, held about $1.8 billion in mortgage loans. They expect to more than double their business over the next 10 years.

Mortgage investment trusts, a newcomer to the housing field, held about $1.5 billion in mortgage loans at the beginning of 1970, up from $400 million a year earlier. They are expected to hold more than $5 billion in mortgage loans within 10 years.

Many State and local governments have established residential credit programs to meet the needs of returning veterans and families of low and moderate income. Funds are obtained by borrowing in the tax exempt municipal securities market. The total mortgage holdings were about $3.3 billion at the beginning of 1970. They are expected to more than triple over the next 10 years.

The Government National Mortgage Association (GNMA) will guarantee about $1 billion in 1970 securities issued by pools or trusts backed by federally insured or guaranteed residential mortgage loans.

Federal credit agencies insured or loaned about $4.7 billion in one to four family home mortgages and $800 million in multi-family residential mortgages in 1969. This was an effort to strengthen the sagging residential mortgage market. GNMA guaranteed about $1 billion in securities issued by pools or trusts backed by federally insured or guaranteed residential mortgage loans. Most of this was for multi-family residential mortgage loans.

Individuals and other lender groups —including fire and casualty insurance companies, college endowment funds, labor union general or welfare funds, personal trusts and estates, and savings bank life insurance companies—are estimated to account for up to 10 percent of the total mortgage lending. However, no accurate records are available.

Back in 1949, the U.S. Department of Agriculture received authority to carry out a small farm housing loan program. This program was delegated to the Farmers Home Administration, and was part of a national goal of "a decent home and a suitable living environment for every American."

Loans were available at 4 percent interest for periods up to 33 years. But only farmowners unable to get credit elsewhere and having farms that produced at least $400 in agricultural commodities could qualify. With such stringent regulations, less than $200 million was loaned over the next 10 years. This was only enough to finance about 3,000 houses nationally each year.

Several legislative actions have been taken beginning in 1961 to amend, broaden, and improve the original farm housing loan program. Today, the Farmers Home Administration is authorized to make housing loans in rural areas including open country and towns up to 10,000 population, as well as on farms.

Due to these changes, the number of Farmers Home Administration housing loans jumped to 50,000 annually in 1969, and 80,000 in 1970. The number is expected to double to some 150,000 in 1971 with $1.5 billion projected for loans.

The bulk of Farmers Home loans today are made to low and moderate income families who cannot qualify for credit from private sources. Loans are made to buy, build, or improve their homes. Most loans are for new construction. Maximum loan repayment period is 33 years.

The current interest rate is $7\frac{1}{4}$ percent. However, if the family's income is inadequate, this rate can be trimmed to as low as 1 percent. Family income is checked regularly. If it goes up, the interest subsidy may be reduced until the family is paying full cost of the original loan.

"Our biggest area of activity is in the Southeastern States and Texas," says Housing Director Malotky of Farmers Home. "This is where most of the poor housing is, and the density of rural population is higher there than in most other farm States.

"As contrasted with 10 years ago when all our loans were for housing on farms, today over 90 percent of our loans are for people who have nothing to do with farming."

Mexican-American children play outside home in Texas.

Farmers Home Administration records show that the average annual income for families getting rural housing loans runs about $5,800. Three-quarters of the families have incomes below $7,000, but only 15 percent were below $4,000. About 17 percent of the agency's new borrowers have incomes so low that the interest they pay on loans is reduced all the way to 1 percent.

Besides its own homeownership loan program, the Farmers Home Administration is responsible—under contract with the Department of Housing and Urban Development—for the administration of section 235 Federal Housing Administration insured mortgages in rural areas.

This function performed by Farmers Home is basically the same as that performed by the Federal Housing Administration Insuring Office.

The agency accepts the applications, determines the applicant's eligibility, appraises the property, makes commitments, and then supervises house construction.

Farmers Home also makes loans to individuals, corporations, and nonprofit organizations to provide rental housing for low and moderate income people in rural areas. This is an expanding program.

The Housing and Urban Development Act of 1969 also gave Farmers Home two additional authorizations that will help stimulate development of more new housing in rural areas.

One permits Farmers Home to make conditional commitments to builders. Builders who plan to construct homes in rural areas for rural families can obtain these commitments. The commitment provides that the home will be acceptable for a rural housing loan if it is built for a given price in accordance with the proposed plans and specifications. The agency has found widespread acceptance of this approach among builders.

Farmers Home is also able to finance purchase and development of building sites to be used for housing for low and moderate income families. These loans are available to local nonprofit groups.

88

They make possible in rural areas for the first time the providing of good residential sites that offer the same types of services and facilities available in and around large cities.

As we move through the seventies toward the year 2000, a very active Farmers Home Administration program totalling $1.5 billion in loans annually is operating in rural America.

In the urban areas, a multibillion dollar Federal Housing Administration credit program is available. Additionally, giant investors from the private sector are capable of putting large amounts of mortgage money into the housing market in both urban and rural areas.

Certainly, with these resources in hand, our Nation has the wherewithal to provide decent housing for those now without it as well as for the 33 million new families that may be joining us.

The need is there and social and moral obligations oblige all of us to work diligently toward solving a serious national problem.

A Giant Step
for Families of
Low Income

LORIMER D. ELWELL and
WALTER Y. FREDERICKS

M OVING DAY. It was almost like a dream to Mr. and Mrs. Samuel Credit, of Faulkner County, Ark.

They could hardly believe that they, and their five children, were moving into a home of their own. It was their first new home as husband and wife, and the very first solidly constructed house in which either had ever lived.

The Credits were proud of their new brick home. They were eager to show the modern kitchen, with running water and plenty of built-in cabinets. Not only was there a full-sized bathroom, but also a half-bath. There were four bedrooms and electric lights in every room.

The house the Credits moved from was a stark contrast to their new home. By any standards it was unsafe and unhealthy for human habitation. The unpainted frame building was almost bleached white, the porch sagged and the steps leading up to it were rickety, and there was no inside plumbing.

The Credits had to pinch themselves to really believe the events taking place on this hot day in August 1970 were actually real.

Like millions of low-income rural people, they had become used to living in dilapidated houses, unpainted, leaning and sagging at the foundation.

With meager earnings, the Credits believed they couldn't even begin to think about buying a new house. Mr. Credit was retired on Social Security disability, and his wife earned small wages as a cook's helper at a nearby college.

But at a church meeting, they were introduced to the rural housing loan program of the Farmers Home Administration. They learned it was for people like them who could not get credit from a bank.

After many agonizing days, reflecting on the dilapidated houses in which they had lived and fearing the prospects of being turned down, the Credits braved crossing the threshold of Faulkner County's Farmers Home office.

Filing an application wasn't too difficult because the lady in the office helped.

*

LORIMER D. ELWELL is Director, Multiple Family Housing Loan Division, Farmers Home Administration.

WALTER Y. FREDERICKS is an Information Specialist in the same agency.

89

Several weeks later, to their surprise, the Credits received official notice from the U.S. Department of Agriculture that their application for a housing loan had been checked and subsequently approved.

The Credits received a $12,000 rural housing loan, and had 33 years to repay it. Because of their large family and relatively low income, they qualified for an interest credit which reduced their payment to only $429 a year.

There are many low-income families like the Credits in our nation's rural areas, but only a small percentage of them have been fortunate enough to improve their housing situations without moving to a larger community.

While the bulk of the Nation's massive housing effort is directed toward meeting the crisis in large- and medium-size cities, many low-income rural people are living in dwellings that only become more decayed year after year.

While the lack of housing for low-income rural families transcends all regions and groups in the Nation, a large percentage of these people are in the South. Many are Indian, Mexican-American, or black.

According to census figures, rural areas and especially small towns account for half the nation's substandard housing even though they contain less than a third of the households.

Some Department of Housing and Urban Development programs operate in the rural areas, but most of these are in communities of 25,000 or more.

Especially designed to serve the housing needs of low-income rural families is the U.S. Department of Agriculture's Farmers Home Administration. During fiscal 1970 about 34 percent of the agency's loans for new housing went to families with incomes of less than $5,000.

The Farmers Home Administration, with a total full-time force of about 7,400 employees in the 50 states, Puerto Rico, and the Virgin Islands, is limited to the rural country-side and small towns up to 10,000 population.

Low-income rural families living in FHA qualifying areas may apply for the agency's basic housing program, the regular rural housing loan. This program also is available to low-income families living in metropolitan areas and working in small rural towns.

The regular housing loan may be used to build new houses, purchase building sites, and buy existing dwellings. It also may be used to make housing improvements like installing a bathroom, providing indoor plumbing, adding an extra room, putting on a new roof, and making other major home renovations.

Low-income rural families receive special consideration when applying for an FHA regular housing loan. Based on family size and income, they may receive credits to reduce the interest rate on a loan to as low as 1 percent. This action reduces total monthly payments of the borrower and allows him to qualify for a loan.

Those low-income families unable to qualify for a regular FHA housing loan may participate in the self-help housing program.

The mutual self-help approach to housing has built-in savings that can bring new housing within the reach of very low-income families. Participants in the program, usually in groups of six to 10 families, do most of the construction work.

Near Edgard, La., for instance, 10 families headed by low-paid sugarcane workers averaging about $1.25 an hour agreed to contribute "sweat equity" (their own labor) in a self-help housing project. They qualified for $5,600 housing loans from the Farmers Home Administration.

Working evenings and weekends under the guidance of a construction supervisor, the self-helpers saved about $3,400 apiece by taking on tasks ranging from laying concrete block foundations to installing kitchen cabinets.

Loan funds paid for material and

fixtures, which the self-help families purchased at a substantial savings through group buying. In addition, the cost of subcontracting skilled jobs like installing electricity and plumbing came out of loan funds.

The results were these: The families became proud owners of homes valued over $9,000. For the first time in their lives, these low-income cane workers could claim a decent house of their own. Gone were the days of the outside privy. Their youngsters could grow up in an improved environment. And the wives learned to work together in developing interior decoration schemes.

The self-help approach is not the total answer in developing housing for low-income rural families, but it can play a significant role in upgrading housing for families with low cash income. Since the Farmers Home Administration made its first self-help housing loan in Goshen, Calif., in 1963, the agency has helped finance construction of about 2,200 self-help housing units.

Of special interest to low-income rural families who own the houses they live in is FHA's rural housing repair loan. These families generally live close to the poverty line. Many are public welfare recipients.

They can use repair loans to correct health and safety hazards in their home. It may mean installing an inside bathroom or replacing a leaky roof, all within the $1,500 limits of the loan. The repayment period on these loans is 10 years at 1 percent interest.

The problem of developing housing to fit the budget of low-income rural families is being approached in yet another direction by Farmers Home.

Under a plan FHA has developed with the Office of Economic Opportunity, borrowers will not be required to provide "sweat equity," yet at the same time they may realize savings up to 50 percent of housing construction costs.

The approach involves a joint effort by FHA and OEO to develop newly constructed rural housing as part of a training program in construction skills for unemployed and underemployed men. Instead of building scale model houses or sections of houses, trainees construct homes on the sites for FHA borrowers.

Generally, FHA selects borrower families for this program who are physically unable to participate in self-help housing and do not have sufficient income to pay the full cost of conventional construction, even with reduced payments through interest credits.

Besides the single-family housing

Mother of 4 discusses Farmers Home Administration loan to build 3-bedroom home in background, in St. Marys County, Md. Husband works as farm laborer. Their monthly payments are $55.

loan program, FHA is involved in a greatly expanding multi-family housing construction effort for low-income families.

What started out as a senior citizen rental housing loan program in 1962 has now blossomed into a rural rental housing program for low-income families regardless of age.

Expanded housing authority made it possible for FHA to finance construction of rental units destined for use as public housing apartments. The agency has financed two such projects, with borrowers in Alabama who leased their apartments to local public housing authorities.

Cooperatively owned housing for low-income families also has been financed by Farmers Home. It made a loan of $150,000 to 18 low-income rural families in east central Arkansas organized as the Poplar Grove Rural Cooperative Housing Project.

Other options are available from FHA for low-income families who want improved housing. The agency can permit borrower construction when it has ample proof of the builder's skill. It can accept note cosigners who pledge to make payments if the low-income borrower defaults.

New developments in construction techniques and improved delivery of credit give prospects of some improvement in solving the housing problems of low-income rural families. With a beefed-up housing program for the 1970's, FHA has as one of its major objectives the task of helping low-income rural families take that giant step into a new, modest home of their own.

As to the future prospects of low-income rural people moving into new or improved housing, the picture is far from clear.

There is no doubt that industry can provide modular or manufactured housing in sufficient quantities to meet the demand. The question is whether industry is able to provide this instant type housing at a cost within reach of low-income rural families.

On the other hand, the Federal Government has resources that would go a long way toward relieving the squalid conditions of far too much of our nation's rural housing occupied by low-income families. For instance, new programs delegated to the Farmers Home Administration—interest supplements, conditional commitments, and rural site loans—can play important roles in bringing new or improved housing within realistic reach of the Nation's low-income rural families.

Housing Migrant Workers

CARL F. SHAW

THE PLIGHT of the neglected migrant worker was thrust into the Nation's spotlight again in 1970 through a series of hearings held by a subcommittee in the Senate.

Subcommittee testimony spotlighted the despair-filled life of men, women, and children who migrate with the harvest seasons seeking the only kind of work they know: picking fruits and vegetables.

No segment of the subcommittee hearings raised the ire of Americans more than that dealing with housing. The hearings established that for too long there has not been enough emphasis on decent, healthful, sanitary, and adequate housing for migrant workers.

Housing has always been a problem. Most growers need the workers for

*

CARL F. SHAW is an Information Specialist with the Rural Electrification Administration.

Farm labor housing near Granger, Wash.

only 4 to 6 months. The houses are vacant the remainder of the time.

Local housing authorities who turn to government assistance in the form of loans depend upon rental income to meet their mortgage payments. If the houses are vacant for considerable periods of time, public bodies have difficulty meeting these payments. This is one of the reasons that some of the government loan money available for labor housing has not been used.

Private growers, on the other hand, usually do not charge their workers rent and are not faced with a loss of income when the workers depart. This generally is the only housing available and most of it does not meet suitable standards.

A 1969 Hired Farm Working Force survey of USDA's Economic Research Service revealed that the domestic migrant working force consisted of 257,000 persons. This was about 12 percent less than in 1968 and a continuation of the decline—which started in 1965—in the number of persons doing such work. There is every indication that the number of migrant workers will continue to drop.

Farm and vegetable growers who depend upon migrants are banding together and providing some type of year-round work, establishing a new home base for the worker and thereby taking him out of the migratory class.

California, Michigan, Texas, New York, and Oregon rate highest in employment of migrant workers in peak seasons. Florida, California, and Texas rank highest among the States that provide most of the migrant workers.

A subcommittee on Migratory Labor was created in the U.S. Senate in 1959 and established as a full standing subcommittee in 1969.

As a result of the 1970 hearings by the subcommittee, two amendments to the Housing Act of 1949 were passed. The amendments go a long way in providing more accessibility to loan funds and grants of the Farmers Home Administration in the U.S. Department of Agriculture.

Title VIII of the Housing Act of 1970 provides loan and grant eligibility to nonprofit organizations, extends the grant portion to 90 percent of the total cost, allows loan funds to be used for furnishings, and reduces the interest rate on selected loans from 5 percent to 1 percent.

During fiscal year 1970, Farmers Home budgeted some $4 million for loans and grants for labor housing. The 1971 fiscal year budget was upped to $13.8 million for the same purposes.

The money budgeted by Farmers Home for loans and grants for labor housing has not always been used. Builders often could not come up with the necessary funds to provide furnishings for the new housing. But the new laws which provide for loan funds to cover such costs, coupled with the eligibility extension to nonprofit organizations, may now boost the applications for such funds.

Some States have come to grips with the problem of adequate housing for their migrating workers, although not by any means solving the problem. But recognition of the problem and desire for improvement are among the first steps.

Florida is on its way to housing improvements with extensive Federal Government assistance. Oregon is providing adequate housing largely through farmer or grower money with minimum government assistance.

The southern portion of Florida is a fall, winter, and spring vegetable producing area and has a longer season for migrant farm workers than any other area in the country. Beginning in September, the work force increases until a peak of 27,000 migratory workers is reached by January.

To help meet the housing requirements for these workers, Farmers Home has made nine loans and grants totaling $12.6 million for housing units in Palm Beach, Brevard, and Dade Counties.

Of the nine borrowers, six are successful, three in financial trouble.

The three borrowers in difficulty were eligible for loans only, not for grants, and the facility depended solely on rent income for repayment of the loan. Many barracks-type single rooms were constructed which proved unsatisfactory since the single dweller was unreliable both in working habits and the length of time he might stay.

Three successful units were constructed also with loans only, but the operation of the units was handled entirely by the growers and no rent was charged to tenants. The farm organization maintains the property,

A family home for migrant labor in Florida.

bears the repayment costs, insurance and taxes. These successful units consist of individual and duplex housing complete with bedrooms, living room, bath, and kitchen. There are no single rooms.

The most successful of the nine borrowers are Public Housing Authorities eligible for loans and grants.

In the Belle Glade area, a complete subdivision with 645 family units, one to four bedrooms, was built. The local housing authority consists of five unpaid commissioners who have a desire to provide decent, safe, and sanitary housing for farmworkers. Many tenants are so well satisfied that in order to keep their house, they pay rent during the summer months while they are not working in Florida.

In the City of Homestead, a similar type operation exists with 572 houses of one to four bedrooms each. Two sewer plants, streets, and landscaping completed the project.

In Oregon a study was made of four areas in the State where the work season ranges from very short to comparatively long. The survey was a joint undertaking of USDA's Economic Research Service and the Agricultural Economics Department of Oregon State University.

Approximately 85 percent of migrant housing in the area is on farms where the migrants work. The rest is in off-farm camps sponsored by growers' associations, housing authorities, and processing firms. About 85 percent of the housing was used for families, the rest for single workers.

Oregon growers long ago recognized that, more and more, workers were returning to areas where housing was adequate. Growers either banded together to build a co-op type camp to house large numbers of workers, or obtained credit to build individual housing for their own workers. Many growers were aware that Farmers Home loans were available for labor housing; they arranged financing according to their own resources and individual needs.

As late as 1963, there was total housing capacity throughout the State of Oregon for 33,000 migrants. Most housing met the standards of suitable, sanitary, and adequate housing for agricultural workers.

Housing standards set by the Bureau of Employment Security, U.S. Department of Labor, in late 1968 have gone a long way toward improving the available housing for migrant labor.

To use the services of a government recruiter for agricultural workers, growers had to meet the housing standards set in the 1968 law. Some growers bypassed the government recruiter and did their own hiring, but many States have passed housing requirement laws with more stringent standards than those set by the Federal Government.

In researching this chapter, I talked with people in USDA, the Department of Labor, and the Subcommittee on Migratory Labor in the Senate. Many of them are directly involved with problems confronting the migrant worker.

Some believe that it is not up to the Federal Government to provide financial assistance to house the migrants. Some believe growers are solving the problem by sharing their housing resources and finding year-long work for the migrant, thereby taking him out of the migratory class. Still others think State governments are on the verge of solving the housing problems within their own States.

All of these views have some validity. Even though they differ, there is a consensus that the renewed interest shown by both State and Federal governments, along with the increasing concern of the grower, will lead to a better life for all agricultural workers.

It is a long road from oblivion to the reality of solving the migrant worker housing problem. The road will not be traveled overnight. But the migrant is at last in the spotlight and concern for his welfare will not fade.

Remodeling Rural Homes

ERNEST D. DARLINGTON and

RUDOLPH A. CHRISTIANSEN

BUILDING a new home is a little bit like buying a new car. At the outset, at least, there are no wornout or broken parts to replace. Everything looks shiny and fresh. But maybe the second-hand car was still the best buy, or the old rural home was still the best investment.

Remodeling or rebuilding an existing rural home can be a real challenge. It often takes exceptional foresight and imagination. The basic reason for going ahead with a remodeling job is to add to the "livability" of the home, to make it a safe, more comfortable, more enjoyable, and more modern place to live in.

If modernizing can be done at reasonable cost, a strong case for major remodeling can be made. Experts say that if the cost of remodeling is more than half to two-thirds of the cost of building a new home, remodeling might not be wise.

In the United States, substandard housing is a serious problem. Only about a third of our population now live in rural areas but half of our substandard housing is located there. Many rural families cannot afford to build a new home to correct their housing problems. Remodeling or repairing the old house is often their only solution.

There are many aspects to remodeling, ranging all the way from a simple paint job to adding rooms, stairways, hallways, or a garage. But whether they involve major or only minor structural changes or just a general face lifting, they all help to enhance America's rural landscape by contributing toward the gradual elimination of our substandard housing problem. It is important that the remodeled house retain the dignity of good architecture.

Should I go ahead with the remodeling job? This is an early question which must be answered. Every situation is different but there are some basic points which seem to have general application.

Location of the structure to be remodeled should be considered first and foremost. A location too close to a public road, for example, can be a definite disadvantage. A setback of at least 40 feet has been recommended. Good drainage away from the building is a requirement. Winds blowing in a direction to make livestock odors a nuisance are an undesirable factor.

Maybe some of these location elements can be solved without moving the house. If the house has to be moved, investment in remodeling is seldom justified.

If the location is acceptable, then the next important point to consider is the soundness of the structure to be remodeled. This can be a difficult decision. There may be deteriorated parts that are not noticeable. Most important is the condition of the foundation and the framing. If these are sound, it probably pays to go ahead.

A cracked foundation or one that is badly eroded or out of square could be a bad risk and major remodeling may not be justified. If the rest of the structure is in good shape, however, moving the building might be a possibility. Relocation is practical only when the basic structure is sound.

Framing defects such as a lopsided, sagging roof, walls that are out of line, shaking floors, or a bad infestation of termites should discourage a

*

ERNEST D. DARLINGTON is a Program Specialist—Rural Housing, Farmers Home Administration, Madison, Wis.

RUDOLPH A. CHRISTIANSEN is an Agricultural Economist, Natural Resource Economics Division, Economic Research Service, Madison.

remodeling project. However, if the building has remodeling possibilities, a specialist ought to be called in to make the final decision.

Of course the general layout of the living space, besides location and structure, is of vital importance. Many rural homes, particularly old farm houses, have plenty of space but should be reorganized and updated. Ten-foot ceilings often need to be dropped to eight. Many rooms are large enough to provide adequate built-in space for storage and clothes closets, perhaps a bath, or even a modern kitchen.

Now take a step back and visualize how the remodeled home will look compared with a new one. Will it serve the family's needs 10, 20, or even 30 years from now? If the decision is still "go", the time has arrived to consider plans, specifications, and cost estimates.

A detailed plan will help to assemble all the remodeling and repairing ideas in one place. It is less expensive to erase lines on a plan than to tear out partitions after construction has started. Your own thoughts plus suggestions from others will provide a picture of the whole job. It will help to establish priorities and will assist in determining the cost. The planning steps should involve the following:

First of all—make a complete list of all exterior and interior alterations to be considered. Included will be all major and minor structural changes plus all nonstructural changes.

Major structural remodeling could include such things as changing the front or rear entrance, repairing part of the foundation, removing supporting walls, adding a fireplace, dividing or combining rooms, modernizing a kitchen, or adding a bath.

Minor structural changes might involve adding or changing windows, adding storage space, supporting a sagging door frame, finishing off an unimproved room, or leveling a floor.

Nonstructural changes could include finishing or refinishing floors, walls, or doors; improving storage; modernizing or changing or adding a heating system, air conditioning, electric wiring, lighting, plumbing, sewage disposal, and water supply.

After examining the prepared list carefully and if remodeling still appears the most feasible and practical thing to do, then you should have some rough sketches or preliminary plans drawn up.

Decide what outside help is needed. It is important to obtain the services of the right man. He should be experienced in remodeling.

Read all the reference material available from businessmen and lumber dealers, libraries and magazines. Discuss your problems and plans with the County Extension Service, the home economist, the Farmers Home Administration county and home supervisors, and the FHA engineers.

Talk about your water and sewer systems with your local sanitary officer. Obtain the latest information on local building codes or regulatory legislation. Secure all necessary permits in advance.

Decide now if the planned improvements are actually worth all the additional investment and if they will add sufficiently to the house's resale value. Ask this question of some qualified person such as a realtor or assessor, or some other disinterested, qualified person.

Next, check on the availablity of credit. Determine the terms available such as interest rates and amortization periods.

You are now ready to have an experienced person prepare a set of specifications and a working plan.

After the detailed plan has been completed, get several cost estimates. If work is to be contracted, bids should be obtained.

Before making the final decision to go ahead, review the list, the detailed plans, and the cost estimates or bids. Is this what you and your family want? Will the remodeled home provide safe, comfortable living quarters in future years?

Finally, are the cost estimates reasonable? If so, you're ready to roll.

According to one farm family from southeastern Wisconsin, remodeling their old farm home was a lot of fun but mixed in were hours of hard work. It was back in 1963 that the 10-member family, consisting of both parents and eight children, decided to go ahead with major remodeling.

Before spending large sums, this family figured long and hard deciding if the old house was worth it. A careful check was made of the foundation, the basic framing, the chimney—all seemed to have stood the test of time. In addition, the house was located on well drained soil with good air circulation and good accessibility.

Equipped with a list of things they wanted done, plus some rough sketches, the family contacted several local lumber yards and builders. The modernizing would cost about $10,000, plus lots of family labor.

Final plans drawn up by one of the local building suppliers considered the following major remodeling items:

A new entrance and door plus a concrete floor in the basement.

A new hot air oil furnace to provide automatic and even heat throughout the house.

Installing a complete bath in the room originally used as a pantry.

Removing the wall between the old kitchen and the small living room or parlor to create a larger combination kitchen and dining room.

Providing a new septic system complete with seepage bed.

Installing 18 feet of new kitchen cupboards including necessary storage and work space.

Removing old and installing new insulated siding for the entire house. Also replacing the old roof with new fireproof shingles and insulating the attic.

Removing the entire open porch on the south and east sides, and insulating the exterior walls.

Replacing all rotted window sashes and frames with new modern windows.

Installing new outside doors and frames. Leveling floors and putting down new underlay where necessary.

Constructing a new family or TV room utilizing the old open porch space on the south side.

Besides the major work just listed, countless other jobs were performed either by members of the family or hired workers. This was truly a major remodeling and renovating. Every room from basement to attic was affected in either a major or minor way. But from an architectural standpoint, the appearance of the 65-year-old home was not materially changed.

The old, open porch is gone. In its place are neat, small steps and a porch leading to the front door. Light, which heretofore was blocked by the overhanging porch, can now pass unobstructed into living areas of the home. This helps provide a pleasant space where family life can thrive.

The remodeling and general renovating of this rural home adds to the beauty of the American rural landscape. The large, spacious, well-kept yard with its majestic trees provides an excellent background for the recently dressed-up rural home.

Industrialized Housing May Hold the Key

JOSEPH W. SIMONS and
EARL R. BELL

WHEN INDUSTRY made the change to mass production, housing was left far, far behind. Nearly everything you buy today has come off a precisely engineered production line, but probably not the house you live in. It was put together stick by stick or brick by brick, in a process that was at the mercy of the weather and the outmoded handicraft methods used in the past to construct houses.

As a result, the land of plenty is drastically short of housing. More living units are needed each year than are being built.

When a family does find a house, more than likely it won't be able to afford it.

All this may have improved had we listened to Leonardo Da Vinci when he told us in the late 1400's to "Let the houses be transported and arranged in order, and this can be done with ease because these houses are first made in parts upon the open places, and then fitted together with their timbers on the spot where they are to remain." Da Vinci may have been the first to recommend industrialized housing to society. However, the idea did not catch on.

The first apparent introduction of off-the-site fabrication in the United States was in 1624 when the English brought a wooden panelized house to Cape Ann. But that did not catch on either. The art of constructing houses progressed very slowly for about three centuries. The original breakthrough for industrialized housing possibly began in the early 1910's when precut pieces for a specific house became available for families to construct their own house.

The housing industry progressed slowly then through the "LUSTRON" house of the 1940's and the "LURECO" house of the 1950's. In this period of the fifties many systems of prefabrication, as it was known then, appeared on the market. The most popular at that time were the panelized houses in the Midwestern States and the shell houses of the South Central States.

The 1960's introduced the sectionalized house as a derivative of the

*

JOSEPH W. SIMONS is Leader, Rural Housing Investigations, Agricultural Research Service, stationed at Athens, Ga.

EARL R. BELL is an Engineer in the Rural Housing Division, Farmers Home Administration.

mobile home industry. However, the public was apprehensive of accepting any shelter that rolled down a highway and attempted to become a permanent dwelling. When the social sciences catch up with the progress made by the technological advances of the last 30 years, then industrialized houses will be more acceptable to the public.

Mobile homes have boomed because permanent housing is not readily available nor economically feasible for many beginning families and fixed income retiring persons. These families of our society take the mobile home temporarily until they can increase their income and settle into a more permanent home. We are moving rapidly in the direction of industrialized housing. Today we have many types and systems in use and other systems are in the experimental stage.

Some building manufacturers estimated that by the end of 1970, some 75 to 80 percent of all new housing would in some degree be produced in the factory, and that by 1980 completely manufactured homes will account for the major share of the new home market.

This means that moderate and high-income families as well as low-income families will be supplied with manufactured houses of quality, design, and size in keeping with their accustomed manner of living. In this era with craftsmen becoming more scarce and labor more costly the builders will become increasingly dependent on factory-produced housing in one form or another.

It is not always possible at the present time to reduce costs greatly through industrialization. However, industrialization has many benefits. It allows the use of materials, methods, and tolerances that cannot be duplicated on the housing site.

Manufacturing takes place within a structure and thus is virtually unaffected by weather, temperature, mud, and other factors that seriously affect onsite work. Labor is more

99

plentiful and more easily controlled to meet changing production schedules. The quality and delivery of material is also more readily regulated and material may be stored out of the weather, thus preventing damage that is a very costly element of onsite construction.

The industrialized approach toward the production of millions of housing units during the present decade requires the best brains available. Intense coordination of the design process is required as well as close attention to details in the construction phase. This must be done if we are to approach the optimum in economy, esthetics, function, environment, and other factors.

The systems presently available might be classified in four general types: (1) panelized, (2) sectionalized, (3) modular, and (4) complete houses. Precutting lumber for constructing a house has been revived after a long period in which there was little activity in this direction. Packaged precut framing and roof trusses are available on the market. The onsite carpenter needs only hammer and nails.

Prehung doors and other millwork items are obtainable as a package. An interior finish package may include prebuilt stairs ready to install. Actually, almost a complete house may be obtained precut with most items included except cabinets, plumbing, wiring, and heating.

Many panelized systems have been developed and used in this country and abroad. Wood frame panels were first on the scene but other materials such as steel, aluminum, concrete, and plastic have shared in the promotion of this type of system.

Some panels may be unfinished on one or both sides or they may be completely finished on both sides including windows, doors, electrical wiring, and plumbing installed. Floors, walls, and roofs may be furnished. Wall panels may be 4 x 8 feet in size for easy handling or may be a full wall

section requiring a crane for lifting in place.

Use of lightweight concrete in making precast prestressed panels reduces the difficulty encountered in handling and provides a better insulative value than regular concrete. Prestressing the reinforcing adds to the stiffness of structural members and it reduces the amount of reinforcing steel because the dead weight of the concrete is less. This type of panel has become more common over the past few years.

In sectionalized housing a complete house is built in the factory in two sections, each section usually being 12 feet wide. The width may be more or less depending upon the limitation in each particular State for transporting over highways.

These sections are transported to the site, rolled onto the prepared foundation, bolted together and to the foundation. Once the utility hook-ups are made the house is finished.

Most sectionalized houses are of wood frame construction with many variations in exterior and interior finishes. In the past some have not been built rigidly enough to stand the racking of highway transporting. As a result joints have opened up and difficulty has been met in getting the house square and plumb. Prefabricators have found it necessary to improve the structural strength or provide adequate bracing in order to have a satisfactory finished product.

The board chairman of probably the largest home manufacturer in the United States has predicted that within the next 10 years modular construction will emerge as the principal method of building homes.

One important result of modular construction claimed by the manufacturers will be significant reductions in cost. Mass production will be used more. As the market expands, handwork would be virtually eliminated. The manufacturing process envisioned would be more like making an automobile—perhaps mainly stamping and assembly operations.

100

Time will tell whether or not the prediction comes true. Nevertheless the factory-built module eventually may be the answer to many problems which puzzle the building industry today.

Modular construction has not been perfected. Actually the ideal module of the 1970's has yet to be conceived. Material used in such a module probably is not manufactured at present. The equipment required for such a production process has yet to be placed on the drawing board.

Modular construction might be termed as "stack up" or "building block" construction. Large sections are generally preassembled in the factory. These modules are trucked to the site and may be fitted together in various arrangements.

Often construction begins with a floor on a transportation frame on wheels. All utilities including air conditioning, furnace, kitchen, and bathroom equipment are installed at the factory. The ground floor modules generally rest on piers and perimeter foundations. Second floor units are easily placed by means of a crane.

The first modules produced were generally of wood construction. However, lightweight reinforced concrete, concrete and steel, and steel construction are common today. Plastics have been tried. Foamed sprayed concrete as well as fiberglass coating over foamed polyurethane or polystyrene are under study.

Among new materials in use by one manufacturer is a gas-fired concrete which is a fifth the weight of sand-gravel concrete. It is placed with either epoxy glue or fiberglass chips and can be put together at almost any temperature. This material is being used in virtually all the concrete construction in Germany, Sweden, and England.

The same manufacturer is experimenting with a new type of sewerage system which proposes saving about 12,000 gallons of water per person per year and a considerable reduction in installation costs.

Other developments include lightweight concrete modules which may have steel wall columns to carry the structural load of housing. Some are finished with brick veneer at the site.

Modular construction can be erected rapidly. In typical operations only 2 or 3 weeks are required from the time the units are delivered to the site until the housing is completely finished including utility hookups, the exterior surfacing, and landscaping.

In one typical operation, the labor on individual modules before delivery to the job site may be about a seventh of the total cost. Labor onsite may amount from a quarter to a third of the cost of materials.

Thus, the labor might amount to 25 percent and the materials 75 percent of the total cost as compared to 50-50 or perhaps 60-40 percent for conventional construction. These labor and materials relationships may not be representative for all manufacturers.

Generally, a 300-mile radius between manufacturing plant and building site appears to be an economic limit for normal transport. It is not uncommon, however, to transport over distances of 700 miles or more.

Completely finished homes are sometimes built in a factory and moved up to 40 miles to a prepared foundation. This requires a movable type of factory and adequate space. It is doubtful if this technique will become widespread except perhaps for large housing developments.

Our problem in industrializing the housing industry has not been primarily technology. You never get a worse house—most often the manufactured houses are better. Generally the structural materials are better. Glue with nails or staples machine-applied will provide a more rugged construction than used in ordinary site-built houses.

More rigidity and quality are necessary because of the cross-country movement it will take; it will suffer some strains that a site-built house will never have to experience. The built-in-place house merely has to stand there and resist stresses caused by weather.

One of the strongest barriers to industrialized housing has been the lack of a large enough market in a single sales area or what is called an aggregate market. Regional planning including urban as well as open country and places with countable populations using the well-planned cluster system—mixing single family detached houses, row houses, town-houses, garden apartments, high-rise apartments and the immediate amenities, such as parks, playgrounds, schools, churches, shopping, and other applicable commercial industrial complexes—will aggregate the market.

We still dream the impossible dream of an English manor house on a green estate, and settle for ticky-tacky houses all in a row with white picket fences. We simply have to learn to live closer together.

We are not yet learning from experience. We tend to forget that remarkable civilizations flourished in attached dwellings of Greek and Roman towns.

We should discover the rewards of planned clustering instead of suburban sprawl.

The advantages of density are to save common land for leisure and recreation. We have to build privacy and quiet into the structure and not hope that a slim strip of green grass will create them.

When we look at the economics of industrialized housing, we have to recognize the values and beauty of houses that are simple in design, modest in cost and plain in color, yet made of steel, glass, aluminum, and plastic.

Natural materials like wood, brick, and stone, with their unmatched human appeal, will hold a place as veneers and finishes to bring individuality to exteriors and warmth to interiors. But houses made primarily of natural materials may be hard to come by in the not too distant future. They will be supplanted by manmade materials which may be more readily adapted to precision-machine fabrication.

Hopefully, the change to synthetic materials will then help reduce the cost per unit. Heretofore, the higher costs have been another barrier to the industrialization of housing construction. Until the markets have increased and been brought together in a single sales area, the costs of manufactured houses will necessarily remain at about the same or slightly higher than site-built houses.

Industrialized housing is here. The Department of Housing and Urban Development has sponsored "Operation Breakthrough" in which 22 competition winning companies will construct 2,000 housing units across the country. This may be the impetus necessary to provide a change in public attitudes, building codes, and community zoning, while adding to our technology experience.

Let us not forget, when we in these United States become convinced of a tremendous need for the preservation of our freedom and comfortable survival, we work together for the common cause. Industrialized housing may be the one big answer to the present poor housing situation in our land-of-plenty.

New Look Dwellings and Towns

RICHARD H. SLATER

A NEW housing unit every three seconds! We will really need to keep our cool to meet the housing needs of the 100 million or so more people added to our present population by the turn of the century. Besides upgrading existing substand-

Modular, reinforced fiber glass bathroom.

A common misconception about Breakthrough is that it applies only to densely populated areas. Not so. Spin-off benefits of the program have broad application to rural America.

If these benefits are to be realized, rural Americans must be prepared to receive them. Some are quite radical. Completely molded bathrooms containing all walls, ceilings, floors, and fixtures—right on down to the soap dish—have gone beyond the drawing board stage and are currently on the market. All that needs to be done is hook them up to a water supply and a waste system.

Electrical wiring flat as a ribbon that can be pasted to the wall and then painted is being developed.

As building technology advances further in developing new methods and materials, the life style of the housing occupant is bound to change.

Most Americans are accustomed to living in compartments. Each compartment is assigned a definite activity, one for living and entertaining, one for dining, one for cooking, one for sleeping, and one for taking care of the bodily functions and bathing.

These compartments are arranged under a roof supported by walls which sometimes, and quite commonly, take on the appearance of an 18th century dwelling or facade made up of decorative elements of the past which have little relationship to today's world.

Innovative methods and materials imitate this traditional plan and style. Present manufactured housing is, for the greater part, doing just that. However, with a more understanding and permissive market, housing can take on new form in style and plan more adapted to the building system and material. The American public has permitted the automotive industry to do this, but it may take considerably more time before we are ready to break away from the sentimental trappings of the past that are reflected in our everyday surroundings.

The general public is gradually realizing the desirability of open planning. It has taken time, but the advantages

ard dwellings, and replacing homes lost, destroyed, worn out or abandoned during this period, we'll need to produce an adequate housing unit every three seconds of each working day. We're already way behind.

HUD Secretary George Romney thinks we can do it by mass production methods, and revisions and updating of building codes to include time-saving innovations. Along with expeditious and low cost financing, that's what Operation Breakthrough is all about.

One of the greatest successes of Breakthrough is that the public has come to recognize there *is* a housing problem and that steps are being taken to solve it. The program has awakened industry to branch out into the housing game, and put some of its production principles to work in housing manufacture.

*

RICHARD H. SLATER is an architect in the National Office of the Rural Housing Division of the Farmers Home Administration.

Top, balanced community of Reston, Va., with variety of
dwellings, shopping area, and industrial area (background).
Above, underpass at Reston. Right, forerunner of underpass
at Greenbelt, Md., pictured in 1937.

104

are there, especially in low-income housing. Multi-purpose areas which include everything from ironing, to cooking, TV watching, and dining are being seen more and more in our rural homes.

Though there is little more area than before, the space appears larger, due to the disappearance of confining walls. The lady of the house likes it because she has company while she does her household chores and the kitchen-dining-family room is the center of the action.

As for allowing the innovative materials to express themselves—and not simulate another material such as wooden ship-lap siding, cedar shakes, or mock-brick—this will take a little longer. But it's coming. Just you wait.

Innovative planning does not stop with the dwelling unit. Planners are concerned with producing a well balanced community where people living in harmony with each other can take advantage of the latest technological developments. This all-encompassing planning ideal is finding expression in many locations in the United States and throughout the world.

The U.S. Department of Agriculture under the Resettlement Administration carried out successfully a number of schemes for model towns in 1935 which have been used as archetypes. Twelve model cities were planned and three were built. The most noted of them is Greenbelt, Md.

Greenbelt and its two sister cities, Greendale, Wis., and Greenhills, Ohio, were new towns patterned on the philosophy of the first modern planned community, a garden city, Letchworth, England, built in 1903. The innovator, Ebenezer Howard, envisioned the English project this way: "A Garden City is a town planned for industry and healthful living; of a size that makes possible a full measure of social life; surrounded by a permanent belt of rural land; the whole of the land being kept in public ownership or held in trust for the new community."

Though some of the pleasant advantages of Greenbelt were destroyed by encroaching highways, it remains an example of what can be done in planning new towns. A study of the events making possible the construction of the highway through its heart can be a lesson to all who wish to preserve those features which give towns their individuality and rustic charm.

With the increased pressures of city living, the crowds and congestion, and the many types of unhealthful pollution, Americans are looking to the countryside for new communities which can give the tranquility that large urban centers lack.

Development of our highways and transportation facilities have enabled new communities around the large urban centers to take advantage of the planning and experience Greenbelt offers. Among the new towns are Columbia and Crofton, Md.; Reston, Va.; Flower Mound, Tex.; California City, Calif.; and several retirement communities like Sun City, Ariz., and Port Charlotte, Fla.

An important element in planning these communities is demographic balance. A mix of people of all ages, various economic strata, education, race and religion as well as gainful employment and industrial opportunity on the site, makes the community a real part of the world.

Innovative methods of housing and planning, used to a degree today, forecast a future that will revolutionize our way of living as we now know it. We are going through the growing pains of discovery that will lead us to this change.

Emphasis on the planned environment for living, rather than an individual unit, is the ultimate society we are approaching. This environment will include all those necessary wants, needs, and a life style for the man of the not too distant future. The individual unit promises to be only a small part of the system.

Building and planning technology is pointing in this direction. The garden, or Greenbelt-type community, is a step. Each new step has gone further. Words like "archology," a combination of architecture and ecology, are being formed to describe this new way of life and planning. Environment control—including control of pollution, temperature, humidity, and transportation—is an important element in planning a new community.

The first enclosed community is now underway in Alaska. A site of 3,200 acres to be linked by monorail to Anchorage, two miles away, will be the first city in 50 years planned to be totally free of automobiles. The new city, called "Seward's Success," is scheduled for completion by 1990 at a cost of $800 million.

Eventually its population is expected to reach 55,000. It will have a climate-controlled environment, providing clean, humidity-regulated, 68° weather throughout the year.

Seward's Success will have all the facilities for day to day living, including townhouse type dwellings, churches, schools, hotels, shopping, and recreation. These will be interconnected by temperature-controlled malls and an automated transportation system powered by electricity to move people and materials.

The total environment concept is not a new thing; ancient fortified towns were essentially just that. Communities like Seward's Success are modern, sophisticated versions of Carcassonne or of Machu Picchu, planned communities that contained all the elements needed to support their inhabitants.

The principal difference of the contemporary new towns may be their reasons for existence and a more democratic form of administration. However, they bear a marked similarity to their venerable French and Inca counterparts.

Designers and planners are looking for and finding building systems which will allow the enclosure of vast areas of land. Seward's Success is only the beginning of planned communities under a roof. Advocates of weather control and the fight against all types of

pollution are discovering that an enclosed community is a solution to these challenges.

The U.S. pavilion at Japan's Expo 70 covered an area 265 feet wide and 465 feet long with a low profile air-inflated structure. This is simply a translucent fiberglas fabric supported by cables anchored to a concrete ring wall and kept at a constant blown-up shape with high power blowers.

It is said that the area enclosed in this fashion is practically limitless. Imagine complete towns covered this way! Preliminary planning of balanced communities that look as though they came right out of Buck Rogers are currently being studied by far sighted designers and the general public.

To meet our housing goals, we must be ready to accept new ideas of planning, new materials, and a different way of life. Drastic revisions in building codes will be needed, along with labor union acceptance of new materials and methods.

Mobile Homes and Parks

ROBERT W. MURRAY JR. and
CHARLES E. WALSH

MORE THAN 6 million Americans live in about 2½ million mobile homes. That is more than live in any one State except the eight largest, more than the total who live in both Israel and Ireland.

Mobile homes in the past few years have suddenly and strikingly become a way of life for millions of Americans who prefer it to other types of housing. The Federal Government has begun to include mobile homes in reports on housing starts, and Congress has

A mobile home.

passed a number of laws to pave the way for further gains in mobile home living.

Not that the road has become easy for those who want to make and sell these homes or for people who want to buy them. Many a community raises (often unfairly) zoning roadblocks against the rising flow of mobile units. And many built-in barriers exist, like the high cost of land in metropolitan areas where most people who need low-price housing live.

Nearly all these new type homes go into rural America and on the outskirts of small and medium-size cities. Their greatest impact has occurred in the South, where about half of them have gone in the past few years. Yet a glance at the list of States where most sales have been made shows how widespread public acceptance has been. Greatest sales growth has come in this order: Florida, Texas, Georgia, North Carolina, California, Michigan, Pennsylvania, Ohio, New York, and Indiana. Hawaii alone has not shared in the trend.

Thus through most of the country, mobile homes have provided suitable dwellings for large numbers of families. Sales hit the 400,000 mark in 1969 and

*

ROBERT W. MURRAY, JR., is Special Assistant to the News Director, Department of Housing and Urban Development (HUD).

CHARLES E. WALSH is Assistant Commissioner for Property Improvement, HUD.

1970, and last year nearly one out of three single-family dwellings produced was a mobile home.

Furthermore, as Secretary George Romney of the Department of Housing and Urban Development (HUD) has pointed out, last year 96 percent of all single-family homes priced at $15,000 or less were mobile homes, "filling a major need."

Without question, the basic low price of these units accounts for their great popularity in these days when prices of conventional housing have risen beyond the means of most families.

The mobile home industry says prices range from $4,000 to $18,000, with the average retail price at $6,300 for a mobile home with 684 square feet of living area. The price includes furnishings and appliances, lamps and draperies.

This $6,300 price contrasts sharply with the average $23,000 sales price of conventional new houses recently sold (which includes land and appliances but no furnishings).

Another key difference is in initial payments. The down payment on a $6,000 mobile home ranges from about $900 to $1,200, compared with $2,000 to $5,000 down on a $20,000 house that a modest-income family might afford.

No wonder then that so many families now buy the mobiles; these are the only dwellings a lot of families with modest incomes can afford. A study sponsored by HUD shows that the typical owner of one of these units is a young blue collar worker with an income below the national median.

On the other hand, the poorest families can hardly afford mobile home living. Time purchases are costly; interest rates are high. Conventional lenders in recent years have collected 12 to 15 percent simple interest on mobile home loans.

These loans are usually on 5- to 7-year terms. Thus, a $4,000 loan paid back over seven years will cost a borrower $1,931 at 12 percent or $2,483 at 15 percent.

Bear in mind, also, that the owner must pay a monthly rent for the space his unit occupies, and utility bills, as well as repay the loan on the home. Mobile home park operators collect anywhere from $25 to $100 a month per "pad" in their parks. Thus the buyer of a $5,000 mobile home might have total monthly housing costs of $150. This equals 30 percent of the earnings of a man with a $6,000-a-year income.

Nevertheless, countless poor families are living in mobile homes today, paying monthly housing costs of $100 or even less. These are the families whose homes are seen on backroads in most parts of the United States. They have bought hand-me-down old mobile homes and placed them on rural lots they or relatives own. The 1970 Census will probably show a very large count of these homes—and a large number of them probably are in substandard condition.

One of the many unknowns is how long a mobile home lasts. They are not built as sturdily as conventional houses. Most of them take a heavier beating from constant family use in small quarters. Guesses as to their length of useful life range from 10 to 20 years. Some will no doubt last longer than others because they are constructed of better-grade materials.

The question of durability will not be answered until the government completes a study on this important matter. (Government housing officials need to know how long the mobiles last in order to determine how many housing units of all kinds are required to fill the Nation's total housing needs over the long run.)

Every buyer of a mobile home has a stake in this matter of durability. The buyer needs to know at what rate his home depreciates in value, how much he loses of his investment over the years. Some dealers tell buyers that the values do not drop and can even go up, especially if the homes are located in the best planned mobile home communities.

But there is much evidence that points to rather sharp value declines for these units. In many ways the mobile home industry is patterned after the auto industry. Model styles change often; dealers have the same kind of "floor financing" for their inventory in both industries; both have "blue books" that suggest the resale values of units made in recent years.

Values of mobile homes are said to drop by 15 to 20 percent after one year and to drop by 50 percent over the first five years. After that, depreciation is much slower. The industry blue book lists thousands of home models and suggests the price dealers might well pay for each and how much to resell it for. As a rule, the book suggests that dealers offer a third less than they expect to sell for. This is important to owners, for most sell to park owners and dealers when they want to trade up for a new model or move into conventional houses or apartments.

Maintenance problems vex many a mobile home owner. The metal roof often warps and develops leaks and usually must be sealed again after two years. Doors may twist away from their frames when homes settle on their cinder block bases. Plumbing leaks sometimes rot the plywood flooring.

A survey of mobile home owners in 1970 showed that more than half the owners complained of noisy furnaces and about how hot their homes

108

were in summer. But this study, by Owens Corning Fiberglas Corporation, turned up much less response about construction or other problems than favorable response about mobile home living.

Several surveys by government and industry show that most people who live in modern parks enjoy the life there. In fact, Owens Corning found only about 8 percent dissatisfied.

Few mobile homes are truly mobile. Not many move again after being towed to the first location. Families can hardly afford to pay hauling costs to move them. For example, an owner must pay $754 to have a commercial mover tow his 12-foot-wide, 60-foot-long home the 722 miles from Washington, D.C., to Nashville, Tenn. This charge, fixed by the Interstate Commerce Commission, covers highway tolls and escorting required in some States.

In the words of Richard K. Beitler, a Hinsdale, Ill., mobile home consultant, "The mobile home is *easily* mobile only from factory to site. The average mobile home owner is as permanently fixed to his pad as the site-built home's owner—5 years. The trend today when families move is to sell the mobile home where it is and buy another in a new location."

This trend is reinforced by the growing practice of park owners and mobile home makers to run "closed" parks. This means owners must buy units from parks and sell back to the parks when they want to move elsewhere.

Around some cities, land developers are catering to the new breed of mobile home owners, with lots laid out specifically for the larger units up to 24 feet wide.

About half of new mobiles go to private sites, often for lack of spaces in parks. These park spaces have become hard to find. Many buyers must wait months before they can find available spaces. In recent years, far fewer parks have been developed than needed to meet greatly rising demand.

Somewhere between 15,000 and 20,000 mobile home parks have 15 or more spaces each (not including spaces for camping vehicles and other smaller mobile units). Many are in out-of-the-way places where most new owners do not work or live. And many are small, without laundry buildings or other features families want.

Some 13,000 of the better mobile home communities with about 900,000 spaces are listed in "Woodall's Directory of Mobile Home Communities." These are rated with one to five stars, more stars going to parks with the best features and best management. Only 1,400 parks rated four or five stars in 1970.

As the shortage of good spaces grows, complaints increase that park owners are hiking rents and stiffening rules. This space shortage hurts mobile home makers, too. Many, especially in the North and West, admit that their sales have slowed as a result.

Many new parks are coming along, with large national companies getting into the lucrative park developing business. And the government has a new program to help the trend along toward larger and better park communities with a full range of neighborhood facilities. HUD now will insure mortgage loans on parks like these—and it requires that the park owners rent to families with children and to those who buy their homes from other dealers.

Congress has also given savings and loan associations the right to make loans to mobile home buyers, has authorized HUD to insure loans on mobile homes, and has even approved a 1970 law to let the Veterans Administration guarantee loans on the homes as well as lots to place them on.

All in all, the mobile home concept has a lot going for it. Its solid base is low-cost production in factories and almost no costly labor on site. Today's wide highways make deliveries easy. And plenty of plant capacity has been built all over the country close to where the buyers want to live.

Further, the mobiles have improved in appearance, in their floor plans, and in size and comfort. Some of the "double wides" with up to 1,600 square feet of living space can, when landscaped, look just like site-built houses. Not a few well-to-do buyers of middle and older ages are among the growing number of enthusiasts.

Against all these pluses, the industry still faces a strong drawback from out of its past. Many Americans still think of mobile home dwellers as "gypsies" who move often and have no roots (and pay no taxes) in the community. Several studies have shown this to be false. More people probably use the old term "trailer" than "mobile home," though the family auto will never tow the large modern unit.

Local groups often succeed in passing anti-trailer ordinances that reflect old fears rather than reality. Some diehard opposition will continue, but part of it will fade away as the public sees more of the better new parks and learns that the mostly young new neighbors in them are as respectable as anybody else.

Mobile homes have by now provided good homes for millions who can live decently only in these low-cost, low-price homes. The Nation's housing shortage and rising costs have left other millions of people poorly housed in large cities where the mobiles are impractical. Federally aided housing programs must help largely to solve that problem, and subsidized housing—through HUD and the Farmers Home Administration—is needed in rural and smaller-city areas.

These subsidies call for large outlays of public funds. One fact is certain: if the mobile home trend had not come on so strong, far more public funds would be called for to help solve a much greater housing crisis in the United States.

In coming years, more and more Americans will come to know mobile home living at first hand. Some experts predict sales will hit the 600,000-a-year mark in the seventies. One reason: most buyers are in the young and old age brackets—and these groups will increase by great numbers while the middle-aged will rise slowly.

Others see mobile homes reaching an early sales peak, perhaps no higher than today's level. One reason is that rapid changes are taking place in housing technology. Oddly, strong competition is rising out of the mobile home industry itself, as many firms shift to factory-built "modular" homes selling at lower costs than heretofore.

Yet all signs indicate that mobile homes are here to stay as a major segment of the Nation's housing supply—serving the needs of a broad spectrum of U.S. families.

Good Planning Is Essential in Landscaping

CRAIG S. OLIVER and
LARRY D. LEUTHOLD

WELL-LANDSCAPED grounds are an attractive asset for the individual home property, and they improve the neighborhood's environmental quality as well.

Good landscaping is an art—the art of shaping spaces and blending family needs, physical features, and existing exposure into a functional design.

All who can do so should employ a professionally trained landscape architect or landscape nurseryman to plan and develop their home grounds. Some may prefer to have the planning done by an experienced designer, but carry out the actual development themselves. Others may want to prepare and develop their own plan.

Regardless of the procedure chosen, good planning is essential in landscape development. Without good planning, the final result will be considerably less than expected.

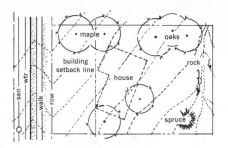

A plot plan.

In landscaping, careful study is vital so that the trees and shrubs chosen will withstand the rigors of outdoor living. Plants and structural features make up the furnishings of your home grounds, creating the outdoor rooms. The lawn is the carpet and the trees become the ceiling, providing shade and enclosure for the outdoor space.

More people will view the exterior of your home than the interior; therefore, it should at least be as attractive.

For those who want the fun and satisfaction of preparing their own landscape plan, this chapter outlines the following steps in landscape development to assist you in reaching your goal:

1. Preparing the Plot Plan.
2. Site Analysis.
3. Dividing the Property Into Use Areas.
4. The Public Area.
5. The Private Area.
6. Selecting Trees and Shrubs for the Landscape.
7. Planting Trees and Shrubs.

The Plot Plan

First step in creating a landscape plan is to make a graphic record of all the details presently existing on the property. A plot plan, then, is a guide to orderly development of a property

*

CRAIG S. OLIVER is Associate Professor of Ornamental Horticulture Extension, The Pennsylvania State University, University Park.

LARRY D. LEUTHOLD is Extension Specialist in Ornamental Horticulture, Kansas State University, Manhattan.

as well as an opportunity to examine ideas about how the property might look without actually planting. By examining a proposal on a drawing, you can avoid making permanent mistakes later.

A plan must be prepared to scale. The first task is to measure the property boundaries. Exact location of the house on the lot can be measured from any two adjacent boundary lines. Next, transfer all measurements to a piece of graph paper, using one square on the graph paper to represent 1 square-foot. If graph paper is not used, a scale of ⅛ or ¼ inch equalling a foot will be satisfactory.

Put all details existing on the property in the plan. This includes location of the walks, driveway, house, and on-hand plant materials.

Site Analysis

Physical site factors as well as needs of the family determine the usefulness of a particular property. The homeowner cannot normally change the physical factors, although they may be modified to suit family needs. The following items are important when considering site utilization:

Topography, or surface undulations of the land—Obviously, a very steep slope requires different landscape solutions from a very gentle slope. Because there are practical limits as to how steep a driveway, walk, or grass bank can be, several possibilities can be considered in solving unusual property undulations.

Views—Property is frequently developed to create or enhance a pleasant view. The view may be artifically created, or it may be the natural offsite or onsite view. If the property has a view, plantings can be arranged to preserve and accentuate the view. If the offsite view is unattractive, an effort to avoid or obscure the view may be justified.

Drainage—Provision for the discharge of surface runoff from roof gutters and from adjoining properties is an important factor to consider when studying the site. Low areas in

111

the yard can be graded, and surface runoff can be diverted from the house if corrective measures are needed before planting grass, trees, and shrubs.

Orientation—The relationship of a property to the prevailing exposure is more important than generally realized. Many plants will not grow well in sunny or windy locations; therefore, plants must be selected in relation to their adaptability to the individual situation. Thus, it is important to know where north, south, east, and west are in relation to the house and property. This will help in locating trees to provide shade in any given area.

Family needs are important considerations in landscape planning. Size of the family, hobbies, and special interests may greatly influence layout of the landscape. A family with one or two young children requires an open play area for location of a sandbox or swing. Other possible considerations are a patio for cookouts, an area for hanging laundry, and an area for a vegetable garden. These needs and desires will be different for each family.

Use Areas

The next step in the design process is to divide the total space of the property into areas according to use. These are the public or access area, living or private area, and the service area.

Division of the site into these three areas is the same for all homes. Only the details differ as affected by house orientation, topography, views, and the family needs.

Landscape development of each use area will create a composite design for the property. Each area may be considered independently in the initial design process. However, there must be an interrelationship between areas to create design unity in the final plan.

The Public Area

The access or public garden needs very little planting. A well-kept lawn, shade trees, and a few well-placed, low-growing shrubs and vines to give the house a setting should be adequate in most cases. The most pleasing front yards are those where the front lawn flows uninterrupted by plantings, walks, or fences from one property to another, and where simplicity of design is well employed.

It is not necessary to have a solid planting of tall shrubs across the front of the house. In some cases, a ground cover or a very low planting of deciduous or evergreen shrubs is sufficient. Style and construction detail of the house will dictate to a great extent the type of planting needed.

A home with an unattractive high foundation will need more plants across the front for screening than a new home with a low foundation. Plants should provide a setting for the house rather than the house provide a background for plants.

A combination of deciduous and evergreen plants can be effectively used in the public area. Deciduous plants usually grow faster than evergreens and offer this change throughout the year: flowers in spring, fruit and foliage in summer, color in the fall, besides interesting bark effects throughout the winter months.

The public area will need trees for framing and shade. Before you place

Consider the property as being divided with three areas—public garden and access area, living or private area, and service area.

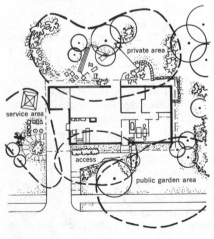

Left, the public garden should be an expression of individual thought. Right, the patio is an extension of the house outdoors.

trees, decide the points which best enhance the appearance of your home. Stand at these points and envision what height and form of trees will best suit your needs.

Smaller flowering trees may be suitable if your lot is small and the house is low, such as a ranch home. In some cases, a large tree will be appropriate to one side of the front yard and a smaller tree on the other.

The dominant area in front of today's modern house with an attached garage is the drive-walk approach. The entrance should be the most attractive, interesting, and inviting portion of the public area. This can be accomplished by careful use of plants for contrast in form, texture, color, or size.

Regardless of what you do, it is important that plants be positioned in the landscape according to a need or purpose. A simple, uncluttered design with an open front lawn area will create the most attractive landscape.

The Private Area

Development of the private area depends upon your interest in outdoor living, gardening desires, and family needs. Unfortunately, most homeowners plan a minimum of landscaping for this area. In reality, a well-planned backyard will serve a more functional purpose and give more satisfaction than the landscaping in front of the house.

Landscape development of the private area is very flexible, and there is no set pattern or formula to follow. A large family may desire more open space for outdoor living while another may want a swimming pool. An avid gardener will wish to develop the area for annual and perennial flowers and possibly a vegetable garden.

Thus, many factors will determine the design of the private area. However, the two primary factors are (1) analysis of the physical resources available; and (2) creation of a plan which will make maximum use of these resources in meeting family needs.

The first step in developing the private area is to consider dividing it into two units—the outdoor living area and the open backyard area. The major portion of backyard landscaping is usually directed toward developing the outdoor living area. This area should be considered as an extension of the house outdoors.

The terrace or patio is located in the outdoor living area. Size of the terrace or patio is also a matter of

113

concern, both in terms of design and use. A terrace or patio that is too small is a nuisance; yet, if it is too large, it is uninviting.

As a general rule, the paved outdoor living area should be the same size as the living room or, at least, provide a minimum of 64-square feet per family member.

Shape of the patio or terrace—whether it is rectangular, free-flowing, or angular—will depend upon individual tastes and the arrangement desired for the remaining yard area. Construction will require that careful consideration be given to drainage and grading before the surface material is put down.

Paving materials selected for the patio must be durable and blend with the house and other features of the landscape. Never select materials just because you like them or because they are inexpensive unless they complement or blend with adjacent landscape features. The patio will be a permanent addition to the home and careful selection of the best materials to suit the purpose is essential.

When locating the outdoor living room area, an important consideration is the addition of enclosure and screening for privacy. The amount of enclosure and screening will depend upon individual desires and the proximity of other homes.

Too often, a poor effect results when homeowners construct a low wall, fence, or plant border around the patio area. Plants and construction materials used in this manner often confine traffic movement and provide little if any privacy. The outdoor living area should provide free movement of traffic to the recreation or rear yard area.

Privacy and enclosure of the outdoor living and recreation area can be accomplished most effectively with a space divider. A fence, plants, or a combination of both can be used for this purpose.

A fence is often disliked by many homeowners because it brings to mind the unattractive mental picture of a

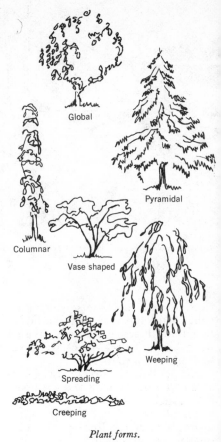

Plant forms.

chain link fence which has been so characteristically used to surround properties in many surburban areas.

Actually, if properly used and constructed of suitable materials, a fence adds instant privacy, beauty, and contrast to the landscape and can be of value both to neighbors and to you.

Development of the private area can be either extensive or limited. It depends upon individual tastes, desires, and budget. Usually an irregular, asymmetrical layout is better since symmetrical balance tends to be rigid and formal and not conducive to today's family living. Maintenance is also easier in a free-flowing design.

Selecting Trees, Shrubs

Thousands of plants are suitable for landscape use. Some may be woody

114

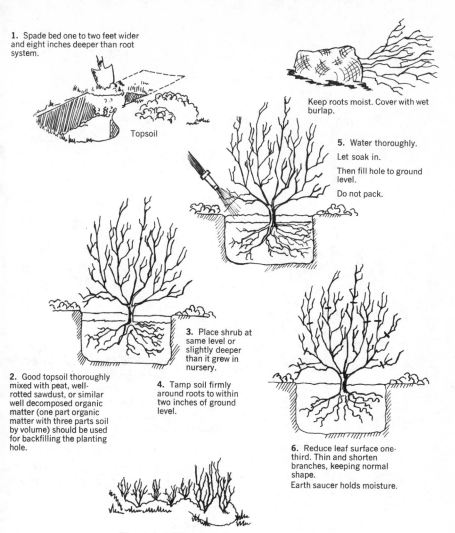

1. Spade bed one to two feet wider and eight inches deeper than root system.

Topsoil

Keep roots moist. Cover with wet burlap.

5. Water thoroughly.

Let soak in.

Then fill hole to ground level.

Do not pack.

3. Place shrub at same level or slightly deeper than it grew in nursery.

2. Good topsoil thoroughly mixed with peat, well-rotted sawdust, or similar well decomposed organic matter (one part organic matter with three parts soil by volume) should be used for backfilling the planting hole.

4. Tamp soil firmly around roots to within two inches of ground level.

6. Reduce leaf surface one-third. Thin and shorten branches, keeping normal shape.
Earth saucer holds moisture.

Zig-zag placing gives best effect. .

Planting bare-root shrubs.

deciduous plants, others evergreen, or you may even use herbaceous plants.

If they are evergreen, they will be either the needle-type like the pines, or they will be the broad-leaved forms like the hollies and rhododendrons. Deciduous plants may be flowering shrubs. The herbaceous materials will consist of annuals and perennials valuable for their flowers and habit of growth.

All these plant materials will have a relative growth habit. Some will be tall, others medium or small, and they may be either spreading, upright, or trailing. Some will do well in combination with other plants; others will do better when alone. These characteristics of plants must be studied before selecting plants for the landscape.

Plants should be selected to carry out the desired objective or arrangement subject to the elements of size, form, texture, and color. However, selection of the right plant is also a

115

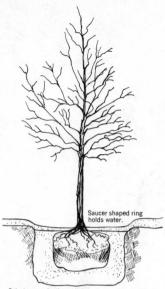

Saucer shaped ring
holds water.

Set at same depth or slightly deeper than it stood in
nursery.

Cut back and roll down burlap to base of ball.

Follow steps already given for planting procedure.

Planting a balled or burlapped tree or shrub.

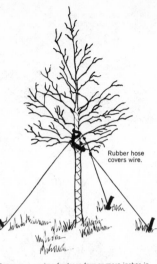

Rubber hose
covers wire.

Three-way guy wires for trees four or more inches in
diameter.

Guying trees.

matter that is dependent on the soil
and climatic conditions. Avoid exotic
plant material that may not be
adapted to your area. A visit to your
local nursery or garden center will
help you determine what is best for
your situation.

Planting Trees, Shrubs

Proper planting of trees and shrubs
is one of the key factors in landscape

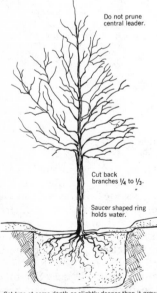

Do not prune
central leader.

Cut back
branches 1/4 to 1/3.

Saucer shaped ring
holds water.

Set tree at same depth or slightly deeper than it grew
originally.

Follow planting procedure steps.

Planting a small deciduous tree bare-root.

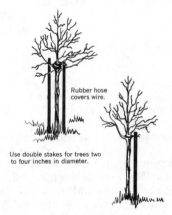

Rubber hose
covers wire.

Use double stakes for trees two
to four inches in diameter.

Use a single stake for trees less than
two inches in diameter.

Staking trees.

116

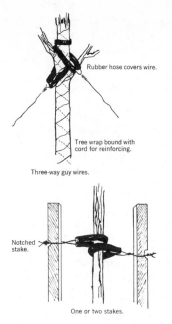

Guying, wrapping, and staking details.

improvement. In any planting operation, the effect of moving a living
plant from one place to another should
never be neglected.

When you dig up a plant, its food
and water supply is interrupted.
Hence, a general rule is to make the
period of transition from nursery to
homesite as brief as possible. Even
with the greatest care and least possible loss of time, there is still an element of chance in any transplanting.

When planting trees and shrubs, it
is essential to dig the planting hole
large enough and to modify the back-
fill soil before planting. Common materials used for modifying soils are
peat, well-rotted sawdust, or leaf compost. Following the planting operation,
proper watering and precautionary
procedures to prevent insect and disease problems are essential.

Summary

Developing a pleasing, functional
landscape is not as simple as most
people think. Each individual property presents a special landscape situation. Borrowed ideas that look good

on other properties usually will not
fit your landscape scheme.

A landscape plan must be tailored
to fit individual family needs, and
embody good design principles. There
are many elements and variables to
consider and unite into the total plan.
However, total effect is the most important in the final analysis.

Professional help is money wisely
invested. Work closely with the person
who prepares your plan to inform him
of your needs and personal tastes. By
understanding and appreciating the
principles involved, you will be able
to work more efficiently with a landscape architect or landscape nurseryman to develop a satisfactory plan.

Creating beauty through your own
efforts is immensely rewarding and
satisfying. The landscape around your
home is on public display every day
of the year. Make it a standout in
your neighborhood and be proud that
you have contributed to improving
the quality of our environment.

Soil Problems
on Homesites
Can Cost You

DIRK VAN DER VOET and
A. A. KLINGEBIEL

H UGH CRAIG was transferred
in the late summer from
a city in the Midwest to one in the
East. He and his wife, Doris, had to
move with their school age children
and get settled before school started.
They decided to buy a house already
built.

After selecting a qualified real estate
agent in the new city, they narrowed
their search to one neighborhood. The

schools were good; there was a hospital and adequate police and fire protection; there was a nearby public library; and a church of their faith.

The real estate man showed the Craigs nearly 30 homes in the neighborhood. They considered the design and construction of each. Doris Craig carefully checked the arrangement of rooms, closet space, cupboards, and, in particular, the kitchen. Hugh Craig examined the basement, heating and air conditioning systems, the garage, and storage space.

Their search soon centered on seven homes. But before they made their decision, the Craigs read a story in the real estate section of the local paper which described some of the problems in selecting not a house but a lot.

"We've studied the houses far more carefully than the lots," Hugh Craig admitted to his wife, "yet this story says that soil problems on the wrong lot can cost a homeowner thousands of dollars."

Acting on advice from the real estate editor, Craig looked up the local office of the Soil Conservation Service, U.S. Department of Agriculture, and made an appointment to see the District Conservationist, Charles Brown.

Brown explained that soil maps and descriptions were available for each of the seven homesites that interested the Craigs.

He said there are thousands of kinds of soil, and every one is different. Some soils are wet; some flood; some are steep; some are clayey; some are sandy and gravelly; and some are shallow. Some soils are ideal for building homes; others are not.

The soil map showed the different kinds of soil and their location and extent on aerial photographs so they can be located readily.

"If the kind of soil is known,"

*

DIRK VAN DER VOET is Assistant Director, Soil Survey Operations, Soil Conservation Service.

A. A. KLINGEBIEL is Director, Soil Survey Interpretations, Soil Conservation Service.

Brown said, "then the kinds of problems which may be expected are known and also the additional expense which the homeowner or builder may incur."

Hugh asked how he, as an average citizen, could be expected to recognize or evaluate the many different kinds of soil problems, or how he could overcome the limitations. The District Conservationist then discussed with the Craigs the interpretations which soil scientists had developed to accompany the soil maps.

These interpretations give the limitations of the soils for many different uses which are of interest to the prospective homeowner, such as homesites, septic tank absorption fields, artificial drainage, irrigation, lawns and shrubs, and local roads and streets.

The soils have been rated, based on their individual characteristics, as having slight, moderate, or severe limitations for the various uses. Significance of the slight, moderate, and severe ratings is as follows:

Slight limitations: Soils with properties favorable for the intended use. Soil limitations are minor and can be easily overcome.

Moderate limitations: Soils with properties moderately favorable for the intended use. The limitations can be overcome or modified by special planning and design and good management.

Severe limitations: Soils with properties difficult and costly to modify or overcome for the intended use.

Brown then determined from the soil map the kinds of soil on each of the homesites the Craigs had selected. He explained to them the characteristics of the soils and the problems these characteristics can cause the homeowner. He also described corrective action, if any, that could be taken to correct the problem.

The first site they discussed was eliminated by the Craigs because the soil map showed the soil was wet and had severe limitations for use as a homesite.

Since it was now early August and

This site appeared desirable when home was built during dry season. Soil survey would have indicated extreme wetness after heavy rains or spring thaw.

there had been no rain for a long time, the site had appeared desirable to the Craigs as there was no outward evidence of wetness. Had they seen the site following heavy rains or after the winter snows had melted, it would have been obvious to the Craigs that it was wet and soggy. Many homes have been built on such sites, resulting in wet basements and soggy backyards when the water table has risen near the surface of the soil.

Brown explained that some soils are wet only for short periods of time, and corrective measures can be applied successfully. This kind would have been rated as possessing moderate limitations.

Other soils are wet over half the time; and corrective measures are usually difficult, expensive, and often only partially successful. In some instances, tile drains and sump pumps can be put in to alleviate the problem; but this is costly after the house is built. Once it is built, shallow surface drainage ditches and diversion terraces may be of some help.

Effluent from septic tank sewage disposal systems cannot be absorbed in a wet soil and will collect on the surface of the ground, causing severe health problems. There is little an individual homeowner can do to improve the absorptive capacity of the soil, and

homes may be condemned by the health department.

Next they discussed a homesite which had been quite attractive to the Craigs because it was close to a pleasant little stream.

The District Conservationist told them that problems might not develop for several years if they should select this site. But then the once in 5- or 10-year-frequency storm could come; and the home be flooded by the stream to a depth of several feet with severe damage resulting.

He also explained that possibility of flooding was increased because several subdivisions, shopping centers, and parking lots had been built upstream. Water that had once entered the soil now poured down over the roofs and asphalt-paved streets and parking lots and into the stream, causing it to overflow its banks.

Dikes and levees can be constructed to protect sites from flooding if the flood waters are contained within the levees.

Upstream flood-control structures are also a form of protection.

These structures are built to control flooding of certain frequencies and are not a guarantee against all flooding. Although the Craigs liked this homesite, they decided against it because the risk of flooding was too great.

119

Homes on floodplains of streams run risk of flooding, with heavy property damage and possible danger to human life as well.

The third homesite discussed by the Craigs and Charles Brown was also desirable from an esthetic point of view. It was located on a hillside and had an excellent view of the surrounding countryside.

The Craigs had questioned this site themselves for they had read news accounts of houses sliding downhill in California and other places where homes had been built on steep slopes.

Brown explained that during periods of heavy rain, certain kinds of soil become saturated with water; and because of the weight of the soil and steepness of the slope, masses of soil slide down the slope.

Even the house itself can go downslope from its foundation and be destroyed. Commonly, soils slide down the slope and into houses below.

Brown pointed out that diversion terraces and subsurface drain tile can be used to divert the flow of water from the home. Other measures can be used also to stabilize soils on steep slopes. The restriction of building to more gentle slopes and on soils not subject to slippage is the surest method.

The Craigs considered this homesite because the soil map indicated a soil not subject to slippage.

Doris Craig had been particularly impressed with the layout and closet space of the next home and favored it for this reason. Hugh, however, was concerned with what he thought were cemented-over cracks in the basement wall.

Brown explained that according to the soil map this home had been built on a clayey soil with a high shrink-swell potential. When wet, the soil swelled and exerted considerable pressure; after it dried out, it contracted and settled.

If the pressure of swelling takes place against a basement wall, cracks

Soil saturated with water slides down steep slope, damaging home.

120

Sidewalk damage from clayey soil with high shrink-swell potential. Soils of this type have same effect on basement walls and floors.

may develop in the wall; and if the pressure is great enough, the wall may collapse. Pressure from below on a cement basement floor may result in the cracking and breaking up of the floor.

Cracks may also develop in the plaster walls and ceilings of rooms built on soils with a high shrink-swell potential.

Brown stated that methods to meet these soil problems are available but need to be used when the house is being built, and some required careful monitoring to keep them effective. They are generally too costly to put in after the house is built.

Septic tank sewage disposal systems do not function effectively in most expansive clay soils. The soil does not absorb the fluid from the filter fields, and the effluent will appear on the surface of the ground causing a health hazard. There is little that can be done to correct this soil problem.

According to the soil map, the District Conservationist said, the next site considered by the Craigs had sandy and gravelly soils. They are droughty and require special care and attention to establish lawns, flowers, shrubbery, and trees; but they do provide a firm foundation for the house, Brown continued. Organic matter needs to be added to the soil when lawns, trees, and ornamentals are planted. Peat moss, grass clippings, manure, leaves, compost, and other organic matter help.

Irrigation of lawns and shrubs is required more often on sandy soils than on other soils. Eight to 12 inches of topsoil placed on top of these very sandy soils provides a better base for grasses and many ornamentals, but to do this is costly.

Hugh asked if there were any problems with septic tank sewage disposal systems in coarse-textured soils. Brown replied that there is if water is obtained from a nearby well or spring. Effluent from such systems may move through the soil and contaminate the water supply. Such disposal systems must be installed a sufficient distance away to prevent contamination.

The Craigs and Brown then discussed the next to last homesite. Doris Craig had noticed an area in the back garden where the grass was greener and the vegetation more lush than the rest of the garden.

She asked if the soil map explained why this might be. Brown replied that only a few feet of soil covered bedrock here, and the public sewer had not yet been extended to that section. The lush vegetation was the result of overflow from the septic tank sewage disposal system, which does not function properly in soils shallow over bedrock.

He further explained that shallow soils are problems in the excavation of basements and for utility lines like water and sewage. Most contractors write into their contracts that if bedrock is met, additional costs will be added for blasting and removing the rock.

Brown added that layers of hardpan

121

and other layers in the soil of a similar nature present like problems, but perhaps not of like intensity.

The final site was examined on the soil map. According to the map, the soil at this gently sloping site was deep; had fairly rapid movement of water through the soil; had no restricting layers; had no danger of flooding; and had no high water table. The District Conservationist described this as the ideal soil for a homesite. This kind of soil presents the least amount of problems, and normally no corrective measures are needed.

The house on this site, although not the first choice of the seven under consideration, was attractive, well built, and quite adequate to meet the Craigs' needs.

Before the Craigs finally decided, however, Conservationist Brown suggested they make an onsite study of the soils on the site selected.

He suggested that an excavation for a basement, a utility line, or a road cut be looked at if available on the site. If none is available, a hole should be dug on the site to a depth of several feet. One should be able to determine from this hole or excavation if the soil is sandy, gravelly, or clayey.

Clayey soils are sticky when wet and can be molded with the fingers. Water appearing in the hole indicates a high water table. Grayish and bluish colors and reddish spots in the upper 18 inches of the soil indicate wetness. Depth to bedrock or other restricting layer can also be determined by digging in the soil.

Brown further recommended that a consultant be engaged if the site selected had soil limitations that required special care or if there were a need for soils information at depths greater than 5 or 6 feet.

He finally told them that in addition to the problems they had discussed, there are other kinds of soils that may present problems when used for homesites. Among these are organic soils, very stony soils, extremely acid soils, very strongly alkaline soils, saline soils, and soils with a high corrosion potential for concrete and metal.

The Craigs decided to purchase the house which had not been first on their list but was located on the deep, gently sloping soil with no high water table, no restricting layers, and no danger of flooding. This decision was based on the information from the soil map with its interpretations and by their personal onsite study of the soil.

Owning a home can be a pleasure, or a costly problem. A careful study and investigation of the soils, such as the Craigs made, can help to make homeownership a pleasure. The soil survey will provide a most valuable tool and guide for you in carrying out this study of the soil just as it did for the Craigs.

Sewage effluent ponds on surface where septic tank absorption field failed on a clayey soil. Disagreeable odor and health hazard result.

Rural Housing Contrasts, a European View

HOWARD E. BRACEY

THIS ARTICLE compares U.S. and European philosophies on rural housing and country and town planning, from my standpoint as a European who has visited the United States and studied these subjects in both continents.

In Europe, as in the United States, big towns are getting bigger in population and area. And, as standards of living rise, more people are buying more cars to clutter up more freeways, tollways, and other improved roads.

From an ever-widening rural area around towns or cities in Europe commuters pour in each morning by bicycle, auto, bus, and train. Villages that are 10, 15, or 20 miles from town and considered remote a decade or so ago are now within the employment orbit of their nearest town.

With urban expansion has marched rural depopulation, both in Europe and the United States.

Generally, the comparison between Europe and the United States ends here, but in detail one can see many similarities for, after all, people are people. Even in the broad trends above, there are significant differences in the forces operating in the two continents which cause houses to be grouped together or spread across the countryside.

Americans had more autos earlier, massive road building programs have been in operation 20 or 30 years, cars are bigger, real wealth in total and per capita is greater, and there are two or more cars per family in many cases.

Most important, Americans have lived with the car problem longer.

This does not mean they have solved it, but simply that it has influenced their solutions for good or ill. Thus shopping centers, industrial sites, and commercial locations in U.S. towns, cities, and villages have massive (by European standards) parking lots, which swallow up a great deal of land.

U.S. towns and villages are loosely held together and the huge parking lots do not seem terribly out of place. But I believe these lots not only increase present housing problems, but complicate future development, since each individual expects to be able to accommodate his own car at home, at work, and at play according to his own choice.

Europe is certainly tending this way. But with the awful example offered by the once-rural areas around certain American cities, most European countries are determined it will never happen to them. Their optimism is based on certain essential differences from the United States, some natural, others acquired.

In Europe there is a regard or sentiment for the countryside and the rural way of life which I have not found in the United States, a regard based largely on past centuries of settlement but also on an earnest concern for centuries to come. Dereliction and pollution actually hurt.

A European's contact with the countryside is not restricted to vacations. Each weekend the inhabitants of every city in western Europe pour out in their millions seeking fresh air, pleasant scenery, a place to picnic, fish, or dream.

A second home in the country or at the sea is commonplace in Sweden and is becoming more frequent in Britain (an old cottage restored) and in France (an old chateau divided into apartments). Traditionally in these

*

HOWARD E. BRACEY, a rural sociologist, retired in 1970 as Senior Lecturer at the University of Bristol, England. He was Visiting Professor at Louisiana State University in 1963–64, and in 1959 at Ohio State University.

countries, the wealthy had their own town houses and their country mansions. This kind of tradition did not obtain in the United States.

In France, Norway, or Austria there would be very real concern over agricultural decline in the countryside. This concern would be not so much with the loss of economic output as regret that a way of life was passing; that land worked for centuries was reverting to scrub; that the peasant, who had been at the base of the rural way of life, was disappearing. In these countries the whole structure of rural society is seen threatened when the traditional agricultural way of life is under pressure.

It is all very emotional to listen to a Frenchman arguing about the threat to the nation because peasants are leaving the family farm for factory jobs; one wonders what century we are living in. Yet to a Frenchman, the peasant is still the mainstay of the French way of life despite supersonic jets and atomic programs. For him, the peasant is something immutable.

In most continental European countries, abandoned farm buildings and workers' cottages and uncared-for fields are an affront. Great and painful efforts are made to support the near-subsistence agriculture, the economically too-small holdings, by subsidies or support prices geared not to the big efficient farmers but the medium sized and smaller ones. While this is not true for Britain, it is true for the Irish Republic.

In Switzerland, the high operating costs of small family holdings are supported by industry and tourism.

In Norway and Austria as in Switzerland a new generation of small mechanized tools has been developed to cope with cutting hay, plowing small fields, etc., yet hay is still cut with a scythe by hand and hung on racks to dry. Little of the improved land may go out of use but the young people continue to leave for better paid, more congenial work in the towns and cities, while country areas show low birthrates and high death rates. The only new houses built are for newcomers—the retired or the visitors.

Even in the newly settled, newly drained polders of Holland the young people look for jobs in Amsterdam, not on the farm. The peasants of the southern toe of Italy get jobs up north, in Milan and Turin, and return home on holidays only to show off their new wealth, such as a Fiat or Volkswagen.

I have said that this "unreasoning" emphasis in some countries of Europe on maintaining the traditional rural way of life, at high cost to the national community as a whole, is based on centuries of living close to the soil. An entirely different background is shown clearly in the form of American villages and country towns.

Admittedly, some American land has been in agricultural use for 150 to 200 years; Ohio was settled around 1800. But for the whole of that time the emphasis has been cash crops, growing food and fiber for sale off the farm and often for eventual consumption great distances away.

European agriculture grew out of a subsistence existence. In Britain, virtually every village and town was a little agricultural center in the year 1100 AD. Each settlement developed as a self-contained community with farms and cottage homes grouped around the church and manor house.

A similar development took place over much of Europe with variations according to the system of land tenure or internal or external national security. But almost everywhere there were landowners, living in manor houses in England, chateaux in France, castles in Germany, with ordinary people dwelling close against the lord's residence for safety and patronage.

Each settlement grew as a separate little territory where the next village represented the outside world, and over the hill was far away.

Except where industrial development radically changed the whole concept of living, this local rural existence carried right into the 20th century.

European countries with early industrialization, like Britain and Germany, broke away from this rigid form of local living, beginning in the early 19th century.

In countries slower to experience industrialization, like Spain, Portugal, or Greece, the rural inhabitants are not very far removed from their medieval ancestors today. In other countries where agriculture is still important to the national economy, as the Netherlands or Italy, brand new farms and agricultural hamlets and villages have been established, in the Netherlands on the reclaimed land of the polders and in Italy by breaking up old estates.

Between 1931 and 1951 the number of Italians working in agriculture increased, but from 1951 onwards the trend was reversed. The number dropped from 8,261,000 in 1951 to 5,657,000 in 1961 and 4,660,000 in 1966.

European countries know that farms must increase in size to survive economically, and that more mechanization must take place. This leads inevitably to fewer workers, and therefore fewer farm dwellings. Yet throughout Europe you will rarely see an abandoned farmhouse or cottage except high on the more inaccessible moors or mountains—never in the plains.

One sees many abandoned rural dwellings in the United States where three factors operate—distance, product, and materials. Farms in the United States have always been larger than in Europe. U.S. farm buildings, new to the territory being developed, were built at the most convenient location; usually on ground giving access to the nearest service settlement which might be upwards of 25 miles away in the Middle West to 50 or 100 miles distant in the Far West.

When the land gave out the buildings were abandoned because land was cheap and available elsewhere.

Finally, because of the abundance of woodland and often a shortage of building materials like stone and brick clay, Americans used timber for their houses, a material with a shorter life. German and Scandinavian settlers of the Middle West built houses and huge barns reminiscent of their homeland. Wealthy planters of the South raised antebellum mansions patterned on the stately homes of England. But always they built of wood. Some of the mansions are preserved with pride. Many more are tumbledown.

In Europe, only in areas where wood was especially plentiful were rural houses built of timber. This is especially true of the agricultural regions of Norway, Austria, Switzerland, and some of the higher parts of Germany. But, fundamentally different from the United States, these rural homes are built in, or close to, settlements. The actual fabric of the buildings may have been renewed, or rebuilt, many times over during the last 800 to 1,000 years on the old brick or stone foundations.

Throughout France, Belgium, Britain, and most of Germany, rural buildings have always been built with stone or brick. These materials have a long life and can be used many times over.

At Woodchester, England, the walls of farm buildings contain fragments of pottery and bricks from a Roman villa whose tesselated floor and foundations alone remain today. This material must be at least 1,500 years old. English manor houses, built in the 13th century with later additions and alterations, are still lived in today.

Since Medieval times, in England the nobleman and the lord of the manor, in France the seigneur in his chateau, in Germany the count on his estate, have taken pride in maintaining not only their own homes but those of their employees. Many cottages 300 years old are still in use.

In Britain, substantial government grants are available for renovating old houses. The grant pays for sewer connections, bathrooms, running water, and central heat. Aims of the grants are to maintain the national stock of homes and the traditional appearance of the British countryside in which the nation takes pride.

Government intervention brings one to what in the United States is known as zoning, in Britain as town and country planning, in Germany as "planung," and in France and Belgium as "planification."

In my experience, Americans accept government interference in the form of zoning for towns with a "blighted area" which their consciences tell them must have something done to it. But they tend to regard as infringement of personal liberty the zoning laws which are applied with any real effectiveness elsewhere. If the control becomes too tight they move to a town or subdivision where zoning is less strict.

This last solution is fine for Americans, but in Europe where the population density is so much higher and all usable land has been effectively employed for some purpose or other for many centuries, you cannot opt out in this way. Until quite recently there has always been somewhere else for the American speculative developer to go and, to a foreign observer, it appears that virtually uncontrolled urban sprawl has become a national habit.

In most European countries, government zoning or planning is based on British experience although some countries, notably Holland, have in several respects improved on the British pattern.

In Europe, zoning is seen as a national responsibility, not a State or local responsibility as in the United States. The need is to provide homes for people, sites for industry and commerce, and the necessary infrastructure to maintain a healthy agriculture and a pleasant countryside, in which homes, farms, farm buildings, roads, bridges, fields, and woodland combine in a harmonious whole.

With the expectation of perhaps another 100 million Americans around the turn of the century, the United States is only now beginning to appreciate what Europe learned the hard way many years ago:

The supply of rural land any nation can afford to use for residential and industrial development is limited and it must be controlled by the nation, for the individual will only suit his selfish wishes.

In Britain, and in most other countries of western Europe, zoning or planning can be divided into two broad sections—development planning and development control.

Every planning authority proposes how land in its area should be used and the stages by which it should be developed. This plan is reviewed every five years.

Permission must be obtained to develop land. The planning authority considers each application in relation to its development plan.

An application for development must be published (or displayed) by the authority and where necessary a public hearing held so objectors can state their views.

Besides new buildings, development covers alterations to existing buildings, and change of use.

Thus you may not switch your somber brown roof tiles for brilliant red or sickly green without permission. You may not use the yard of your home for trucks, materials, and equipment of your building business without a permit to do so.

The European landscape was once largely forest, scrub, and swamp. It is now, after 2,000 years of occupation by civilized man, predominantly man-made.

During that time Britain's population increased from a quarter million to 55 million.

Germany and France, from populations only slightly larger than Britain's in the first century A.D., have grown to approximately 60 million and 50 million respectively.

Britain has 90,000 square miles. France 200,000 square miles. The United States covers $3\frac{3}{4}$ million square miles, but it also has over 200 million people. Much of its acreage is too mountainous or too arid to do much with, for the foreseeable future at any rate; the easiest land to develop is usually the best for agricultural use.

When developing land for residential or industrial use, individuals tend to consider only short-run interests. But, in my view, the United States is approaching the day when it will have to pay far more attention to long-run costs.

These must include the high cost of open development in terms of highways for commuters who travel daily up to 50 miles each way, and the cost to communities of providing services like water, waste disposal, police and fire protection, and schools.

"Infilling" means nothing to an American. To every knowledgeable Englishman it means building on the uneconomic bits and pieces left over from the days before planning or zoning when there appeared to be plenty of land for all. It means splitting up one or two acre lots to accommodate dwellings for a dozen or so extra families in the village.

In a broader context, planning means swallowing up several square miles of once-agricultural land and engulfing several villages to provide homes for half a million or so people in a new city.

Or, in one case, the building up of a sleepy country town in the middle of the hill country of Wales, so the new industries it attracts will provide jobs for rural workers displaced from the land by a contracting agriculture.

In other words, the new town or new city will function as a "trigger area" for a long depopulating neighborhood—as has proved successful in Norway.

We in Europe, whether British, German, Dutch, or Scandinavian, do not like this planning process particularly. But after nearly a quarter century of planning control in practice, while we see that planners sometimes need themselves to be controlled, we recognize that we have to live with planning in town and countryside to retain a harmonious environment, one which took many centuries to create, and of which we are reasonably proud. The alternative is chaos.

Housing
for the
Elderly

JAMES E. MONTGOMERY

F OR MANY older Americans, the national housing crisis has become a plight. Large numbers of them, rural and urban, find it impossible to secure decent, suitable, and comfortable housing in which to live out their remaining days in dignity and hope. This is because of their greatly limited incomes, and the relative indifference of the public.

Older persons in general occupy a more limited life space—physical, social, and psychological—than do younger adults. Their mobility and movement decrease. They spend a large proportion of their lives in and about their dwellings; this is especially true of the poor. For the enfeebled, their physical world is reduced to a dwelling, an institution, a room, or even a bed. The way the elderly cope with their infirmities, and the degree to which they are able to prolong their independence, depend largely on the nature of the immediate environment, their housing.

If they are to be safe, comfortable, in touch with others and psychologically stimulated, the aging must have functional and satisfying housing. As Marie C. McGuire has said, "Safe and suitable housing is probably the most important single environmental factor in the well-being of older persons . . . for the aged it may mean the difference between living independently or in an institution; between

*

JAMES E. MONTGOMERY is Professor and Head of the Department of Management, Housing and Family Development, College of Home Economics, Virginia Polytechnic Institute and State University, Blacksburg.

solitude and socialization; between safety and danger; or in extreme cases between life and death."

In recent decades housing aspirations and standards have increased, but many of the aged find it difficult to participate in the benefits of our technology and affluence. Three years ago the median income of families whose head was 65 and older was only 46 percent of that of younger heads of families; 9 years ago the figure was 51 percent.

Incomes of older rural persons are lower than those of their urban counterparts. The rural aged have fewer community services and facilities to aid them.

Less than 40 percent of the Nation's aged live in nonmetropolitan areas, but in these smaller communities and rural areas are found at least two-thirds of all substandard housing.

Contrary to the stereotype "65 and over," the 20 million older Americans are far from similar. They vary in age, sex, income, marital status, education, race, subculture, health, interests, abilities, life styles, and places of residence. James E. Birren has said that older persons differ probably more than any other age group because of the major decisions they have made throughout life about such matters as education, occupation, marriage, and outside interests.

Since they do differ greatly one from another, this implies that each community, large and small, needs a variety of housing options available to the elderly. The issue, then, is not whether to provide one type of housing or another but rather to provide for varying needs. Here are the major types of living environments that should be included in community housing inventories for the aged:

Single-family housing—The individual house represents the dominant housing image in America. In rural communities this type of dwelling and mobile homes comprise a majority of the housing inventory. The disparity between incomes and housing costs means that usually only older houses and mobile homes are within the economic reach of the elderly.

Apartments specifically designed for the aged, dispersed and segregated— The debate as to whether independent housing arrangements for the aged should be dispersed or in concentrated complexes and projects continues.

On the one hand, Irving Rosow, in a study of older persons in Cleveland who lived in apartments having varying proportions of older persons, concluded: "Our data show that . . . *Dense* areas produced isolated residents only half as frequently as less concentrated apartments."

Frances M. Carp, in a study of older residents living in Victoria Plaza, a public housing complex, found they became more involved with life and showed improvements in morale and self-concept contrasted with comparable individuals who remained in private housing.

On the other hand, Sussman and Steinberg wrote of what happened to older people living in public housing apartments exclusively for the elderly in these words: "Without so being designated, such a building actually is an old age home. Residents often are just as enfeebled and unable to care for themselves as in any officially labeled institution for the aged."

Retirement communities—Starting around 1950 a number of retirement communities have been built and occupied. Occupants of this type of housing have relatively high incomes, good health, and more than the average facility for restructuring their life styles.

Undoubtedly the most serious question about these retirement villages is what will happen as the population grows too old to live independently.

On balance these communities should be encouraged since they meet the needs of certain types of people. However, we should avoid concluding that the communities are within the financial and psychological reach of a large percentage of the aged.

Congregate housing—For persons whose health is waning, congregate housing may provide a setting where they have their own space and facilities for living, sleeping, and bathing, but take their meals in a central dining room prepared in a central kitchen.

This kind of housing helps prolong the person's ability to remain independent, and at the same time ideally provides a variety of adjuncts to living—nurses, clinics, and recreational programs.

Intermediate care homes—Persons not well enough to live in any of the types of housing mentioned earlier, but who are not sick enough to require a nursing home environment, may preserve a semblance of independence by living in a setting that provides some personal care along with room and board.

As Marie C. McGuire has said, "Intermediate care facilities are required to have a responsible staff person on duty at all times, develop a program of social and recreational activities, provide at least three meals a day (including arrangements to provide special diets where needed) and provide for certain limited health care services."

Nursing homes—Undoubtedly few words used in connection with the elderly elicit as many feelings of despair as "nursing homes." They are frequently described, with considerable justification, as places where the enfeebled are "warehoused" until the ebb of life ceases.

At best nursing homes are highly worthy institutions, but many of them need to be better located, designed, staffed and operated.

Despite our negative attitudes, nursing homes are an absolute necessity in American society. The better ones are finding a way to operate in a manner that supports life in dignity, comfort, and reassurance.

Major problems are met in providing housing for the elderly at the community level.

First of all, the majority of older Americans, rural and urban, simply are financially unable to afford suitable housing. Thus far, as a nation we have not made a sufficient commitment to meet these financial constraints by an adequate level of public subsidies.

Our failure to understand what kinds of housing environments older persons want and need greatly restrict the end products. Research has failed to provide action programs with adequate insights into housing needs of the elderly.

Many programs of assistance are available to the elderly, but often neither the aged nor their would-be benefactors are aware of what they are and how to use them.

In smaller communities, obstacles to better housing for the aged include: very low incomes and restricted local credit resources; a paucity of utilities—like water and sewer systems; an absence of larger builders; limited transportation facilities; a dearth of such life supports as hospitals, physicians, clinics, and recreational programs; a wide dispersal of the elderly who have need of various kinds of housing; and a lack of public awareness of needs.

To date as a nation we have assigned, perhaps unconsciously, a low priority to needs of the aged, especially in housing.

However, within the last two decades or so the Nation has become increasingly responsive to housing needs of the elderly. Some major programs currently in operation are:

• Subsidized public housing. Theoretically this program is available to the elderly regardless of the size of their community.

Local housing authorities, in metropolitan areas as well as small communities and rural counties, provide subsidized housing for the elderly. This approach, instituted in 1937, began in 1959 to make special provisions to serve the elderly. Since then it has placed increasing emphasis on housing needs of the aged.

By December 31, 1968, annual contribution contracts had been signed for a total of 183,154 dwelling units designed specifically for the elderly. Of these, approximately 62 percent were in projects with all units for the

elderly and almost 38 percent in projects with mixed age groups.

Since 1963 the Department of Health, Education, and Welfare has had an agreement with public housing to assist in providing food and community services which complement housing.

• Rent supplements. This program was designed to be used in conjunction with FHA section 221 (d)(3) which assists private efforts to help families and individuals eligible for public housing, including the elderly and handicapped. Rent supplements are also provided under FHA sections 202, 231, and 236.

Subsidies are paid at a rate representing the difference between 25 percent of the tenant's gross income and the FHA-approved rental for the unit. Sponsors of this type of housing may be nonprofit organizations, limited

Public (subsidized) housing for elderly at Villa Tranchese, San Antonio, Texas.

dividend and cooperative housing corporations.

• Intermediate care facilities. It is now possible through FHA section 232 of the nursing home program to assist with the financing of a form of housing for persons whose health requires more than independent living arrangements and less than skilled nursing care. Such facilities may be separate from or a part of nursing care facilities.

Terms and conditions of loans are essentially the same as for FHA-mortgage-insured nursing home facilities.

• Nursing homes. FHA section 232, National Housing Act of 1959, insures mortgages on nursing homes sponsored either by profit or nonprofit organizations. To qualify, the facility must have a bed capacity of at least 20. Minimum requirements for licensing are required.

• Farmers Home Administration Programs. A major source of assistance available to rural low-income elderly are programs provided by the Farmers Home Administration. These programs are limited to areas having a population not in excess of 10,000 and to families having low income.

Older persons who are unable to secure funds through commercial sources may, under the Section 502 program, secure loans to purchase land, a dwelling, construct a dwelling, or make home repairs. Interest rates range from 1 percent to 7¼ percent for a period not to exceed 33 years.

Through the Farmers Home Administration, it also is possible to finance rural rental housing with profit and nonprofit sponsors. For profit, sponsor interest rates are 7¼ percent on loans that may have a duration of 50 years. Loans made to nonprofit organizations have adjustable interest rates ranging from 1 to 7¼ percent.

Finally, the Farmers Home Administration enables cooperatives to secure loans at a rate ranging from 1 percent to 7¼ percent to be repaid in no more than 50 years.

Progress is being made in the public and private sectors of our society to improve the housing lot of the elderly, but here are some concrete suggestions that need continuing consideration:

In rural America, close to a million persons are 80 years or older, of whom perhaps three-fourths are women. Therefore, systematic efforts should be made to coordinate efforts and to "invent" human institutions to care for the very old.

Housing for the aged should be viewed, not as isolated shelter, but as the "hub" of an environmental support system that includes transportation, medical services, recreational facilities, and opportunities to be as nearly independent as possible.

More consideration must be given to the basic social and pyschological needs of the elderly—a wholesome self-concept, privacy, socialization, sense of place, psychological stimulation, independence, and mastery of their immediate environment. These must serve as guides along with the needs for safety, comfort, convenience, and physical well-being.

So far as possible, each community should strive to maximize the number of housing options available to the aged.

More than 20 separate Federal programs are relevant to the housing of older Americans. These programs need to be consolidated, simplified, and broadened. A highly readable layman's handbook should be prepared to interpret available programs to local officials, other interested citizens, churches, *and* the aged.

Local advocates for better housing for the aged should be discovered and encouraged. Many older persons are incapable of seeking or are unwilling to seek better housing through programs now available. The elderly should be significantly involved in the total process of providing housing and related services.

In conclusion, an increased measure of resolution and commitment on the part of the Nation would go a long way in closing the gap between the way its elderly are being housed and the way that they need and deserve to be housed.

131

Rental Housing Aids the Rural Aging, Others

ARTHUR I. STANLEY and
ROBERT E. NIPP

WHO LIVES IN THE poorest housing in rural America? Is it the young farmer? Older farmer? Small town resident? It is none of these.

Those with the least comfort, safety, and convenience in their homes are the single, older women. Most are widows with limited fixed income. But they value their independence and do not want to live with their children.

Our rural, older generation has come up through hard times. They suffered through the stock market crash in '29 and survived the droughts and depressions of the thirties. And it is their group—on small fixed retirement incomes—that is most victimized today by the ravages of inflation.

Many older people have never been able to accumulate wealth or sizable retirement incomes. They live in dilapidated little houses, improvised apartments in big old houses, or shabby rooms over ramshackle store buildings. At best, these are hovels— cold in winter, hot in summer, uncomfortable, inconvenient, fireprone, and unsafe.

As long as "the old folks" can live independently and look after themselves, their younger relatives are interested but not overly concerned. However, they do become anxious and disturbed when "Mom" or "Dad" needs nursing home care. For this reason, most communities have been more intent upon providing nursing homes rather than other types of housing for their older citizens.

Through USDA's Farmers Home Administration, Federal loans are available to provide rental and co-operatively-owned housing in rural areas for senior citizens, 62 years of age or older, for other rural residents, and for low to moderate income urban residents who work in a rural area.

These loans fill a housing credit gap in rural areas and offer an opportunity for senior citizens to maintain their independence and to live out their lives in dignity in the communities where they have spent their working days and where their roots are deepest. This Federal aid also increases the supply of adequate rental housing for low to moderate income families.

A housing crisis developed 6 years ago in Oak Grove, a typical rural Missouri town. Insurance companies decided to discontinue coverage on the 1900 vintage Main Street store buildings unless upstairs tenants were removed. Unfortunately, most were elderly people who needed to live close to grocery and drug stores, and doctors' offices.

The community became aroused over the problem. Mayor Hubert Roach and Banker Hollis Dyer headed a group that wanted some answers. Their search brought them to the doors of USDA's Farmers Home Administration at nearby Independence. There they talked to FHA Supervisor Henry Smith who was administering a large rural credit program in rural Jackson County.

Roach and Dyer told Smith that at least a hundred elderly people were living in makeshift rooms over stores and in other substandard housing in Oak Grove. "Why," they asked, "can't your agency do something for these people?" Smith explained that Farmers Home did have authority to finance rental housing for senior citizens. "However," he said, "no such loans had been made in Missouri."

*

ARTHUR I. STANLEY is a rural housing loan specialist in Missouri for the Farmers Home Administration, with offices at Columbia.

ROBERT E. NIPP is a public information specialist with Farmers Home in Washington, D.C.

On a rainy night in February 1964, a unique cross-section of Oak Grove's residents assembled in a public meeting to discuss what the community could do to secure better housing for its senior citizens.

Present at the meeting were older couples who had long since reared their families, and older widows, widowers, bachelors, and spinsters reluctant to pose a housing burden on their relatives and friends. On hand too were businessmen, clergy, and community leaders who did not want their older citizens to move away.

FHA County Supervisor Smith of Independence was there, accompanied by two housing specialists who had driven the 115 miles west from FHA's State office in Columbia to explain how the agency's loan program could help.

As the night wore on, the brainstorming session revealed that:

• Most of the persons who desperately needed better housing were single women, including widows over 60 years of age but in good health and determined to remain independent.

• One-bedroom apartments with 650 square feet of living area in single-story buildings seemed best suited to the needs of older people. Housing should be located within walking distance of Oak Grove's business district. Rent should be no more than $40 a month.

• Good housing could be built locally for $10 a square foot. FHA could make loans to broadly-based, not-for-profit corporations to establish rental housing—terms to be $3\frac{1}{8}$ percent interest over 50 years. Community leaders were willing to form a nonprofit corporation and work together to support the project.

• The project would set a breathtaking new precedent of rural housing activity in the State, establishing a pattern to be followed by other FHA offices, and County Supervisor Smith was anxious to help get the work underway.

Before breaking up for the night, the group appointed a steering committee to work with Smith. This group met often in the days ahead.

Don Hutson, their attorney, drafted articles of incorporation and bylaws and steered the group through the intricacies of State laws and Federal regulations. He helped them form Oak Grove Civic Improvement Inc., a not-for-profit corporation authorized to own and operate rental housing and eligible for FHA loans.

The corporation's Board of Directors selected a site and obtained a "buy" option. Next, the board arranged for an architect in nearby Kansas City to design the housing and provide the plans and specifications required by FHA.

Finally, the board advertised for bids to construct the project. When these were in, they found that $108,120 would buy an acre of land and construct seven buildings.

Six of the buildings would contain a total of 12 one-bedroom and eight efficiency apartments. The seventh building would house laundry units and a large room for family gatherings and for other group activities.

Board members then developed a comprehensive budget of planned expenses and incomes. They decided to foot the water bill but residents would pay their own electricity, natural gas, and telephone.

The budget revealed that monthly rent of $40 on one-bedroom and $35 on efficiency apartments would enable the corporation to meet its annual payment of interest and principal on a loan, pay regular operating expenses, and allow for a small surplus that could be put away for emergencies.

An FHA loan was approved in July 1964, and the Golden Age Apartments were completed the following March. By mid-April 1965, all 20 apartments were occupied. One year later a second loan for $90,000 enabled Oak Grove Civic Improvement Inc. to provide 12 more apartments at another location in town. The 32 apartments have been fully occupied by senior citizens over the past 5 years.

Thus began the story of rural rental

Top, resident who serves as superintendent mows lawn at 4-plex building in low-cost rental housing project at Mountain View, Mo. Above, newlyweds in kitchen of their Mountain View apartment.

housing in Missouri. W. T. Sparks, Jr., a mortician in Odessa, 10 miles east of Oak Grove, watched construction of the Golden Age Apartments, and soon things were happening in his town. Today, Odessa boasts 21 low-cost rental housing units with central air conditioning.

Harry Fuelling, real estate and in-

surance agent in Rock Port, 150 miles north, attended the dedication of Golden Age Apartments with some of his fellow businessmen. Now his town has 34 new apartments.

Oak Grove became a "visitor's Mecca" for community leaders who had compassion for their older friends and neighbors and the desire to keep their towns alive. Jim Thompson of Madison pushed his Lions Club into action after a trip to Oak Grove. Jim Trainer and Finis Smith took the message back to their small town of Cuba; now it boasts 36 apartments.

A new way to cut building costs developed by happenstance in the Missouri Ozarks. Noval Cantrell of Mountain View and Alba Ray, Jr., and Logan Buckner of Licking established sponsoring organizations simultaneously and—quite by accident—hired the same architect. He developed identical plans for both housing projects. The sponsors liked them.

Since the towns are only 50 miles apart, the architect arranged also to have bid openings the same day. The total size of the two jobs attracted larger contractors. Favorable bids were received. A Kansas City construction company won the nod. A $144,000 loan to each community paid for the building site, six four-unit apartments,

Woman resident of Cuba (Mo.) Retirement Homes chats with a project director.

a small community building, and legal and architectural fees.

The square four-unit apartments feature carpeting in living rooms and bedrooms. All-electric kitchens with range, oven, and refrigerator furnished by the owner, have ample counter space and cabinets. Electric wall outlets are located waist-high to eliminate stooping.

Safety grab bars are available over bathtubs. Electric baseboards heat the well-planned apartments. And the 576 square feet of living space in each unit provides adequate room for a couple to live comfortably. There are no steps.

This is the best housing the residents have ever enjoyed. And it is the best apartment-type housing in the community—making the town a better place to live.

The 24 one-bedroom apartments in each community averaged an investment of $6,000 and were rented immediately upon the completion of construction in late summer 1967. At Mountain View, rent is $50 a month with all utilities furnished. Licking charges $35 a month but tenants pay their own utilities.

These two housing enterprises in the Ozarks have done more than provide a comfortable, modern, and convenient place for 48 senior citizen families to live. Each project has become a showcase for miles around, displaying what a community can do to provide better housing for its people and at a price that those with low to moderate incomes can afford.

Just as Oak Grove, in the northern part of the State, had been an inspiration to leaders at Licking and Mountain View, these two projects in turn came into focus for community leaders in southern Missouri. Many have journeyed to Mountain View and Licking—getting an eyeful of the projects and an earful of community pride and enthusiasm.

They have visited with senior citizens like Mrs. R. E. Jackson, a widow in her late seventies living on less than $100 a month; Mrs. Lee Gutufson,

135

also in her late seventies, who stretches an $85 monthly old-age assistance check plus some help from relatives, to meet her needs; Mr. and Mrs. L. Davis, ages 70 and 63, making do on a $180 social security check; and Arlis Martin, widower and World War I veteran living comfortably on $150 a month. All are enjoying life in attractive garden-type apartments near relatives and friends and a familiar environment in which many had spent their younger years.

Residents at Licking enjoy reading books and magazines provided to their own library by the regional bookmobile. On Saturday nights they have fun playing bingo in their community building. Bill Buehler keeps the walls of the building decorated with his own oil paintings. Oak Grove residents enjoy services held in the community building each Sunday by ministers from all the churches in town. At Rock Port, Lee Fyfer entertains his fellow residents with organ music.

And there are outdoor cookouts, flower growing contests, square dancing, plenty of birthday parties and anniversary celebrations, and other activities to keep residents involved. One active resident at Licking summed up his busy schedule with the remark that he did not know how he could find time to go back to a regular job if he suddenly had to come out of retirement.

In addition to seeing the housing and meeting the residents, leaders from other communities have talked to Board Members Cantrell, Ray, and Buckner about how to start projects in their towns. They learned how to organize a not-for-profit corporation with enough individuals and organizations as members to assure broad-based support for the housing enterprise. They learned how to raise operating capital for the corporation. In Mountain View and Licking, they learned that this had been done by encouraging members to make small contributions.

They found that FHA insisted that the Board of Directors do most of the work involved in organizing and planning the housing enterprise. They learned that the manner in which this work was done indicated to FHA the ability of the Board to manage the housing after it was completed.

For example, the Board was required to make its own market survey. One of the most important results of the survey was a list of prospective residents.

Below left, resident of project at Dixon, Mo., shows grandniece tomatoes grown outside apartment door. Below right, Bill Buehler (L.) with some of his paintings, in community building of Licking (Mo.) housing project for the elderly.

The survey also revealed that though FHA rental housing was available to all age groups, older citizens in towns like Oak Grove, Rock Port, and Licking evidenced the greatest housing need. Community leaders found that younger families preferred to become homeowners through regular rural housing loan programs.

Older residents often are not physically able or desirous of maintaining their own housing. And the expense of hiring help to keep up yards and homes is prohibitive for the elderly on small fixed incomes.

Obtaining a list of prospective tenants gave the Board experience in selling their housing. The list, itself, indicated an actual immediate need for the housing. To prevent overbuilding, FHA limited the number of living units financed to half the number of prospective residents.

Gaining these experiences from Board members who had already been through the mill, and finding that the FHA requirements could be met by folks just like themselves, impressed and encouraged community leaders in 18 southern Missouri communities. They have organized, planned, and completed 392 apartments. Six more communities are processing loans to provide an additional 116 apartments. Twenty of these 24 communities were influenced to go ahead after a visit to Licking and Mountain View.

Progress in Missouri has not been without problems. Property owners in one town took legal action to keep out a rental housing project—believing it would reduce the value of their property. Informed of the problem, board members carried out a public relations sales job. After finding that the new housing would be attractively designed, fully landscaped, and properly maintained, homeowners withdrew their objections. Since the project's completion in 1969, neighborhood property values have increased some 15 percent.

In another case, construction bids were $100,000 above the architect's estimated cost. This was due to many expensive frills incorporated into the housing design and rural contractors not understanding a city architect's plans and specification. The architect offered to resign. The board insisted he stay on, modify his specifications, and assist rural bidders in interpreting his plans. The final result was attractive housing at reasonable cost.

Six other Missouri projects had extensive problems in winter with frozen water pipes and malfunctioning waste disposal systems. Rumors spread throughout their communities, and new apartments remained vacant or became difficult to rent. The water and sewage problems were corrected, but the housing received a poor image which only time and proper housing maintenance will correct.

A fourth problem has been the lack of an aggressive selling program by some boards of directors, coupled with an attitude that the market for this kind of housing is so great that the apartments will rent themselves.

To help overcome this problem, Farmers Home Administration required two prospective tenants for each living unit financed.

A final word of advice: Sponsors of a rural rental housing project need to recognize that success or failure of their enterprise will depend on joint effort, judgment, and competence, instead of the loan check from the Farmers Home Administration. The agency's financing serves only as a catalyst for their action.

Willard Duncan Vandiver, a native son and "turn-of-the-century" Congressman, once said, "I am from Missouri. You have to show me."

And "show me" it is as one community generates the idea and others stand by to watch and learn. Thus as Licking and Mountain View led the way in the south, Rock Port set the example in northwest Missouri, and Madison and Paris in the northeast.

Nationally, 1,258 communities and private entrepreneurs throughout the 50 States, Puerto Rico, and the Virgin Islands have completed—or have under construction—close to 11,000 apartment units, using $90,364,000 in Farmers Home Administration loan funds (as of April 30, 1971).

This is the statistical record for a new program which is just getting off the ground.

In forging this dramatic new concept that small towns and rural America need rental housing, Farmers Home Administration hopes to demonstrate to other investors that the program is an excellent basis for credit investment and thus encourage them to become more active in making such loans. One of the reasons many rural communities have lost population has been the poor housing available, both owned and rented. With modern transportation and communication, a person no longer needs to be on a streetcar line or within walking distance of his job.

As rental housing loans that Farmers Home Administration are making prove successful, other lenders will hopefully change their policies and be willing to provide credit to people or organizations looking for a place to invest their time and money. Those towns in Missouri that have taken advantage of the loans to not-for-profit corporations are showing the way.

Besides the loans to not-for-profit corporations, the Farmers Home Administration offers complete credit service to profit oriented entrepreneurs for rental housing.

One borrower in Missouri started with four apartments 3 years ago and added 12 more for a total of 16 apartments. Winning favorable acceptance, he has had 100 percent occupancy from the time the housing was completed. Most tenants are younger families who are either employed in the area or are attending a rural technical school to improve their job opportunities.

With 100 million or more Americans expected as a result of population increases by the turn of the century, attractive low-cost rental housing in the countryside can well play a significant contributing factor in rural

community development and at the same time help meet our Nation's overall housing needs.

In Missouri, by early 1971, 35 communities had completed more than 800 apartments; all are occupied. Another seven communities were building 144 units. Twelve more communities were getting ready to start construction of 216 units when weather allowed in the spring.

By the end of 1971, almost 1,200 senior citizen families will be living in the best housing they have ever experienced; and all as a result of what happened in Oak Grove that rainy night in February 1964.

Wisconsin Plans for People

HAROLD RYAN and
CAROLYN JOHNSTON

FROM Maine to Californ-i-ay, we plowed and planted—superhighwayed and suburbanized. Mr. & Mrs. America, meet the land you made.

Do you like it? Did you plan it? Did *anybody* plan it?

Out in mid-country U.S.A.—southeastern Wisconsin—the seven counties of Washington, Waukesha, Walworth, Milwaukee, Ozaukee, Racine, and Kenosha *are* planning. Five percent of Wisconsin in size, they pack in 41 percent of the State's population, or more than a million and a half people. And, they're bracing themselves for an extra million in the next 25 years.

How can advance planning help this area of green hills, growing towns, and busy cities provide a good en-

138

vironment for its citizens? Professional planners, town officials, and ordinary citizens are testing some of the answers. Like farmers earlier, these men have turned to the Soil Conservation Service for technical help on the uses and properties of soil and water.

Urban planners know that soil and water use mistakes are no abstraction; they "hit home" quite literally, and affect men and women in very personal ways.

• In Racine County, a 10-year-old boy will leave his Michigan lakeshore home soon and never return. The problem is not a runaway boy but washed-away land. Shore erosion has brought the lake within 15 feet of his expensive house and the steep front slope cannot hold much longer. It's too late to stabilize the area.

• In Washington County, a concerned county nurse called at the adjoining homes of several young children sick with an undiagnosed illness. As she parked her car, she spotted a wet, smelly area along the curb. Sewage was backing up and overflowing. The septic tanks were placed in nonabsorbent soil. The wrong soil for the wrong use had hit home again. Two families are moving.

• In Ozaukee County, a new home-owner was understandably angry to come home one evening and find muddy water ankle-deep in his living room. A floodplain? Yes. A solution? Improved surface drainage on both sides of the house plus a small, water-retarding pond in his front yard. It worked, but it wrecked the bank account.

Bills, ills, and disappearing homes. These are only a few land and water use problems.

Ten years ago, officials and citizens became concerned enough to organize the Southeastern Wisconsin Regional

*

HAROLD RYAN is District Conservationist, Soil Conservation Service, for the Milwaukee and Waukesha (Wis.) Soil and Water Conservation Districts.

CAROLYN JOHNSTON is an information specialist for the Soil Conservation Service, in Washington, D.C.

Planning Commission (SEWRPC) for the seven counties. The Commission oversees a full-time professional planning staff.

The Commission realized that a vital first step was thorough knowledge of the region's natural resources. In 1963, it signed a cooperative agreement with the USDA's Soil Conservation Service for a soil survey, with detailed interpretations for both rural and urban planning uses. The survey was completed two years later and the results made available to SEWRPC, local officials, and concerned individuals.

To put the new information into quick use, SEWRPC, USDA agencies, and soil and water conservation districts agreed to supply technical help to local planning officials and citizen groups. SCS also provided assistance for on-site investigations and special soils interpretations.

Simultaneously, the SEWRPC developed guides and model ordinances for health and sanitary regulations, sediment control, flood plain and shoreland zoning, and subdivision ordinances. Soil survey information was a basic input in all of these.

Today, six counties have adopted flood plain and shoreland zoning ordinances and four counties have passed new sanitary codes. The flood plain ordinances require erosion problems within 1,000 feet of a lakeshore to be corrected according to practices in the Soil Conservation Service technical guidebook. The sanitary codes forbid use of septic tank filter fields in soils unsafe for this purpose.

The sanitary codes are particularly important, since about 50 percent of soils in the 7-county area are "no go" for septic tank systems. SEWRPC officials estimate that use of soil survey information in the selection of homesites alone will save citizens some $300 million over the next 25 years.

Water uses and water problems were also the subject of detailed studies, under SEWRPC auspices, in the Fox, Root, and Milwaukee watersheds. The Soil Conservation Service did the major hydraulic and hydrologic work as well as engineering and economic evaluation of flood control measures for the Fox study, which covers about 35 percent of the southeast Wisconsin area.

This soil and watershed information is applicable to most natural resource planning in the area.

Transportation: A regionwide transportation plan involves a combination of highways and exclusive "busways." Soils information was used in the route planning.

Open Space: SEWRPC laid out a system of environmental corridors and identified 13 regional parksites, using "inputs" of soils and watershed information. A total of 26 major outdoor recreational areas has been recommended by SEWRPC. SCS will provide some services in the development of these areas.

Flood Problems: Good land use is a major flood prevention method. For example, floodplains—the land at the bottom of stream valleys—are the first areas flooded in any rainstorm. Floodplains are designed by nature to soak up rain water like a gigantic sponge. When we cover a floodplain with concrete and cement—without planning a good alternate drainage pattern for the water—there will be flooding problems. Land-use regulations can help.

Water Pollution: Ten of 12 major lakes sampled in one study had coliform bacterial levels too high for safe swimming. Yet the demand for water-based recreation—in fact for all water uses—is rising fast.

SEWRPC planners recommend: more intensive sewage treatment and future urban development on soils that do not readily contribute to water pollution. The Fox Watershed report points out: "(Our) study clearly indicates a relationship between urbanization and stream pollution . . . (so) pollution abatement is, within southeast Wisconsin, basically a problem of land use."

Waste Disposal Problems: As mentioned, four counties have new sanitary codes, and other counties are considering similar safeguards. The local SCS soil scientist estimates he spends approximately 50 percent of his time in on-site investigations.

Overall, SCS people in rapidly urbanizing southeast Wisconsin now spend 40 to 50 percent of their time on nonfarm land and water problems. At the same time, surprisingly, they complete almost as many farm conservation plans as in the "old days."

One SCS service requested by both farm and nonfarm people is help in planning small, manmade lakes and flood control structures. Many building firms and municipal engineers are familiar with planning closed storm drains, but have little or no experience in lake design work incorporating flood control measures. One of the authors has helped plan and design perhaps 500 ponds or small lakes during the past 10 years.

Much of the land and water planning for people is done at the county level.

Green and beautiful Walworth County has 63,000 people in winter—but 350,000 people in the summer vacation months. Half the county's assessed valuation comes from property around its 37 natural lakes. Careful use of soil and water will be needed to keep the natural beauty that attracted people to Walworth in the first place.

A county ordinance prohibits septic tank systems on soils that can't "take it." This is well publicized and enforced. Says county sanitary officer Jim Johnson, "if anybody—attorney, homeowner, contractor—comes in and says he didn't know about this building restriction, we feel he's not being very honest."

Walworth County is currently working on a revised zoning ordinance that includes zones for agriculture and for steep or wooded areas that need special protection from careless or exploitative development.

Another proposed ordinance requires subdivision builders to protect the land, during the building process, in erosion-prone areas.

140

Both present and proposed ordinances incorporate SCS soils information. The two proposed ordinances also incorporate sound technical standards for managing floodplain and agricultural lands, and for conservation methods in urbanizing areas.

Johnson sees increasing acceptance by the average citizen of sound health and land-use regulations. But, "We must apply reasonable restrictions to real problems. If we all get worked up over something that isn't a real problem, we're going to lose ground."

Builders are also taking a longer look at their land before they let loose the bulldozers. Northridge Lakes is an example.

This 640-acre "new town," within the city limits of booming Milwaukee, will eventually house 15,000 people and include a shopping center, schools, offices, and community recreation facilities.

The development centers around three manmade lakes totaling 55 acres. They "work" as flood control projects and "play" as swimming, fishing, and generally attractive lakes.

SCS helped Northridge Lake builders with soil interpretations, lake feasibility studies, and lake designs that incorporate flood prevention features. Floodwater runoff will go through the lake spillways. This should reduce peak floodwater discharge by more than 75 percent with obvious benefits to people in both the immediate area and the downstream urban areas.

The development is proceeding in a step-by-step manner. Only the immediate working area is stripped of protective grass cover. The builders seed temporary vegetation where necessary, and trap much of the soil that does run off through sediment basins on the building site.

SCS people in southeast Wisconsin feel that by sharing their know-how with private engineers and architects, the latter can begin to incorporate similar conservation features in future building projects with little or no SCS help. With the rapid rural-into-urban land changes now occurring, the need is growing for more builders to understand and use erosion and sediment control measures.

A small but perhaps typical result of accelerated sediment production in rapidly growing areas is illustrated by this fact: Milwaukee must now pay half a million dollars yearly to remove silt and sediment from its drinking water; 40 years ago this was no problem.

Are citizen-taxpayers working to clean up their water supply *directly*? Yes.

Little Muskego, in Waukesha County, is one of hundreds of dying lakes in the Nation. Sediment, sewage, and fertilizer runoff are the killers. Two and a half million yards of silt muck up the bottom.

Little Muskego is not an unusual lake, except for one thing, It has friends in the Little Muskego Association and its president, industrial salesman Ron Ford.

Ford and his citizen group hope to clean up the 570-acre lake and restore water depths of 9 to 11 feet. Costs will be borne by lakeshore property owners and the city of Muskego.

After cleanup, the group is urging city officials to enact a sediment control ordinance. The proposed ordinance, enforceable by bond, would require lakeshore builders to use erosion control measures.

Says Ron Ford of the fight to save Little Muskego: "This is only one of many similar lakes. If we reverse the trend here, it may give hope to other areas."

What general conclusions can one draw from Wisconsin's experience?

1. A recognition that "hit or miss" is no good for a growing area. Orderly planning is needed to provide and maintain the life that people want.

2. Planning must be rational, humane, and allow for full citizen participation. It must *precede* land-use changes.

3. The natural environment sustains most physical, and many economic and psychic, needs. When our air,

soil, and water are wisely used, these basic needs are better satisfied.

4. If we do not consciously plan the use of air, soil, and water, life will continue for most Americans. But it will be a harsher, more unpleasant world; one that to many will seem drab, crowded, and bleak. The question is not so much life or death as the quality of life—a better existence or a polluted, deteriorating "live-in" world.

Beyond statistics, regulations, and committees, this is the reason for environmental planning.

Building Codes

PAUL R. CONN

ABILITY of the United States to meet its housing commitment of providing an additional 26 million homes in the 1970's is adversely affected by outmoded, inflexible, and widely varying building codes in use throughout the country.

Out-of-date and rigid codes can increase the cost of the average home as much as $1,000 by excluding the use of improved and less expensive material. The countless differences in building codes from area to area and town to town are unnecessary, confusing, and ultimately add to the cost of housing.

There are codes, for example, which specify that footings for the foundation of a house must be a certain size based on soil with a low bearing capacity. There is no provision in the codes for reducing footings for houses built on firmer soil. Results: an unnecessary added expense to the house.

Other codes specify that galvanized steel pipe or copper pipe must be used in the plumbing system of houses. It has been proven that plastic pipe, which is less expensive, is equally satisfactory. Use of roof trusses constructed of 2 x 4 lumber is forbidden by some codes, although this type of roof support is a lower cost substitute for heavy rafter and joist construction.

The preponderance of local building codes are also roadblocks in the path of mass production of factory built or modular constructed homes. Before going into production, the developer of preassembled housing components is primarily concerned with the building codes in his market area. His housing must meet code requirements of each jurisdictional area, or he must seek changes in the code, or obtain a variance whereby the local code authority authorizes construction even though certain code requirements are not met.

The developer's problem can be compared with the automobile industry's mass production techniques.

Suppose cars had to be manufactured to comply with various local safety ordinances that cover almost every item in the automobile. Suppose some codes required all cars to have eight cylinders and other codes allowed no more than two. Also, suppose some codes required parts of the automobile to be made of wood while others required all metal construction.

On top of all this, suppose the plans and specifications of each car had to be submitted to the local authority for approval before the car could be sold.

It is easy to see that the automobile industry could not function as it does today under such conditions. Although homes are not cars, mass production of factory built homes on a national basis is greatly handicapped by the various local building codes and regulations.

The study of local code requirements, and negotiations to get changes or variance from local authorities, are time consuming chores for the mass

*

PAUL R. CONN is a Rural Housing Loan Officer in the Farmers Home Administration.

producer of factory built homes and—without a doubt—add to housing costs.

The historical migration of people from rural areas to the towns and cities of this country, and the resulting concentration of population, has up to this time made the control and regulation of building construction primarily an urban problem. Most home construction, especially concentrated types of development, has taken place in and around our large cities.

Due to less building activity and more open space, the use of building codes in rural areas has not developed to the same extent as in urban areas. In many rural areas, there are no building codes regulating construction of private dwellings.

It is a recognized fact that building codes serve a useful and necessary function of regulating the construction of buildings, and I see a definite need for more comprehensive, workable, and uniform building codes for rural areas. But a continuation of the type of building codes already in existence must be avoided.

A closer look at building codes in use today shows they exist under the authority of States, counties, and in most cases, local municipalities.

States have played a secondary role in establishing building codes. Some have passed enabling legislation that authorizes local governments to develop and adopt their own building codes. Others rely on their constitutions and the home rule provision that local governments are free to adopt all regulations not specifically prohibited by the State constitution.

A few States have passed State building codes covering private dwellings which set forth certain standards that must be observed throughout the State.

Building codes are not easy to write, maintain, or revise. Anyone who has looked at the plumbing, mechanical, housing, or other building codes of a relatively large city has an idea of the complexity and details involved.

Small towns and counties have difficulty in hiring and retaining the expertise necessary to develop and maintain their own building codes. To minimize the problem, some local governments have chosen to adopt one or more of the model codes developed by such organizations as American Insurance Association, Building Officials Conference of America, International Conference of Building Officials, and Southern Building Code Congress.

The model codes are highly regarded throughout the country. However, in providing a service function to their members and the building industry, these organizations are constantly revising and updating their codes to provide for use of new materials and methods.

This creates a problem for the authority which has adopted them of either continuing with the originally adopted code, or making provisions for keeping it updated—which usually means that the authority's governing body must act on each revision before it is incorporated into the code. This is a time consuming and costly process.

Many counties and local municipalities have not adopted any codes at all due to the problems of developing and maintaining them, and also because of community resistance to building controls.

In these areas, which for the most part are in small towns and rural communities, there is little more than the knowledge, ability, honesty, and integrity of the builder to construct housing which meets what is commonly called minimum standards of health and safety.

Construction requirements of lenders financing new housing may require certain construction standards, and regulate the design, size, and use of materials. Government agencies concerned with financing and insuring funds for construction or renovation of housing have developed minimum property standards that provide for minimum size and spacing of materials, minimum size of doors and rooms, lighting, ventilation, heating, plumbing, and other requirements which the housing must meet.

143

However, these agencies, such as the Department of Housing and Urban Development, the Farmers Home Administration, and the Veterans Administration, each have their own separate minimum property standards that are not necessarily correlated with each other. The differences add to the confusion for builders constructing housing according to these standards.

To resolve this problem, the agencies began work in 1967 on uniform design and construction standards for housing that will be used by all agencies. The standards were to be released in 1971.

Progress is being made in eliminating some roadblocks in the way of factory built homes. California and Ohio, for example, have passed laws establishing uniform codes that apply to factory built houses.

In Ohio, the State code applies to nonpublic buildings which were not included under the previous State building code, especially prefab and modular 1 to 3 family dwellings. A Board of Building Standards is set up in the State to develop performance standards for material and procedures and also to issue model codes for 1 to 3 family dwellings to be made available for adoption by local code authorities on an optional basis.

The "California Factory Built Housing Law," as its statute is called, says in part:

"The Legislature hereby finds and declares that in an effort to meet the housing needs within the State of California, the private housing and construction industry has developed mass production techniques which can substantially reduce housing construction costs, and that the mass production of housing, consisting primarily of factory manufacture of dwelling units or habitable rooms thereof, presents unique problems with respect to the establishment of uniform health and safety standards and the inspection procedures.

"The Legislature further finds and declares that by minimizing the problem of standards and inspection procedures, it is demonstrating its intention to encourage the reduction of housing construction costs and to make housing and home ownership more feasible for all residents of the state."

The California law requires that all housing manufactured in the State be approved by the State and bear the State insignia of approval. Factory built housing bearing this insignia is considered to comply with all ordinances and regulations of any city, county, or district which may apply to the manufacture of such housing. Local code authorities are still required to inspect installation of these factory built homes. Any local requirements such as building setbacks, rear and side yard clearances and arrangements, still prevail.

What can and should be done to update, modernize, and eliminate unnecessary differences in building codes? Perhaps we have reached the stage when State and Federal authorities need more power to control codes, now largely in local hands. At stake is our Nation's current effort to produce housing on a mass production basis.

With perhaps as many as 25 million more families expected by the turn of the century, mass production of housing may mean the difference between adequate housing for all or having a large proportion of the population in overcrowded substandard housing.

Uniformity of building codes cannot come about as long as each local area exercises its power to control them independently of each other. Codes will not be revised to keep up with technological development as long as the controlling authority does not have the resources to keep them updated.

Model codes that are based on performance of materials, a built-in factor against obsolescence, will not be adopted on any uniform basis across the Nation as long as local areas have control. An alternative to Federal or State control would involve a concerted effort by towns, cities, and communities in the same geographical area to develop and adopt building codes for use throughout the area.

services for living

Quality of Life in the Rural Community

DARYL HOBBS

AMERICAN society has long used increase and growth as standards for success in practically all aspects of life. Communities increasing in employment and population are regarded as dynamic and successful while thousands of rural communities declining in population desperately seek new industry and other means of stemming the tide of decline.

As a nation this concern with quantity has paid off in the sense that growth and increase have been achieved. There is more income and more goods, services, and leisure time to spend that income on than any society has ever enjoyed.

However, despite success as measured by increases of quantity, widespread concern recently has developed about the quality of life in American communities. The blessings of our increased income, production of consumer goods, technological development, and population growth have come to be viewed by many as "mixed": mixed with environmental pollution, overcrowded streets and highways, increases in crime and violence, breakdowns in human relations, and other social costs.

While these social costs are largely associated with centralization and industrialization and thus most closely identified with cities, the effects of centralization have had effects upon rural communities as well. Many traditional rural community services have become more centralized, thus reducing the number of services found in rural localities. This trend has not necessarily resulted in a lessening of services available to rural people, but it has modified the function of the community.

We have come to use the term community in many different ways. We often think in terms of an economic or functional concept of the community. This idea about community focuses on the economic base of a locality and the extent of services and population that the economic base is capable of sustaining.

A community thought of in this way represents a good place to live if there are sufficient employment opportunities besides adequate education, health, government, consumer, cultural, religious, and recreational services.

People also often think of community in terms of being involved with other people quite apart from the jobs and services found in a locality. This meaning usually refers to the existence of a *sense of community*—a sense of mutual trust and involvement in cooperative ventures and activities. The sense of community is more concerned with the quality of social relationships in contrast to the quality of public and private services.

Although definitions of quality of life are at best imprecise, there is at least general consensus that both adequate services and a sense of community are important dimensions of the quality place to live.

Our idealistic concepts of community usually envision a convergence of both the economic and social dimensions. Indeed the rural community of the past such as described in Sinclair Lewis' *Main Street* and many similar works was thought of as embracing both meanings within the boundaries of a single locality.

The small locality was both a relatively self-contained economic and service center and the focal point for the sense of community. The com-

*

DARYL HOBBS is Professor of Sociology and Rural Sociology, University of Missouri, Columbia.

munity was small enough to sustain face-to-face relations yet large enough to provide most services demanded at that time.

This shared sense of community served as the basis for people getting together in associations and organizations concerned with solving problems affecting the economic, political, and service dimensions of the community.

The overall trend toward centralization which has been facilitated by technological changes in transportation, communication, and production has greatly modified the interrelationship between the economic community, the social community, and the geographic community. Rarely do the three coincide in present day America.

Towns or localities small enough to sustain a sense of community are often not large enough to economically provide a full range of consumer and public services. Conversely, cities large enough to economically provide all the services people demand are too large to sustain a sense of community on a personal and informal basis.

Communities other than subsistence agricultural communities cannot exist without an economic base: that is, production of some good or service which brings income into a locality. The economic base may be manufacturing, mining, tourism, a college, retirement checks, etc., or any combination of these. For most U.S. rural communities the economic base has been primarily agriculture, although a transition to such basic activities as industry and tourism is occurring in many rural localities.

Basic economic activities like those mentioned above not only provide employment but also generate the income which provides the support for nonbasic employment such as retail stores and community services as well. In a typical community, then, most services exist to the extent that there is an economic base to support the services. An exception are those services provided directly by government as being in the public interest regardless of the economic support base.

Some governmental services provided for the public interest have contributed much to community economic development as well as to relocation of both people and services in rural localities. Such public and publicly regulated investments as highways, railroads, communication systems, etc., often termed the economic infrastructure, serve to link the community with the regional and national economy of which the economy of the community is an integral part.

The economic base of the community depends on the existence of such linkages. Without it the community would be isolated and to a great extent an economically subsistent community. The assumed importance of an economic infrastructure to economic development is reflected in the central place it occupies in development investment both domestically and internationally.

A study in Missouri, for example, demonstrates a clear association between population change and location of towns on major highways. Towns in all size ranges were much more likely to increase in population if located on a major highway.

Facilitated by the economic infrastructure, rural community services have followed a pattern of increasing consolidation and centralization to the extent that few rural localities are the location of even a majority of services demanded by residents today.

The small, relatively self-sufficient economic and service community of yesterday has been largely replaced by the functional economic or service community. This "functional" community as it is often called consists of all the towns that rural people visit with some regularity to obtain services.

For many of the kinds of services rural people demand—such as medical specialists, general hospitals, vocational training schools, commercial airports, department stores—the size of operation necessary to economically provide such service makes it unlikely

147

that they would be found in a city of less than 25,000–50,000 in population. Consequently, the functional economic community of most rural people includes a small city even if 100 or more miles distant, besides nearby smaller towns serving more limited service needs.

For many rural people the functional community thus will include a hierarchy of towns of increasing size, services, and complexity. The smaller nearby places are visited more regularly for services demanded most frequently and the large centers less frequently and for more specialized services.

The functional service community has been replacing the self-sufficient service community in rural areas for two reasons. First, improved transportation and communication has made it feasible. Second, although the location of various specialized services tends to vary directly with size of town, the demand for specialized services generally does not. Rural and small town people want the same kinds of services as city people.

This has been found especially true for health, consumer, educational, and cultural services. For example, a recent study in the Midwest found interest in cultural activities and events was as great in small towns and villages as in larger towns even though professional concerts, plays, art exhibits, etc., are seldom found in towns of less than 10,000 population.

Similarly, the demand for health services is as great in small towns that have no physician as in cities with a full range of medical services.

Insofar as there is an association between quality of life and community services, it is important to know whether the functional community adequately serves the needs of rural people. Centralization and specialization of services (such as the consolidation of schools, medical clinics) presumably lead to higher quality service, but this increase in quality would be of small consolation if the service was inaccessible.

Does the absence of a physician in a locality mean a deprivation of health service besides the inconvenience of having to travel further for the service? Although evidence on this point is not entirely clear, recent studies in the Missouri Ozarks lead to the conclusion that use of health and medical services and availability of these services in the locality are not directly associated.

No difference was found in extent of use—that is, having a family doctor, number of visits to a doctor, number of different doctors seen, use of medical specialists, etc.—between families living in a community with no physician, those living in communities with general practitioners only, and those who live in a community with several types of physicians and a general hospital.

Furthermore, residents of each of the study communities were found to be making extensive use of medical specialists in a city approximately 100 miles from the communities.

Overall use of health services by people in the study area compared favorably with national health statistics for metropolitan areas. The principal conclusion from this research is that although inconvenience may have been caused by loss of some services within the locality, this trend has not necessarily resulted in reduced use of health services. However, further work is needed on the relationship between location of various services, how the services are organized, and how these factors influence use of services by various segments of the population.

In considering the association between community services and quality of life, it is important to take into account not only the availability of services but also what services contribute most directly to quality of life and the elimination of community problems.

It is a matter of nearly universal agreement, for example, that good health is an important dimension of quality of life. But it is less clear that the presence of medical facilities or services in a community necessarily relates directly to the health of the community, even though we often make that assumption.

Health facilities and medical services are generally focused on cure of disease and restoration of health, which are necessary and important functions. However, if community health is the desired objective, greater gains could perhaps be made by adding services addressed to preventing disease.

Similarly if reduction of crime is a desired community objective, services should be provided that are concerned with preventing crime and eliminating conditions which produce crime as well as catching and punishing criminals.

The problem involved in the relationship between community service and quality of life is thus conceived as being of two parts: (1) making existing services available to all potential users, and (2) determining what additional services are needed to more effectively cope with problems generated by a highly centralized, industrialized, and mobile society. Meeting these service needs will require effective planning.

Difficulties of planning for rural community services are, however, compounded by the very trends discussed above. As rural communities become more integrated into the larger economy and as services become more centralized, rural communities lose much of their economic and political autonomy.

The small rural locality that serves as a basis for a sense of community has lost jurisdiction over many of the forces which affect its economic base and over decisions pertaining to many of the services which localities rely on. Thus even though there is more likely to be a sense of community in the rural locality, this sense of community is often not paired with effective means of control over community services.

In planning for rural community services, new mechanisms for both decision-making and financing are needed to at least partially restore a relationship between a sense of community and community control. One such mechanism is the many regional planning commissions which have been organized. These, however, are still in their organizational infancy and have yet to solve many of the problems of participation in decision-making, coordination, and financing of services.

Such planning bodies must be prepared to cope with problems of how to provide services for residents of rural communities of today. But they must also anticipate a probable move back to rural localities by some urban residents. There are indications now of this reverse migration as people begin to despair of the problems of congestion, pollution, etc., which characterize today's cities.

Although predictions vary, many social commentators expect that rural communities accustomed to population decline will be expected to absorb a significant portion of expected population increase in the coming decades. At a minimum, doing so will call for effective planning organizations capable of establishing participatory ways of meeting service needs.

Social Services— The Great Lag

GEORGE L. WILBER

PEOPLE in nonmetropolitan America suffer from inadequate and unequal social services provided through a multitude of Federal, State, and local programs. Yet the demand for services has no boundaries—geographic, age, sex, color, or otherwise. If anything, circumstances dictate a greater need for services in rural than in urban areas.

Three major factors help create a powerful need for improved services in rural America: poverty, inadequate services, and differences in population structure.

Faces of poverty in rural America.

There is a heavy concentration of the poor in nonmetropolitan areas and their poverty is severe. Over 12 million people living outside metropolitan centers were below the officially defined poverty level in 1968.

Nearly one out of five nonmetropolitan people were poor compared with about one in 10 among metropolitan residents, despite the fact that the numbers of poor were about the same in each of the areas.

The greater severity of poverty for the nonmetropolitan poor is reflected by their incomes. The metropolitan poor averaged $538 per family member in 1968 compared to $497 for the nonmetropolitan poor.

Services of many kinds are less often available to both the poor and nonpoor in nonmetropolitan than in metropolitan areas. And where they are available, the services often are inaccessible.

Not only are medical, clinical, and family planning services relatively lacking in rural areas, but also library, legal aid, welfare counseling, and many others. The picture of inadequate services is too huge, and perhaps known too well, for detailed description here.

Both facilities and personnel for providing services tend to concentrate in

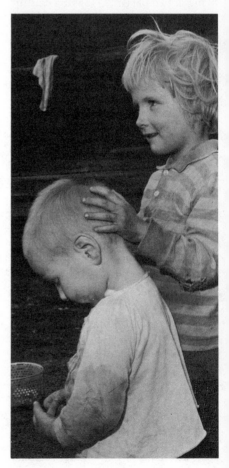

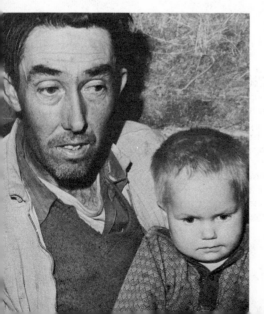

urban centers. The resulting discrepancies in services may be illustrated by visits to a doctor's office. In 1966–67, people in metropolitan areas averaged 4.5 visits, while outside of metropolitan centers nonfarm residents averaged 4.1 and farm residents only 3.3 visits.

Individuals living in the nonmetropolitan areas are essentially the same as their metropolitan counterparts, but the nonmetropolitan population as a whole differs in several important respects. Nonmetropolitan residents are older, more frequently widowed, more often in poverty, less well educated, and have more children.

In 1969, for example, over half of female family heads were widows in nonmetropolitan areas, and 10 percent of all nonmetropolitan residents were 65 or older. These kinds of circumstances call for greater, not just equal, services for widows and the aged.

The number of people living in either rural areas (places of 2,500 or less) or outside of metropolitan areas is not increasing as fast as in metropolitan centers. Nevertheless, the urgency for improved services will grow as many of the projected additional 100 million people by the year 2000 settle outside metropolitan centers.

Although actual numbers are necessarily uncertain, some of the additional 25 million families will undoubtedly live in small cities, towns, and open country. So it is not merely a question of differences in the characteristics of people. Nonmetropolitan areas as a whole are expected to contain *larger numbers* of people from another generation.

Historically, barriers have impeded us from providing the same services for people in less densely settled areas as for those living in urban and industrial centers. In part a sort of inertia has set in which still makes it

*

GEORGE L. WILBER is Director of the Social Welfare Research Institute, University of Kentucky, Lexington. He served as Associate Director of the National Advisory Commission on Rural Poverty.

difficult to extend programs such as employment service or family planning to rural areas.

This inertia is bolstered by the presence of problems not yet solved. The greater cost per person of extending services into sparsely settled areas is a perpetual rationale for not providing services.

Often the sheer logistics of getting the needed service or facility to rural people are exceedingly difficult. Distances and isolation continue to hamper the provision of services to all citizens, but now we have the technology and the skills to solve such problems. What is needed is a strong national commitment to solve them.

Personnel in service professions typically prefer living and working in big cities. This fact alone poses a major obstacle to making services available in small cities and open country. It seems to make little difference whether we talk about lawyers, physicians, nurses, teachers, or social workers. All these people tend to prefer the big city.

Regardless of their reasons, the result is that relatively few trained service people are outside metropolitan centers. Without personnel equipped to provide service, nonmetropolitan people simply do not obtain the service, at least in their home community.

Rural residents, particularly those most deprived economically, lack the resources to effectively demand what they need. This is best illustrated by the poor whites, who have little organization and no real spokesman. Negroes, Indians, unionized workers, and others are organized, vocal, and relatively effective in presenting their case. Not so the poor whites.

While many long-standing obstacles to the providing of services to nonmetropolitan Americans have been overcome, inequities remain.

Family planning services have grown rapidly in recent years, but very little in rural areas. In the rural South, described by the National Advisory Commission on Rural Poverty as "one vast poverty area," benefits under public assistance programs are

151

typically among the lowest in the Nation.

Family counseling and legal aid are rarely available in rural areas. Many counties are without a medical doctor, not to mention a hospital or clinic. Psychiatric service is all but unheard of in rural areas.

Demands for new and expanded services accompany technological and social change. Therefore removal of old barriers and inequities is only a partial solution.

The need for a comprehensive employment service is one of the most evident consequences of changed conditions. Successful placement of workers in agricultural jobs is not enough, for rural America is no longer primarily engaged in farming.

Increased employment of women, many of whom are mothers of young children, requires not only better employment service but also day care services and family counseling. The task of running the household has changed with the introduction of modern labor-saving devices. And the absence of the employed wife has changed family living considerably.

Workers now have much more leisure or nonwork time. Even employed wives may be freed from the traditionally time-consuming household tasks. So an increasingly important question is how this nonwork time is spent.

Not only is there a growing need for recreational facilities and services, but sentiment is strong for opportunities to increase skills and knowledge. An extended education and training program is an important parallel to an elaborate recreational service system.

Expansion of nonwork time for older citizens brings greater demand for services also. Earlier retirement and longer lives have created the demand. Problems of health and retirement adjustment for the increasing numbers of older persons emphasize this demand for services.

Innovative services to replace the "old folks home" are clearly needed. These new services should not only meet the health, housing, and financial needs of senior citizens but also their psychological and social needs. Therefore social and recreational activities appropriate to the nature of the demand must be made available.

The older person may be strongly in need of counseling, but even more critical is the need for programs that help prepare in advance for years of nonwork.

The demand for social justice has sprung into prominence in our big cities and the same thing is likely elsewhere. Too little is known about injustice outside urban centers, but there is no reason to believe the need is any less.

Demand has grown in our cities for improved legal aid, better protection for the accused, an effective and fair probation and parole setup, and overall improvements in police and court systems. So also will these demands increase in rural areas.

If the demand for services in nonmetropolitan areas is to be met effectively within the next generation, plans and programs must be developed and implemented immediately.

Two basic strategies are suggested. The first may be called a catchup strategy. All existing services for all nonmetropolitan residents need to be brought to higher levels so that everyone—not merely "the people left behind"—has an equal opportunity to avail himself of adequate services.

The second strategy is more nearly a go-ahead tactic. Changing conditions and demands for new services must be anticipated and policy and program activated to meet the need for new as well as expanded services.

National policy must provide a basis for necessary services and include an equal chance for everyone to have access to these services.

No single agency can develop a comprehensive service policy by itself. A division of labor among present agencies can implement national policy. But in the absence of clear, unequivocal national goals and standards, individual agencies are unlikely

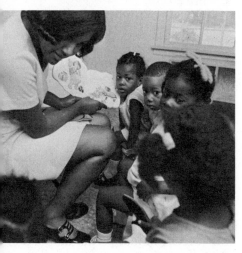

Day care center in Virginia.

to move effectively toward either catching up or going ahead.

Setting priorities is never an easy task. The demands for services seem unlimited and advocates of one kind of service insist that their demand is more important than others. A basic criterion for setting priorities, however, is the social climate and conditions in America today which point strongly to the urgency for removing injustices and inequities.

Many of the problems of urban slums, violence, and protest have their roots in rural areas. Consequently the task of catching up must have a very high priority.

Moreover, if nonmetropolitan areas are to become models for the solution of problems for the next generation, a go-ahead strategy must be developed now rather than later.

Only brief and illustrative mention of more specific courses of action can be made here.

Obviously the lags in health and welfare services in nonmetropolitan areas should be eliminated. Although the costs per person may be relatively high, medical services, for instance, must be made accessible to isolated residents.

If this means mobile units, then they should be provided. If it means constructing and staffing additional clinics and hospitals, then this should be done. If it requires more recruiting and training of medical manpower, this too should be done. If it also requires educating the public about health problems and available services, this should be accomplished.

The objective of providing for better health is already clear. All that remains is to move vigorously and decisively to realize the goal. The same can be said for recreation, education, and welfare services.

Difficulties in providing services are greater when there is less consensus on the nature of the problem and ways to meet the need for services. It is yet unclear whether family planning is primarily a means of improving health, reducing poverty, or slowing population growth. Probably it is all of these and more, too.

But family planning services for rural people have lagged far behind basically because of a void in national policy and the failure to establish equal, if not priority, services in more sparsely settled areas.

Changing Needs Through the Life Cycle

MARGARET I. LISTON

It's a boy! Congratulations! The messages poured in—by mail and phone—to the parents of Richard Rinder, the first born of a couple who recently had moved to *Crossroads USA*.

Not only was the new baby an exciting event—so too was the fact that he was the first to be born in the new community hospital which Richard's parents, their friends, and relatives had worked so hard to get. A Federal grant, generous contributions of many citizens, much planning, and lots of hard work had made this badly needed hospital a reality.

Soon it was time for the baby boy and his mother to go home. Though they would not admit it, the new mom and dad were a bit frightened about being fully responsible for him. But some assurance was felt in the fact that their little town had one of the best doctors in that part of the state. Also, if necessary, they could call on the county's Public Health nurse.

While Richard was "on the way" his parents had taken advantage of special classes for expectant parents. They found these classes very informative and helpful. They were

Couple talking to Farmers Home Administration aide about financing home they plan to buy.

given quite a bit of literature on infant and child care and development. Those from the U.S. Department of Health, Education and Welfare proved very helpful.

Before Richard entered their lives his parents had gone rather deeply into debt. Every month several payments came due on loans. Through the U.S. Employment Service, Richard's mother located a job as a clerk-stenographer. It was pleasant work and the pay check helped a lot in keeping up with the loan payments. For one thing, a new car had become a "must" because they'd had an accident with the old one.

For a couple of years they had been renting a farm. Then, almost over-

*

MARGARET I. LISTON is Professor of Family Environment in the College of Home Economics at Iowa State University, Ames.

night, a chance came to buy some high quality farmland on the edge of town— a chance which seemed too good to pass up. With most of their savings and a loan from the Farmers Home Administration, it became theirs, at least in title. Every now and then they used short-time production credit for operating the farm.

Since there was no house on the farm, they bought one of the older single family dwellings in town. For this they also were helped by a loan through the Farmers Home Administration.

The house seemed a good buy, especially since an agricultural engineer of the State university's Cooperative Extension Service had checked it over and judged it to be structurally sound. Also, with the help of the Extension home economist and the landscaping specialist, they had made some long run plans for remodeling and redecorating the house and for beautifying the lawn and plantings.

So, early in their married life, Richard's parents had had some extensive experience with judicious use of credit in the form of consumer, real estate, and producer loans. And for two years, in fact until shortly before his birth, Richard's mother kept her stenographic job to help pay off the debts.

After the baby came, the debt load seemed far more onerous without the wife's earnings. So she started thinking—to herself, because she feared her husband would not approve—about possibilities for going back to work. Much to her delight she learned that a day care center was to be started in the town because a new factory was being built there and would need women workers. What is more, her old job was to be vacated soon and she would have it back.

At a strategic moment she proposed the idea to Richard's father. At first he was hesitant. Later however, he agreed they both would feel more secure if they could get that debt load paid off a bit faster.

Richard was introduced to his first

"peer world" in the day care center. But other peer groups emerged as he went through preschool, kindergarten, grade school, and high school.

Meanwhile, Richard's sister had joined the family group. As they grew older, both children played in the school band, were active 4-H'ers, and took part in various community recreational and educational activities such as sports, crafts, and nature study. They put this nature study to good use on their family camping vacations in various State and national forests and parks.

One very special event for the whole family was their share in obtaining a community library. An elderly citizen of the community—also a friend of Richard's family—had expressed his willingness to donate a considerable amount of money for constructing and equipping a library in the town.

However, this donation would be made only on two conditions. First, the people of the community would have to round up enough money to match the gift. Second, they would need to organize a community library committee for developing a reasonable plan to operate, maintain, and gradually expand the library services.

Everyone in Richard's family took part in various money-making projects which, fortunately, did yield enough to match the donor's gift. It was a happy day for everyone. But, more important, Richard felt a special sense of proprietorship, a feeling that the library was just a little bit his own. He and his family, along with many others, had made it possible and now were responsible for keeping it going and growing.

Although *Crossroads USA* was just a little town it obviously was "on the grow."

Its people knew they must invest hard labor and public spirit as well as money in the community if their

Worship service at Four-H camp.

own personal needs were to be met by the town.

Encouraged by the success of the library project, interest in a community center soon developed.

Both the teenagers and the elderly needed places where they could gather for activities of special interest to them. A "little theater" was the dream of an amateur dramatics group. Special facilities were in demand with audio and video equipment that could be used by those fortunate enough to travel so they could share with others their experiences of historical, scenic, and human interest.

Desire for an arts and crafts center had been kindled a few years earlier by a demonstration project of the Home Economics Extension Service from the State university.

As a long-time hobby, one of Richard's uncles had written a brief history of the community. Along with this, he had collected quite a few artifacts of the area. These needed to be much more available to the public than was now possible. His uncle met with the town council which, in turn, set up a committee to approach the State's commission on the arts.

With a favorable nod from the Commission and some promising leads about sources of financial assistance, the "local leaven" of the town again became active. After a few years the community center was a reality of buzzing activity.

One day an exhibit in the library caught Richard's attention. A set of large photographs, loaned by the area's Community Action Project (CAP), portrayed the plight of disadvantaged youth in a nearby city. The pathos and futility reflected in the faces and stances of the young folk in the pictures got through to Richard. Something had to be done!

After talking with his folks about it, Richard enlisted the interest of some of his pals. They contacted the county Extension director who advised them to talk with CAP officials. From these efforts emerged a Brother-to-Brother program. Several times Richard and

his friends spent weekends with disadvantaged families in the city while youth from the city visited homes in *Crossroads USA.*

It was not surprising that Richard, sometime earlier, had found it necessary to have a car of his own. Without a car, many of the activities he enjoyed would not have been possible.

During his high school years he had worked most of each summer in a local supermarket. In the fall he raked leaves and in winter he cleared the walks for several elderly townspeople. He saved enough for a reasonable down payment on a used car. Since it seemed to be a good buy he contracted for full ownership through monthly payments to the finance company.

When Richard was a high school senior, his father died suddenly of a heart attack, leaving his mother a widow with two teenage children. Emotionally, the adjustment was difficult for all, but their financial circumstances could have been worse.

Survivors' insurance through social security, although limited in amount, was a dependable source of income. Life insurance benefits not only helped with burial expenses but also provided a reserve for future emergencies or old age income. Equity in the farm enterprise was a comfortable "nest egg."

Richard's mother, who had not been employed since his sister's birth, found her previous secretarial experience an asset toward locating a job a few months after her husband's death.

Richard and his sister usually had participated in Sunday School and youth groups but they never had been regular churchgoers. After the death of his father, Richard felt drawn to greater identification with church activities, especially in the social action programs.

Then, luckily, an evening course on "Leadership and Community Action" was offered in a nearby town by the State university's off-campus program. This was an opportunity Richard could not pass up.

During his high school years, Richard had aspired, now and then, to go to the State university and prepare for teaching social studies. But on the death of his father he gave up this idea, and accepted an offer to work in one of the local banks as soon as he could get some special training in accounting.

A study program of this type was offered in the community college of a nearby city to which he could commute and not have to leave his mother and sister alone.

Oh yes, there was a girl in Richard's life cycle, too. They became acquainted during his study at the community college and found they enjoyed many of the same things. After Richard had worked at the bank for 2 years, they decided to marry and set up a home of their own. Like his father and mother, they eventually had a son and a daughter.

Family interests and work at the bank did not distract from Richard's concern for community service. He often was involved in projects which needed to be done for the library or the community center. He and his wife became members of a "Homes Incorporated" group in the nearby city. It worked with disadvantaged families by helping them to obtain and often to own housing suiting their particular needs.

Eventually, the factory—the one which had been an important factor in starting the day care center when Richard was a baby—was closed down and its production activities were transferred to another State. Many of the people of the town and surrounding area were left jobless.

To help these unemployed families cope with their difficult situations, Richard helped organize a small action group. With the cooperation of the State employment service, the Cooperative Extension Service, and the local churches, this group provided assistance in retraining, finding work, and migration to other communities—if necessary.

A food stamp program also helped those in need.

And then, when Richard was 40 years old, tragedy came to him and his family. He was seriously injured in an automobile accident. Although he was lucky to recover, he was so handicapped physically that he had to be retrained for a job on which he could be seated most of the time. From the State's vocational rehabilitation service he obtained help in both physical and occupational therapy for several months.

But it soon became apparent that his injuries were more deep-seated than had been expected. A gradual paralysis on his left side necessitated his being placed in a nursing home. His wife became the main earner for the family, with various kinds of assistance from her children who still were in high school.

Incapacitated as he was, Richard would not remain idle. His family background and his own life style had been oriented to "action according to need." In the nursing home he found many new ways to foster companionship and to bolster the morale of the other patients as well as his own.

Throughout the life cycle of Richard Rinder there seemed to be a well balanced blend of personal independence and social interdependence. Independently he was alert to his own needs as well as to those of his family and community.

Leadership was one of his strongest qualities. But leadership implies mutual interdependence of members of a group as they strive to achieve a goal. And many social problems require interdependent effort by various types of organized groups.

From Richard's birth in the new community hospital to his residence in the nursing home, the social interdependencies of individual, family, and community were exhibited frequently. He worked with and received help from numerous public agencies, including several from the U.S. Department of Agriculture. These reciprocal relations provide the basic fabric for rural life and growth in our nation.

Rural Schools Renaissance Vital for U.S.

JAMES T. HORNER

W E AMERICANS believe in the dignity of the individual. Education is the cornerstone of dignity and the keystone of freedom. Education is the essence of social and economic progress.

In this chapter I will discuss the scope, functions, and value of education in the United States; changes in education; the rural education situation; and a look to the future in funding.

Education, a $70 billion enterprise, with 127,000 schools, must be considered big business! More than 62 million Americans are engaged full-time as students, teachers, and administrators.

A fourth of our nation, 48 million, are enrolled in elementary and secondary schools alone.

Among the foundation blocks of American education is the concept that public education has a basic obligation to prepare *all* people for their next pursuit, be it an advanced grade level, high school, post high school, technical or college education, or for job entry.

Effective educational programs to combat ignorance and unemployment are costly. But society pays a much higher price to do without it in terms of youth delinquency and waste of the abilities of thousands of citizens who cannot find their proper place in society.

Even at $600 to $800 a year per student, education is a bargain compared to twice that amount for remedial education, three to four times as much for relief of an unemployed worker's family or for delinquent de-tention home care, or five times as much to maintain a criminal in a State institution.

Certainly not all returns on investment in education are in the form of economics—there is preservation of freedom, for example, and self-realization, to name just two.

However, when we treat schooling as an economic investment, what is the rate of return? University of Chicago economist T. W. Schultz, in comparisons with farm investments, states, "Investment in land is large. The rate of return is approximately 5 percent, compared to 30 percent from schooling. Tractors, machinery, and livestock may earn a higher rate of return than land, but not nearly as high a rate as schooling."

John Kenneth Galbraith adds that "... a dollar or a rupee invested in the intellectual improvement of human beings will often bring a greater increase in national income than a dollar or a rupee devoted to railways, dams, machine tools, or other tangible capital goods."

A recent Census Bureau report reconfirmed that the more education a person has the more money he makes—advancing from less than $200,000 expected lifetime earnings for those with less than eighth-grade education to more than $600,000 for those with 5 years or more of college.

U.S. education has amassed great achievements. Barely a century ago only 2 percent of the Nation's 17-year-olds were high school graduates—now 70 percent graduate.

More than two-and-a-half times as many pupils from working class families reach the final year of high school as in England, and over seven times more than in Germany. Likewise, the United States provides substantially greater opportunities for its citizens to enroll in the institutions of higher

*

DR. JAMES T. HORNER is Professor of Adult and Continuing Education, Professor and Chairman of Agricultural Education, and Professor of Secondary Education, University of Nebraska, Lincoln.

159

education and to earn degrees than do other advanced nations.

However, the dynamics of modern society make yesterday's education insufficient to prepare people of today for tomorrow's world. The greatest scientific and technological revolution in the history of man is now in progress—the knowledge revolution.

Educational practices and procedures must change. The traditional pattern—the hoary lock-step curriculum—six periods per day, 5 days per week, 36 weeks per year, 12 years, advancing one grade level per year in

There are encouraging signs, especially in suburbia. To avoid the "evils of the big city," the vast middle class of our nation has migrated to the fringe areas. Suburban educational systems have sprung up.

These schools have the newest furniture, devices, and equipment. They attempt to employ the best teachers available. The deficient educational programs in the city and in rural America are not so often found in suburban schools.

The following depict some of the dynamic changes occurring in edu-

Nucleus of many rural growth centers is an actively growing community college or university. At Western Kentucky University, small town friendliness is still retained in advising on course selection but facilities as modern as color TV are available, too.

a series of self-contained classrooms (with four unyielding walls) each with its teacher and 30 students, is geared to group advancement. Obviously it is exactly right for few, if any.

The schools must perform on a stage set with this backdrop: The scientific and technological explosion. A philosophy of mandatory education for the masses which yields students with wide diversity in terms of intellectual ability and educational background, interests and motivations, geographical orientation, sex, socio-economic advantages, and ages. The concept of comprehensive education, pluralistic in purpose, ranging from moral and ethical teachings to the preparation of doctors, plumbers, and farmers.

cation—all of which help, but none of which is a complete solution.

Individuals are at the center of instruction—

Active participatory, rather than passive, learning is emphasized.

Thinking and problem solving rather than just memorizing facts is stressed.

Effective guidance and counseling is "people oriented."

Individually-prescribed instruction permits a learner to proceed at his own pace.

Flexibility enhances individualizing of instruction—

Flexible and modular scheduling and ungraded systems allow for a variety of types and rates of learning.

160

Convertible, large-small classrooms without walls along with versatile furniture and equipment permit a wide variety of uses for learning activities both immediately and over the long range.

Mobile instructional units on wheels, correspondence courses, and traveling teachers add versatility.

Year-round schools and 24-hour-a-day Day Care/Toddler Education Centers are in operation.

Methods and materials are modern—

New approaches such as discovery learning of science principles and modern math are being used.

A variety of resources supplement books.

Team teaching capitalizes upon the strength of each teacher and adds variety.

Simulation and problem solving give a note of realism to education.

Technology is being used to meet changing concepts of learning and needs of students—

Programmed, machine and computer assisted, television, film and tape instruction add to self-directed teaching and the concept of the teacher as a guide.

The use of "laser link" for transmitting dozens of channels of video lessons simultaneously seems imminent.

Staffing is improved and is concerned with more than the mind—

Supporting the teacher are the professional physicians, nurses, social workers, counselors, psychologists, speech therapists and specialists in administration research and remedial reading.

Para professional aids and technicians round out differentiated staffs.

Curricula are being broadened—

Community centered courses of study developed and conducted cooperatively with the community use all community resources in learning.

The educational programs focus on special needs and the disadvantaged.

Academic, cultural, and vocational aspects of curriculum and guidance are being "integrated" at all levels, prekindergarten through adulthood, and capitalize upon the experience, natural interests, and the motivations of all ages.

General education is oriented to the world of work, while the vocational programs are deliberately designed to lead back into academic work.

New York City, recognizing the importance of work in each family and the community and the need for everyone to have a marketable skill, is requiring *all* students to complete at least a year of vocational education to graduate.

Nationally, for the first time the number of persons attending vocational schools is approaching the number in college—although only one in four jobs requires a 4-year degree. In the past, 80 percent of the educational effort has been college oriented, yet just 20 percent graduate with a bachelor's degree.

Organization has been toward consolidation—

Centralized, unified, multi-purpose programs enhance the quality of facilities, teachers, and the supporting services.

Area vocational schools, university extension centers, and junior colleges pool intellectual and cultural resources with minimal local pressures.

Broader based financing—area, State, and Federal—has helped assure higher minimal educational standards at a more equitable rate.

Granted, education has taken giant steps the past decade. But there's still a long way to go. Any agency which has a dropout rate of more than a third of its clientele is hard put to claim it is doing its job.

We can hope that the Nation, during this decade, will see the gap between educational needs and resources as an important problem— and disoriented youth as social dynamite—and will assign high priority to education as resources are released by relaxing international tensions.

Although the decade of the sixties stirred up a revolution in American education, it has not been equally shared as a reality of rural education. That the benefits should be shared seems undebatable.

However, it does seem appropriate to briefly describe the size and nature of this "disadvantaged minority." Rural America consists of more than a third of all Americans! Only a fifth of them are farmers. To focus upon the significance of status rather than the usual highlighting of trends: If the U.S. urban population did not exist, rural America would be large enough to be classified as the world's eighth largest country.

Further, it could be considered the world's fifth largest underdeveloped country. To the surprise of most Americans, there is proportionately three times more poverty on farms (three in 10) than in our cities (one in 10). One-half of the poverty families, those with less than $3,500 income, are rural families.

Improvements in management and the application of science and technology have made it possible for fewer farmers to produce more food. Their rate of production has increased at twice the rate of other segments.

In only 30 years, the number of people fed and clothed by one farm worker has increased from 11 to 45.

Decreasing the labor requirements on the farm has resulted in accompanying migration of farm youth to seek off-farm agricultural or nonagricultural employment. Decisions to migrate are made hastily and without much information or deliberation—and even less for the poorly educated.

Paradoxically, rural America is not a dying area, as some think.

New manufacturing jobs opened up faster in the last 10 years in rural America than in metropolitan areas.

The shift from a rural population has not been to the cities but to the suburbs, with the cities growing only about 1.2 percent while the suburban population grew by 27.6 percent.

Despite all the change taking place, rural America still retains its distinctive patterns:

The school is the center of rural life.

Values are more conservative.

Rural teachers are paid less, and qualified teachers desiring to teach in rural schools are in short supply.

Farm people as a whole do not see the great economic value of education—in dollars and cents— to say nothing of its other values.

Both the college and occupational aspirations of rural youth are lower.

Farm youth not only complete fewer years of schooling but they also receive inferior schooling. Half again as many urban as rural farm high school graduates enroll in college (48 versus 32 percent) and with half as many deficiencies, too.

Rural youth tend to drop out of school at an earlier age, and they are less successful than urban youth in the sense that they have more trouble getting a permanent job and their jobs are not as good.

Educational attainment of rural adults lags by almost 3 years.

Local rural communities, generally, are not capable of financing needed general and vocational education, although rural areas allocate a larger proportion of their limited resources to public education.

Curricular offerings including specialized programs for the slow or rapid learners, vocational programs, and properly staffed guidance programs, do not have the breadth of urban and suburban schools.

Many buildings are deficient and much equipment and teaching material is unsatisfactory.

One basic difficulty is that both the elementary and secondary rural schools are too small. The quality of the educational job rises significantly as the size of the school increases, at least up to some size that is far above that usually found in rural areas.

James B. Conant has judged that the rural high school with a graduating class of less than 100 is, and unavoidably will be, highly unsatisfactory. Yet a large proportion of all rural and small-town youth go to high schools smaller than this.

Less than a tenth of the 200,000 one-teacher schools of a half century ago exist today. But no informed observer feels that school consolidation has gone far enough; much of the hoped-for gain from it has been wiped out by the continued shrinkage in numbers of farms. The new school may wind up with not many more students than each one of the small schools consolidated to form it.

Outside instructional standards and other influences have been much resisted by rural people. To argue that it is their responsibility and that they must be satisfied is to overlook the fact that the Constitution of the United States provides for the free movement of people and that large numbers of rural people migrate to the city.

Rural and urban must be considered as an entity. All should be concerned about the uses of natural resources—soil, water, plants, and animals. There is a large national interest in the quality of schooling at the local level.

In all areas, rural and urban alike, there is a divergence of interest between those who want good schools for their children and those who resist increased tax levies.

As a nation, we have entered a period of dynamic educational reform. But it is clear that some schools, especially in rural areas, have barely begun to adapt their programs to the new demands and opportunities.

Rural schools as a whole are substandard. A technical study for a recent Conference by the National Committee for Children and Youth concluded, "The specific problems of education in rural areas could be itemized as a minimal level of nearly everything that makes up an educational program."

A renaissance for rural schools is needed. The serious gap in education between rural and urban areas must be closed as rapidly as possible. This is obviously a matter with social and economic implications far beyond agriculture, but it is also basic to agricultural improvement.

School organization and development—education and the development of human resources—are of prime importance to all communities and the nation. Thus, we need to think of the full range of elementary, secondary, college, technical, adult, and community education as an integrated package.

As we look to the future, someone must take the leadership in raising standards of rural education.

The rural educational structure has demonstrated that it alone has neither the administrative, institutional, nor instructional capability for making major adjustments to perform the total educational task.

A system of support on a wider equalization base must be developed for rural areas.

More outside, or even centralized, financial support is needed. Because of the concentration of industry and of nationally operating businesses, much of the income to these concerns, gathered from all over the country, accumulates in about 200 counties.

Only funds from Federal taxes can relieve many of the educational problems of counties and States with a low tax base.

A cooperative and coordinated thrust of all local, State, and national agencies—private and public —is imperative. For example, a unified career information, testing, counseling, preparation, and placement service for rural America should surely be the concern of, coordinated with, and jointly funded by USDA, the Office of Education, and the Department of Labor, in addition to industry and patrons.

Block funds or grants-in-aid should provide resource centers and multi-purpose educational centers. In like manner, USDA, Health, Education, and Welfare (HEW), Interior, and others should be active participants in environment ecology education.

T. W. Schultz implied a responsibility for redirection of programs and interagency cooperation at all levels with this charge, "had the agricultural colleges, the USDA, and the farm organizations thought through and provided the economic rationale for Federal funds for rural elementary and secondary schools, the problem of this part of the necessary financing of these schools could have been resolved long ago."

We must think about America and our rural youth as it will be in 1980 or 2000—a nation with perhaps as many as 300 million citizens, with different kinds of schools and different kinds of teaching and learning programs; and we must do this right now. There is no time to lose. The key to human survival is Education.

Vocational Education

EDGAR J. BOONE,

GLENN JENSEN, and

JERRY KLEMENT

VOCATIONAL education links man and his work. Currently referred to as "occupational education" by many authorities, it should be a vital part of the total process of education. It prepares people of all ages for productive and satisfying occupations in the world of work.

The modern concept of vocational education encompasses all levels of education including secondary, post-secondary, and adult programs, as well as programs for persons with special needs.

Approximately 8 million persons participated in vocational education programs in 1969. The American Vocational Association has estimated that enrollment in all phases will come to approximately 14.6 million by 1975.

The need for functional, expanding vocational education programs in the United States is highlighted by a number of factors. There is no place in the world of work for the uneducated or the educated person who has not learned how to work; just as there is no place for the person who has not learned how to learn. Thus, the total educational process is increasingly tied to the work required by society.

Technology has created a dynamic relationship between man, his education, and his work in which education is placed between man and his work for practically all men and all occupations. Both the nature of society and work have changed. The more rapid the change, the greater the interdependency between education and work.

Acceleration of technology and automation have had a profound effect on the labor market and the kinds of jobs it offers. Examples often cited are automated elevators displacing 40,000 elevator operators in New York City; 15 Census Bureau statisticians in 1970 doing the work that required 300 in 1960; 30,000 cotton pickers replaced by machines in Georgia; 75,000 coal miners producing more coal during 1970 than 400,000 did in 1960.

Although many low-skill jobs have

*

EDGAR J. BOONE is Professor and Head of Adult and Community College Education, North Carolina State University, Raleigh.

GLENN JENSEN is Professor of Adult Education, University of Wyoming, Laramie.

JERRY KLEMENT is a Graduate Fellow in Adult and Community College Education, North Carolina State University.

164

disappeared, new jobs have been created as a result of technological developments. In 1966 the job market called for 1.4 million new workers. This was 600,000 above the number of new workers, aged 18 to 19, who were entering the work force. The 600,000 had to be drawn from the ranks of the unemployed who needed some preparatory training.

Hence, our technological advances have caused an increase in jobs, not a decrease—although there has been a shrinkage in occupations such as agriculture, mining, and some types of manufacturing.

This overall increase in available jobs has resulted in the shortages of many skilled workers in areas for which secondary and post-secondary schools and adult programs have been supplying the workers.

A good bit of the breakthrough in technological developments, and hence the increase in jobs and the need for skilled labor to fill them, is due to research directed at discovering and developing new products for public consumption.

Supporting these technological developments for consumer use are accelerating activities in research and development.

The more than 3 million scientists, engineers, and technicians in the U.S. work force of more than 80 million presages even more rapid technological changes in the future which will affect both occupations and the preparation programs for them.

Results of research on the labor market can best be seen in requirements of the following fields for installation and maintenance technicians:

Systems engineering (mechanical and electronic combined)—involves new developments in power control and the rapidly developing field of fluid power.

Automation engineering technology (production and manufacturing)—requires new knowledge and skill in dealing with power sources, control mechanisms, and study of the economic feasibility of such developments in manufacturing.

Instrumentation technology (hydraulic and electronic controls).

Materials engineering (new synthetics as well as new uses for existing materials)—the production and development of metals, plastics, ceramics, gases, liquids, and fibers.

Biomedical engineering (instruments and devices).

Oceanographic research, including aquanautics.

Astronautical research and developments.

Water use and treatment, including pollution prevention and control, as well as desalinization.

Agricultural technology and research, new sources of food.

Conservation of natural and human resources and technologies.

Government and municipal services and technologies, including law enforcement, food science, and traffic control.

Quality control technology.

These are but a few of the many new occupations which have come into being during the past decade. Well-trained workers possessing high-level intellectual and physical skills are needed in the new occupations. Technological developments in new products and services require precision, accuracy, and reliability. Vocational programs must develop these concepts, skills, and values.

The technological explosion since the turn of the 20th century indicates that the total target population for organized vocational education programs potentially includes the entire labor force.

It is not anticipated, of course, that all of the approximately 100 million projected to be in the labor force in 1980 will be enrolled in organized vocational education programs at any one time. However, it is reasonable to assume that a majority of the labor force, at one time or another in their lives, will have participated in some type of organized vocational education.

165

Vocational education in North Carolina: Machine shop at community college, marine technology, ornamental horticulture, and cosmetology at technical institute.

Alterations in the skill requirements of existing jobs as well as the creation of new jobs will require additional training or retraining throughout man's life span. Many educational experts feel that vocational education should begin with early childhood education and extend throughout the life span.

A number of educators also feel that increased emphasis should be given to conceptual learning and value formation in vocational education at all levels to provide workers with the intellectual tools to perform proficiently jobs that are subject to constant change—the nature and intensity of which are difficult to predict. It is reasoned that as future and present workers use these intellectual tools, they will develop the ability to modify and adapt such concepts to meet and satisfy the changing requirements of their chosen occupations.

More people are now investing more time in education in the early part of their life span in preparation for full-time entry into the work force. The average age of entry of men into the work force is now over 19. Because of the added years of life expectancy, even with the delay in entering the work force, men spend more years working than ever.

Following a decade of studies and discussion, spearheaded by the National Society for the Promotion of Industrial Education, Congress in 1917 enacted the Smith-Hughes Act providing Federal aid to the States for vocational education of less than college grade.

This legislation, which embodies the grants-in-aid concept to the States, specified agriculture, home economics, and trades and industries as occupational categories for which State and local training costs would be eligible for partial reimbursement by Federal funds. Subsequent enactments continued the pattern by designating other occupational categories in which training could be supported.

The George-Deen Act of 1937 added the distributive occupations (that is, marketing, retailing, salesmanship, etc.) and was superseded by the George-Barden Act of 1946, which provided for a major expansion in vocational education. Separate amendments of the Act in 1956 added practical nurse training and comparable preparation in other health occupations, and authorization for training in the fishery trades and industries. The National Defense Act of 1958 authorized training of technicians in occupations needed for national defense.

The Vocational Education Act of 1963 continued the previous authorization for training in specified occupational categories, but added the office occupations. It also permitted States, at their option, to transfer Federal funds from one category to another.

In addition, the 1963 Act offered States additional funds for training specified population groups—regardless of occupational objectives of the training. Target population groups designated in the Act are high school youth, post-school youth, adults enrolled in full-time instruction, youth and adults enrolled in other courses, and people with special needs.

The 1963 Act was amended in 1968 to provide many more "people-oriented" services and activities. This legislation provides funding to promote such activities as cooperative education programs, training for the disadvantaged as well as the handicapped of all ages, consumer and homemaking education, residential schools, and guidance.

The legal bases for vocational education are the Vocational Education Act of 1963 as amended and the earlier Smith-Hughes and George-Barden Acts. All are now administered as a single legislative act.

Besides this specified vocational legislation, reference should also be made to the Manpower Development and Training Act (MDTA) of 1962, which was aimed at serving a growing number of people with special vocational education needs. The special groups include migrants, the educationally deprived, the economically disadvantaged, and the physically handicapped.

MDTA programs are administered jointly through the Department of Labor and the Department of Health, Education and Welfare.

Programs of vocational-technical education aided by the Federal vocational education acts are the largest component of the Nation's organized efforts to reduce unemployment and eliminate occupational shortages.

These State-Federal cooperative programs, supported by the U.S. Office of Education, are supplemented by other programs for specified groups (for instance, high school students, out-of-school youth, neighborhood youth corps participants). However the State and local programs partially funded by the Federal Government remain the major permanent thrusts for preparing entrants to the labor force and improving the productivity of those currently at work.

Each State is responsible for its vocational education program. The State board of education or a separate board for vocational education serves as the responsible administrative agency. The U.S. Office of Education deals with this one central board or agency having responsibility for vocational education within each of the 50 States, Puerto Rico, and the District of Columbia.

Supplementing these efforts of the official board or agency in each State is a State advisory council appointed by the governor or by an elected State board of vocational education. Advisory councils are authorized to obtain the services of professional, technical, and clerical personnel needed to carry out their functions.

A State plan for vocational education must be prepared in consultation with the advisory council. The public must be given an opportunity to express its views on program matters and the council must provide one public meeting for this purpose.

The State board of education or board of vocational education has the responsibility of seeing that the State plan and recommendations of the advisory council are put in effect.

Organization of vocational education varies greatly at the local level. In most States, administration is conducted through local boards. Exceptions include State-operated vocational schools that serve an area of several school districts and correctional schools. In many States county administration also rests between the State and local levels. The county administration usually serves several local levels.

Institutional arrangements and program offerings vary greatly at State, area, and community levels. The range of program offerings has broadened in recent years to include training or retraining in most occupations other than those designated "professional" by the U.S. Commissioner of Education or those that require a baccalaureate or higher degree.

A growing trend in program offerings has been the combining of two or more related fields, like marketing and agricultural production courses.

Most vocational education offerings in secondary education institutions are under the auspices of programs authorized by the vocational education legislation at the Federal level. Some of the major program offerings at this level include agriculture and agribusiness, home economics, distributive education, trades and industrial education, practical nursing, and office occupations.

There is no one single pattern of institutional arrangements or program offerings in vocational education at the post-secondary level in the various States. Programs are offered by a variety of institutions, which include high schools with evening adult programs, area vocational schools, technical institutes, community colleges, special State schools, and the 4-year senior colleges and universities.

Many high schools are expanding their programs to offer vocational courses that are taught during the

168

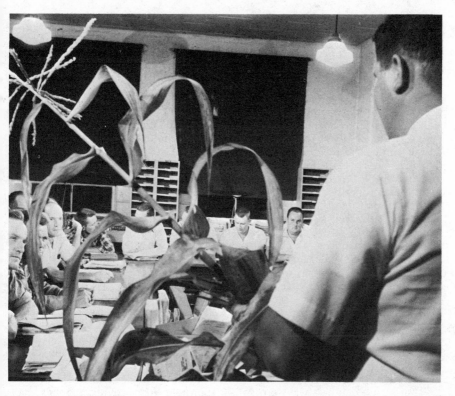

Ohio farmers in a Federally-supported vocational agriculture program listen as the instructor discusses diseased corn stalk.

evening hours, especially for adults. These usually include agriculture and agribusiness, home economics, distributive education, industrial and technical education, and office jobs.

Some high schools offer adult basic education designed specifically to help adults acquire the necessary skills needed to read, write, and compute at a level at which they can function in society.

The area vocational school usually is operated as an adjunct of secondary schools in a particular area. However, these area schools also include program offerings for out-of-school students. High school students are bused to the vocational school from surrounding high schools for a part-day program. The vocational area school also may enroll special students in Manpower Development and Training Act programs and, at night, enroll adults in vocational programs.

Course offerings in the area school range from simple crafts to highly specialized technical areas.

Technical institutes and community colleges are gaining in prominence in the American educational system. These institutions provide vocational and technical education programs.

The technical institute offers vocational programs consisting of courses and curricula designed to equip persons for a particular trade, such as agricultural and biological, art and design, business, and engineering technologies; health occupations; and public service technology.

Community colleges differ from technical institutes in that besides offering comprehensive vocational and technical education programs and general adult courses, they have a 2-year college-parallel curriculum.

Generally, both technical institutes and community colleges have an

169

open-door policy and will admit to an appropriate program all persons who are high school graduates or are 18 or older.

An estimated 3.5 million adults participated in vocational and technical education programs offered by technical institutes and community colleges in 1969. There are currently over 1,000 of these establishments in the United States.

Four-year colleges and universities also are deeply involved in vocational education programs. Almost all offer vocational-oriented curricula at the baccalaureate and subbaccalaureate levels. Curricula are generally available in agricultural, engineering, health and medical, and business technologies.

Besides formal organized vocational curricula in the secondary, post-secondary, and higher education institutions, many other sources of vocational preparation exist in the United States. Among these are private schools, home study schools, and business and industry.

There is no one best way to organize, plan, and conduct vocational education programs at each of the several levels of government. The number and types of program offerings depend upon such things as sources of funding, and the philosophy of administrators and institutions, as well as labor needs evident within a given geographic setting.

Future effectiveness and impact of vocational education programs obviously will depend largely upon the leaders in that field (1) maintaining a continuing sensitivity to the vocational needs of people and (2) developing programs specifically tailored to meet such needs. Opportunities should be provided for related agencies and organizations to become involved in planning and putting in effect vocational education programs at the local, State, and Federal levels.

CAMPS—Cooperative Area Manpower Planning System—is an example of a planning effort whose objective is the coordination of policies, plans, and activities of all agencies, institutions, and organizations involved in carrying out manpower development programs.

Included in activities of this group are many programs directly related to vocational education, such as New Careers, Neighborhood Service Centers, and others. The program operates at four levels—national, State, regional, and local. U.S. Department of Agriculture representatives at all four levels are among the personnel of eight Federal agencies designated to participate in CAMPS.

Technical Action Panels (TAP's) represent a second type of educational activity at all levels. A TAP coordinates the program efforts of all Federal agencies in a rural area in developing and carrying out rural community development programs. Primary responsibility for TAP programs lies with USDA. Planning for and coordinating occupational education programs might be one of the activities of a TAP.

USDA representatives also are responsible for providing many supportive roles to local occupational education programs. High school vocational education efforts, technical institutes, area vocational schools, and other programs can benefit from contributions by many of the USDA agencies.

Vocational education is becoming a dynamic force affecting the thought procedures, habits, economic status, and social interaction of people from many walks of life throughout the country. It is becoming a major, integral part of the American educational system.

As vocational education expands and improves the quality of its program offerings, continuous attention should be given to the concept of vocational education in a complex, changing society.

The Advisory Council on Vocational Education in 1968 provided these thought-provoking ideas about an expanded concept of vocational education being needed to service

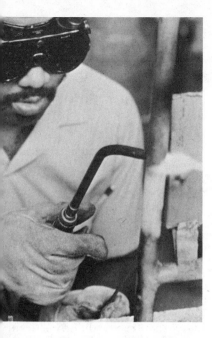

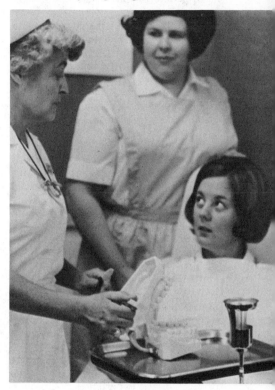

Modern rural vocational education includes not only basic industrial skills like welding but service vocations like dental assistant and nursing. Many skills are needed for a growing rural America.

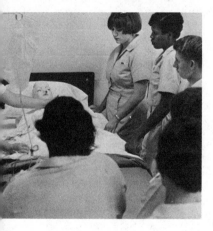

future occupational needs of the American public:

• Vocational education cannot be limited to skills needed for a particular occupation. It is more appropriately defined as all those aspects of educational experience which help a person discover his talents, relate them to the world of work, choose an occupation, refine his talents, and use them successfully in employment.

In fact, orientation and assistance in vocational choice may be more valid measures of employment suc-

171

cess, and therefore more profitable uses of educational funds, than specific training.

- In a technology where only relative costs, not engineering know-how, prevent mechanization of routine tasks, the age of "human use of human beings" may be within reach —but those human beings must be equipped to do tasks which machines cannot do.

Where complex instructions and sophisticated decisions mark the boundary between the realm of man and the role of the machine, there is no room for any division between intellectual competence and manipulative skills and, therefore, between academic and vocational education.

- In a labor force where most have a high school education, all who do not are at a serious competitive disadvantage. But at the same time, a high school education alone cannot provide an automatic ticket to both satisfactory and continuous employment.

Education cannot shed its responsibilities to the student (and to society in his behalf) just because he has chosen to reject the system or because it has handed him a diploma. It is not enough to dump the school-leaver into a labor market pool. Society must provide him a ladder, and perhaps help him climb it.

- Every educational experience must include some type of formal occupational experience. Although final occupational choice may well be delayed until all the alternatives are known, no student should leave the educational system without a salable skill.

In addition, given the rapidity of change and the competition from generally rising educational attainment, upgrading and remedial education opportunities are a continual necessity. Those who need occupational preparation the most, both preventive and remedial, will be the least prepared to take advantage of it and the most difficult to educate and train.

172

School Bells Ring for Adults Through Life

CHARLES W. MCDOUGALL and EUGENE WELDEN

IT MIGHT be a good idea to inscribe on every college diploma a warranty that reads, "This education is valid for 24 months or 24,000 miles, whichever comes first." Perhaps we then should offer each college graduate a "tuneup" in education every 2 years.

The dynamic world we live in requires that each adult American update his supply of knowledge frequently.

The young scientist, farm manager, or engineer may find, as he steps out of college and into his first job, that many of the techniques and much of the theory he has learned already have been superseded by better ways and fresher ideas. He then realizes it is not possible to have a "completed" education that will satisfy his lifetime needs.

An insurance executive recently pointed out that we now move from new idea to application almost "overnight." In contrast, it took 112 years for the process of photography to develop. The telephone took 56 years, radio 35, television 12, and transistors 5 years.

The time span from idea to application has been drastically reduced. This same insurance executive predicts that 9 years from now most people working in industry will be making products which have not yet been invented.

Contemporary systems of continuing education have their roots in the basic notion that knowledge and skill are means of self-improvement, and ultimately lead to the resolving of group and community problems.

Continuing education, as a label for the activities of lifelong learning, is most closely associated with opportunities provided by colleges and universities. But continuing education, of course, takes place in a wide variety of other settings. Programs are offered under the auspices of public schools, business and industry, government agencies, volunteer and professional organizations, libraries, museums, and religious institutions.

One of the largest of these systems is the Cooperative Extension Service. For almost 60 years, the U.S. Department of Agriculture and the land-grant universities have been actively engaged in continuing education through State extension services.

These services link the land-grant universities with rural and urban communities through county or area extension offices staffed with professionally trained agents. They constitute America's only national network of continuing education with a unique Federal-State-county cost sharing structure.

The Cooperative Extension Service is devoted to human development through the fuller realization and use of individual capabilities. It helps to show how new possibilities, satisfaction of needs, and new qualities of experience can be fulfilled by the individual through continuing education.

Extension's informal teaching is designed to help individuals, families, businesses, and communities identify and solve their problems. Local advisory committees participate in the planning and operation of educational programs. Their effectiveness is enhanced and multiplied through

*

CHARLES W. MCDOUGALL is Deputy Administrator of the Extension Service.

EUGENE WELDEN is Chief of Planning and Evaluation, Community Service and Continuing Education Programs, Office of Education, Department of Health, Education, and Welfare.

the services of more than a million volunteer workers who are trained to assist with the informal teaching of farmers, homemakers, youth, and community and agri-business leaders.

This continuing education process often is carried out through existing local organizations. The flexible arrangement is further supported by teams of State Extension and research specialists from the land-grant institutions who provide knowledge and expertise of application.

Cooperative Extension Service is best known for its educational programs in agriculture, home economics, 4-H youth activities, and community resource development. Needs of a rapidly changing society have stimulated further expansion of programs and audiences reached.

Major program areas emphasized by Extension in the 1970's include improved systems of agricultural production, management, marketing, and distribution of food, along with wise use and development of our natural resources.

Rural communities will be given more assistance in identifying problems and evaluating the relative feasibility of alternative solutions. Extension also will help them analyze costs and benefits of shaping their future development to provide better facilities, services, job opportunities, and increased income.

Home economics programs will continue to stress improved quality of living at all levels of society. Special programs are being directed to reach low-income families, minorities, handicapped persons, and the elderly. Programs for youth will be broadened.

Developing countries, too, are looking to the Cooperative Extension Service for assistance in making the best use of their human and agricultural resources. This assistance is being provided through the Agency for International Development, the Food and Agriculture Organization of the United Nations, and other international agencies.

173

USDA's Extension Service, in co-operation with other Federal agencies and the State land-grant institutions, will continue to strengthen programs of continuing education and seek to obtain more resources to help people improve their ways of living. It will be concerned not only with traditional educational services, but also will cooperate with other systems of continuing education for the betterment of our people.

One of the great American ideals has been equal education opportunity for all. Our land-grant college system, other State-supported universities, and locally supported public education generally are evidences of this emphasis.

Continuing education too often is thought of as being apart from the traditional education process. It is seldom integrated with our public school systems and its importance is not well recognized by the educational establishment. Nor has it achieved full commitment or support and understanding of the general public.

Those enrolled in continuing education often pay a fee, or their employer or professional association assists in subsidizing them. Many branches of government, foundations, schools, and institutions underwrite costs to the students, or adjustments are made according to one's ability to assume the costs.

For the individual, limited education becomes a handicap in obtaining employment or in moving up the status ladder as jobs become more specialized, and technical-educational requirements increase.

Once a person is employed, he seeks to maintain or improve his position. Some companies have tuition-assistance programs for employees who take university courses on their own time.

A number of large corporations provide a broad program of continuing education that is developed and managed by the company. Western Electric, International Business Machines, and General Electric are outstanding examples. Many programs are carried on with colleges and universities—both in on-campus residential centers and at in-plant locations.

Professional associations also have initiated a host of programs for their members. The Academy of General Dentistry, American Bar Association, and American Medical Association report increasing participation by members in programs to help them keep up with the knowledge explosion.

Answering one critical need for continuing education is the Department of Defense, which offers to train each year up to a half million men and women rejected by the military services for educational or physical reasons. These are dropouts who experience the disparities of life.

Although the professional, the farmer, and the business manager appear to have choice opportunities for life-long learning, blue collar workers have not yet found their way in sufficient numbers into the upgrading process. National attention has been focused on the disadvantaged and entry level jobs, but the gap between the educated and undereducated widens.

A large share of the continuing education programs fail to attract the disadvantaged, the alienated, or the undereducated. Instead, these programs draw largely from middle class and better educated groups. The reasons are many and often difficult to analyze. One factor is cost.

More funds are needed to permit appropriate instrumentalities to provide leadership and develop cooperation among the many organizations serving adults.

Fortunately, some types of education are becoming more accessible at low cost or no cost to the individual. Educational television and radio provide opportunities for the professional as well as the least educated among us.

The gradual growth of support

from some sources is encouraging. But much more can and should be done to alleviate the inequities between States and between areas within States. The current challenge is to provide a realistic basis for determining the needs and goals, and for implementing programs of continuing education to meet national objectives and priorities.

As our time for leisure increases, we have the opportunity for cultural education. Creative writing, art, music, and drama allow individuals to seek new goals and values that emphasize personal cultivation for its own sake. Both President Eisenhower and Winston Churchill were "Sunday painters." Since such activities are so widespread among business and political leaders, Jacques Barzun was moved to note that: "The fine arts are acquiring the respectability of fishing and golf."

Art institutions, in addition to regular exhibitions, offer a variety of learning opportunities for adults such as classes, art mobiles, and film showings. The Metropolitan Museum of Art is cooperating with the Book-of-the-Month Club to offer "Art Seminars at Home." The brilliant film series "Civilization" has been shown at the National Gallery of Art and in other galleries and libraries throughout the country and on television.

Growth of the community theater is a striking development in America. There are now about 3,000 theater groups in villages, small towns, and major cities. They offer a good opportunity to develop skills and techniques for producing and performing. Such activities provide a means of personal expression as well as a basic understanding of the history and theory of the performing arts.

Music study tours, lecture-concerts and church music workshops provide new ideas through demonstrations, as well as social and recreational opportunities.

In our society, we permit the aging population to rest and recreate. But, says Jack London of the University of California, "Recreational activities are not sufficient to maintain mental abilities, contact with society, identity, and sense of significance as a person." The common view that education is for children inhibits many senior citizens from engaging in this exciting adventure. Continuing education can help to expand horizons, develop understanding, create meaningful activities, and possibly bridge the generation gap.

Pollution, racial discrimination, and other pressing issues demand that we acquire insight and understanding about the conditions—and the causes —that directly affect us. Survival of a democratic society depends on our ability as adults to acquire a critical perspective and a desire to make needed changes in that society.

We hear a lot about educational hardware—like computers, television, teaching machines, and multiplex FM radio. Tape recorders and cassettes are becoming as common as TV. The audio-visual revolution is upon us.

Soon an instrument "no bigger than a breadbox" will allow you to see and hear almost any program you want at a time you choose on your home TV. The programs can be bought in stores, rented from libraries, or borrowed from a neighbor. The TV set will become as versatile as the phonograph and the telephone.

In Canada, a major oil company is working on a plan for auto drivers to rent tapes on the history, economy, and culture of the areas in which they are traveling. Drivers will be able to turn in the tapes at any company station along their route.

We are all familiar with classroom group-learning, but as adults continue their education, new methods and techniques are being used. The "Great Decisions" program of the Foreign Policy Association was based on issues. Printed materials and discussion were the basis of the program.

175

Ideas were examined and clarified in the crucible of analysis. While there was rarely a consensus, each learned from the others as well as from the written words.

The expanding interest in human relations has encouraged development of new settings. Such programs focus on learning about one's self in relation to others, based upon personal experience of the participants. In the final stage, the participants take responsibility for directing their own learning.

There is no single institution or agency where an adult can engage in study related to all his interests or pursue one such concern throughout his lifetime.

Thus some seers have proposed creation of a new community agency for continuing education—the Open University—which would offer a total curriculum, relevant both to community life and the lives of individuals. This new institution would seek a way in affluent America to properly balance entertainment and instruction in the regimen of man.

Counseling Aids Job Seekers

C. B. GILLILAND

PEOPLE in rural areas and small towns need help to improve their occupational skills and find jobs or more satisfying employment. Often they must move away to obtain a new job, or they need training or retraining, for a different occupation. Since 1940 around 28 million people have migrated from farms—most of them to the cities—seeking jobs.

Conditions are rapidly changing both in job requirements and places of work. Employment counseling, including mobility counseling, consequently can become vital to making the best use of manpower and enabling workers and their families to adjust satisfactorily to their new places of employment and residence.

Counseling on the requirements for a good job is among the most important needs of job seekers. How often has a rural resident said, "If I just knew someone who could tell me something about the new jobs in that industrial center, I would know whether to move my family from our little farm here in the country."

This has been a tough problem for many farm and rural nonfarm workers in recent years as rapid mechanization of farming has greatly reduced the number of jobs in farming areas.

Employment counseling is relatively new, or nonexistent, in most small towns and rural areas. The overall counseling shortage has intensified in recent years because of the demand for counselors in public schools, private industry, and government. Limited services are available through the U.S. Department of Labor, State employment services, and private agencies. Most high schools have full-time guidance counselors.

The usual counselor or adviser in rural areas for many years has been the local minister, the family doctor, the local banker, a county Extension worker, or the local school administrator or teacher, none of them skilled as a job counselor. However, they help as much as they can.

Good counseling can help individuals achieve a more satisfactory work and life adjustment. This will enable the nation to develop and use its human resources more effectively. We have approximately 60,000 counselors in the United States, chiefly in the

*

C. B. GILLILAND is Program Leader for Manpower Development in the Extension Service.

public schools. Another 6,000 are available for counseling adults and school dropouts through the State employment services. Demand for counseling service in the school systems and other Government positions is increasing rapidly.

The school counselor has many tasks. He helps gifted students see opportunities for the advanced education required to make the best use of their talents. He works with potential school dropouts, to motivate them to finish high school. He tries to get the dropouts back into school or else into vocational and technical training programs.

Approximately 75 percent of the professional counselors are employed in public schools. This increase in personnel requirements stems in part from rising public school enrollment. It also stems from the need to reduce the available counselor-student ratio in high schools from the current figure of about one per 500 to the generally recommended average of one counselor for 300 students.

In addition, extension of counseling and guidance services to the lower grades is of great importance in aiding all students to obtain appropriate orientation and education earlier in their school careers, and thus reduce the number of school dropouts. Extension of counseling and guidance services to 7th and 8th grade students has been made possible by recent Federal legislation.

The Federal and State governments provide some manpower training and placement programs so greatly needed by rural residents. Counseling and guidance are the chief means of making such programs available to the people for whom they are designed.

What is employment counseling? It is the process whereby a counselor and an applicant work together in order that the applicant may gain a better understanding of himself and knowledge of the world of work so that he may more realistically choose, change, or adjust to a vocation.

An important element in success of the new manpower training programs has been the incorporation of counseling in the regular procedure for both occupational training and retraining of unemployed and underemployed workers.

Counseling is also a key ingredient in the many important pilot projects being conducted under the Manpower Development and Training Act. This counseling is especially helpful in effective use of the new legislation providing for basic education of jobless adult workers who need it to qualify for occupational training.

In rehabilitation of physically, mentally, and socially handicapped people, counseling is a basic requirement. Recent estimates indicate more than two million people in this country need rehabilitation counseling. Those least likely to receive it are handicapped citizens living in small towns and rural areas.

To meet the basic need of rural communities, we must try new experiments in counseling. These might be patterned after the Smaller Communities Survey Teams of the State employment service. Also, a mobile counseling service similar to the rural library service might be tried.

A mobile counseling center staffed by four counselors serves high schools in four counties of southern Indiana. Operation of the center's activities is designed to enrich, supplement, and improve the quality of counseling services for the area's secondary students. The mobile center also serves as a model to stimulate development of top-quality guidance services in regular school programs.

The community has an important stake in any program that promotes the employment and occupational adjustment of its members. Communities will accept new employment counseling programs if the people are kept informed.

A planned and sustained public information activity will aid greatly in securing widespread public support and cooperation. The local informational program should be built around the local office and stress its goals with respect to the vocational adjustment of applicants, its facilities, and its outstanding accomplishments.

A good job is a key to a happy life in either rural or urban communities. But the opportunity for a satisfying job is only half as good in rural America as in the cities.

Unemployment and underemployment are twice as common in rural areas and small towns as in metropolitan areas.

This disparity would be even greater had not so many of the rural people moved to the cities. They made the move because they wanted a job that would pay enough to meet their needs and their family needs.

Some found a job. Many did not. Many merely exchanged life in rural poverty for mere existence in an urban slum at a large cost to themselves, the cities, and rural America. (When large numbers of people move from farms and small towns, the costs to those remaining behind are greatly increased. This includes the per capita costs for maintaining roads, schools, churches, electric and telephone lines, and other community facilities.)

Elimination of these desperate choices between two evils by making available a third choice—of realistic employment opportunities in rural America—is one of the greatest needs of this generation. Currently only a few urban dwellers return to the rural areas or small towns, for part-time jobs or retirement.

Mechanization of farming, along with new technology in producing, processing, and marketing agricultural commodities, has reduced the number of jobs in agriculture and related industries in rural areas.

New machines and methods increased farm output in the United States by some 40 percent between 1950 and 1970. This reduced farm employment by about 50 percent during the same period and it has continued downward to the present time. There is evidence that the reduction in farm employment will continue, but at a slower rate, during the next decade.

This reduction in jobs in rural areas is at the root of rural poverty. Most of the rural poor do not live on farms. They live in the open country, in rural villages, and in small towns.

Contrary to a common misconception, whites outnumber nonwhites among the rural poor by a wide margin. However, an extremely high proportion of blacks in the rural South and Indians on reservations do live in destitution.

This rural poverty, which shows the great need for counseling and jobs, is evidenced by the following:

• Hunger and malnutrition leading to disease and handicaps, especially of children, often beyond cure.

• Disease and premature death. Infant mortality is far higher in rural areas than among the least privileged groups in urban centers. Medical and dental care are inadequate and often conspicuously absent.

• Poor schools. It is estimated that 3 million rural adults are illiterate. In both educational facilities and opportunities, the rural people have been shortchanged.

• One in every 13 houses in rural America is unfit to live in. These houses are often in depressed and poverty-stricken rural communities.

As communities deteriorate, they offer fewer opportunities for anyone to earn a decent living. Inadequately trained young people leave the rural areas and small towns in search of better opportunities elsewhere. Those who stay behind have few resources to earn incomes adequate for a decent living and for the revitalizing of their communities.

The huge urban renewal program has not been extended to rural areas. Unfortunately, as public programs improve the lot of the urban poor without making similar improvements in conditions for the rural poor, they provide fresh incentive for rural poor to migrate to the central cities.

Some jobs have been retained in rural areas because of the type of business enterprise. Most urban occupations do not allow for gradual retirement. Farming, and to a lesser extent other rural occupations like small business ownership, provides the opportunity for a reduction in work responsibility or the elimination of some work roles rather than complete retirement.

The self-employed entrepreneur or farmer is not forced to retire at a specified time. In fact, he may not be able to retire because he is unable to sell his business or because he lacks an adequate retirement income.

Greatly increased manpower and job development efforts are needed to improve employment opportunities for people living in small towns and rural areas. Improving the operations of the private economy in order to provide better opportunities for jobs and a decent living is a need in practically all rural areas.

There are rays of hope. Some progress is being made in improved job opportunities through the programs developed under the Economic Opportunity Act and the Economic Development Act. Also, assistance is available through loans and technical assistance from the Farmers Home Administration and the Small Business Administration.

A limited study of trends during the 1960's indicates more industries are moving to rural America.

About half the gains in manufacturing employment in the smaller or nonmetropolitan labor market areas, or approximately 20 percent of the national total, stemmed from new plant locations or expansions in rural communities.

Among major contributory factors were: 1. Progress on interstate highway systems; 2. improvements in processing, marketing, and transportation technologies; and 3. increasing attractiveness of selected small cities and towns as places to work and live.

However, the pace is far short of the need. Total rural employment in 1980 is projected as 22 million, an increase of around 5 million over 1960, which will be insufficient to stop net out-migration and establish a satisfactory employment rate.

It has been said that every American has a heritage of mobility—from the first adventurous settlers to the pioneers who moved west to tame and settle the wilderness, to the millions of migrants who came from many lands seeking new job opportunities.

The American worker has usually been ready to pull up roots and go wherever job opportunities were better. This mobility has been a keystone of our national growth and underlies our progress and development as a nation.

However, the unemployed and underemployed in all areas must know where to find jobs. This knowledge is almost always lacking in the small towns and rural areas. Youths and adults who leave the formal school system as dropouts do not understand job requirements.

Special attention is being given in limited areas through consulting assistance to "boxed-in" farmers and other low-income rural families.

Mechanization of farming since World War II, combined with changes in the plantation or farming system, has speeded up the migration of farmworkers to the city, particularly from the South. This heavy migration in many instances has resulted in overcrowded cities.

However, flexibility afforded by the automobile and advances in communication and transportation have brought on another kind of mobility called suburbanization. Families with average or higher incomes have tended to move to the suburbs, leaving the central cities with disproportionate numbers of the poor locked into slums and ghettoes.

Many of these urban poor are recent migrants from farms and small towns in rural areas. They lack the skills and education needed for the new jobs in industrial centers.

Age is also a factor in mobility. A 1964 study shows that one out of 25 workers aged 55 to 64 changed jobs during the year, compared with one out of 10 aged 35 to 44 and one out of five young men aged 18 to 24.

Older workers are reluctant to leave jobs where their seniority may give them some degree of employment security and where they may have earned higher rates of pay and become eligible for longer vacations and other fringe benefits. Leaving the job might mean the loss of a part or all of these hard-earned benefits.

Another reason for not changing jobs is that many employers are reluctant to hire older applicants, especially those who need training for the jobs at hand.

A 55-year-old man who works until he is 65 will have one or two jobs during this period. In contrast, a 21-year-old man will probably average eight jobs during a 32-year period in the labor force.

Low-income families have special problems, too. When a low-income family moves to a new and strange community, the kinds of help needed often go beyond financial aid. Such help includes preparation, information, and social guidance before relocation, as well as friendly and interested help in the settling-in process in the new community.

Supportive social services like individual and group counseling, informational programs, and special followup services are being made available in some relocation areas to help the new workers and their families adjust.

An example of a need to relocate workers is a rural area in Appalachia with approximately 30 percent of the workers unemployed (primarily because of lack of skills and age of workers). Effective counseling, training and retraining, and moving to the job opportunity area all are required to relocate these workers in a growing industrial center in the same State with from 2 to 3½ percent unemployment.

In a recent study in Appalachia, it was shown that about three-fourths of all relocated workers were satisfied with their jobs and their new community.

The dissatisfied in this study indicated that the social adjustment was more difficult than the training and retraining. Unhappy workers returned to the rural area saying the city was too large and too lonely, and people were too busy. One worker is quoted as stating, "It's hard to rest where everything around you is moving so fast."

In the successful relocations it was pointed out that the worker has improved his economic situation with a minimum of social and psychological difficulties in adjusting to the new community.

Efforts are being made by industry, local government, and the Federal Government to insure that the benefits of automation do not increase the burdens of widespread unemployment. Improved planning and expanded efforts will be required by all of these units to assure that adult men and women, and especially young people, will be trained and available to meet the changing job needs brought on by improved technology.

People most reluctant to move to new job opportunities are those with limited skills, older workers, and the handicapped.

Many new programs are being tried to improve job opportunities through making moving easier.

The State and local employment services are working with other government agencies, private organizations, and individuals in an effort to provide the many kinds of services that persons moving to new areas may need. They do not always have all the experience needed. But cooperation between social welfare organizations, local school administrators, civic associations, and employers is making possible a rapid adjustment to changed employment opportunities.

By working together, these agencies are providing greater assistance to the untrained, unemployed worker. They are helping the worker get a steady, productive job in the area where jobs exist and also helping ease family and community adjustment problems that sometimes overshadow all else.

180

Health Services for Rural Areas

EDWARD W. HASSINGER

KNOWLEDGE and techniques in medical practice have advanced rapidly. At the same time, as a nation, we have taken seriously the principle that high quality medical care is a right of all people. Yet delivery of health services has not kept pace with these developments, resulting in an "application gap." This problem affects us all, but for certain groups—the poor, the immobile (because of, for example, age), and the isolated—it has become critical.

For rural people the problem is often focused on the lack of personnel (particularly physicians and dentists) in rural communities. Metropolitan counties have between 3 and 4 times as many doctors per 1,000 population as counties with no urban places, and the deficiency in dentists is similar.

Within the metropolitan areas, of course, there are extremes in availability of health personnel, so residents of the inner city may be more remote from services than residents of sparsely populated rural areas. It does not change the fact, however, that hundreds of small towns which had a physician 10 or 20 years ago are without one today, and countless places are seeking a resident physician without success.

It is unlikely that availability of physicians will improve in rural areas. Doctors in many small towns are nearing retirement age and in many cases prospects for their replacement are dim.

Serious efforts have been made by medical schools, foundations, medical societies, and communities to recruit or direct doctors to rural areas. For the most part, these efforts have failed to maintain the status quo, let alone improve the situation. To understand the reasons, we must look at some of the changes that have taken place in the practice of medicine. Doing so may suggest solutions.

Traditionally the rural doctor was a general practitioner in solo practice and the bed of illness was in the home. Many places were one-doctor towns and the local doctor provided most of the professional medical care to most of the people. The "family doctor" meant friend and advisor as well as healer.

Then, too, medical technology was relatively simple and the doctor could carry the tools of the profession in his "little black bag" which he took into the homes of the community as he made his calls.

To be sure this is a description of things as they were in the past but since doctors are notably immobile once they have established a practice, their present location may reflect a situation that existed as long as 40 years ago. This description is also the basis for the expectation that every place should have the services of a physician.

Medical practice has changed in many ways. Because of the explosion of knowledge in medical sciences, no one physician can know all there is to know in the science and art of healing. This has led to specialization within the medical profession and most new doctors specialize in some field. Since specialists almost always locate in urban areas, the consequences are especially important for rural areas.

The apparatus needed for practicing medicine has also increased greatly so the doctor is no longer able to carry his essential equipment in a "little black bag" nor contain it within the walls of an office in many cases. Hospitals, clinics, and laboratories are illustrations of the added facilities required by modern medicine.

Of course, added personnel including many new types of technicians are

*

EDWARD W. HASSINGER is Professor of Rural Sociology, University of Missouri, Columbia.

needed to provide services. Today physicians represent less than 10 percent of the personnel employed in providing services to the ill, and the health industry is the third largest employer in the Nation.

A related change is the greater dependence on hospitals in treating illness. Such facilities cannot be located in each trade center. However, many small hospitals have been constructed in rural areas often with partial funding through the Federal Government. But as in the case of the general store and other small town service institutions, rural people frequently bypass smaller hospitals. The result is that these institutions are often underutilized and may gain a local reputation for being inferior or at least limited in the services they provide.

Not only do doctors tend to locate near hospitals in which they are willing to practice (many of the small hospitals are unable to maintain a staff), but they also find advantage in formal or informal group practice relationships with other doctors. This allows them to share expensive equipment, make more efficient use of auxiliary personnel, and obtain relief from practice for short periods of time.

So we find physicians in fewer places but with the likelihood of several doctors practicing in the same place. These locations may not be classified as rural in the Census although the physicians provide service to rural people.

When we look at these developments in a broad sense, it is apparent that the changes in location of medical services are related to other changes in the rural service community. Medical services are concentrated in fewer places, but so are retail stores, schools, and other service institutions. People are able and willing to travel greater distances for services they find more desirable.

In view of the larger rural service community, it has been suggested by some that doctors and hospitals are still located in too many rather than too few places.

In emphasizing location of physicians and health facilities, we may be asking the wrong questions. What is important is not so much *where* facilities are located but whether people have access to them.

To be located across the street from a fine medical facility is of little advantage if cost or hours or impersonality limit its use. On the other hand, through provision of transportation and use of "outreach" personnel such as visiting nurses or health aides, people at some distance from services might have relatively easy access to them.

It should be emphasized that what is needed are points of entry which will assure people, wherever they live, of orderly access to comprehensive health care.

Besides efforts to recruit physicians to rural areas, a number of things are being tried to meet the problems associated with delivery of services in these areas.

An obvious way of expanding medical services is to increase the efficiency of doctors already providing services to rural people. This is the purpose of a number of efforts to train auxiliary personnel. Of course, nurses have always worked in this role, but now there are training programs for physicians' assistants, nurse midwives, and pediatric associates.

A program of this type which has received much attention is MEDEX. Conducted by the University of Washington Medical School, it provides a 15-month training program for armed forces medical corpsmen upon their return to civilian life. These men have had training and, in many cases, vast experience in medical care.

The purpose of MEDEX is to extend the arm of the physician by providing trained assistants. Under the supervision of physicians the MEDEX assistants may perform such tasks as: taking case histories, performing parts of the physical examination prescribed by the physician, screening patients, providing home and nursing home care to chronically ill patients, performing

182

minor surgical procedures (applying and removing casts, suturing minor lacerations), and assisting the physician in surgery.

A major part of training in the MEDEX program is apprenticeship with a physician in community practice. While the program is applicable to urban areas as well as to rural communities, initially most of the trainees are being placed in rural areas with the expectation that they will remain there as an associate of the physician with whom they trained.

One estimate is that the MEDEX practitioners will allow the doctor with whom they work to care for 20 additional patients a day. Early indications are that the MEDEX practitioners are well accepted in communities.

In other situations, nonprofessionals have been trained to act as health agents or health aides. They are used, for example, in the migrant health program to bridge the language gap and social distance between migrant workers and clinics set up to serve them. Use of similar "agents" would be a possibility in any situation where a link is needed between individuals and medical service units. They could be used, for example, to provide transportation for elderly people to the medical facilities and back home again.

A number of projects have been developed providing comprehensive medical care units to serve rural people. These are often initiated and in part supported by universities and the Federal Government to demonstrate the feasibility of the approach.

Projects of this kind show what can be done, but have little overall impact until they are accepted and implemented by communities.

The Office of Economic Opportunity has supported development of a number of neighborhood health centers which provide primary medical services for residents of a neighborhood. The first and best known attempt to provide services in a rural area under this concept is the Tufts-Delta project.

Tufts University School of Medicine, located in Boston, Mass., has undertaken development of a program to provide comprehensive medical services in a low income area of rural Mississippi where the population is predominantly black.

The area is approximately 400 square miles surrounding the town of Mound Bayou and it includes about 14,000 people. A survey found serious health problems including malnutrition and conditions which modern medicine has long had the ability to conquer.

In November 1967, after almost 3 years of planning, a health center was opened in a remodeled church parsonage. Late in 1968 a new facility was opened in a modern 24,000-square-foot building where office space was provided for three family care groups, each consisting of an internist, pediatrician, general practitioner, community health nurses, nurses' aides, and sanitarians.

There is additional space for an obstetrician-gynecologist, a surgeon, and a psychologist which serve all three groups. Also, there is an emergency room and other facilities including a delivery room, x-ray facilities, record room, lab, and pharmacy.

A feature of the Tufts-Delta project is involvement of local people in the program. This is done in two ways.

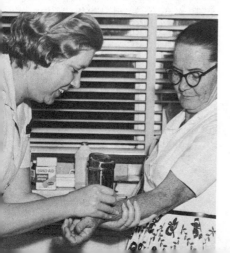

Community spirit and determination created a small health care facility for Morgantown, Ky., population 1,400. Residents found they could work together for such projects by starting on smaller projects—such as painting mailboxes—together.

The center employs many local people on its staff and has a program for training them as nurses' aides and home health aides. Also, local health associations have been organized in the several neighborhoods of the area which in turn have representation on an areawide planning council. This council is involved in setting priorities and in planning the health center program.

It is expected that eventually the council will share completely with Tufts University School of Medicine in planning, managing, and directing the entire program. The council provides an important means for educating the public regarding health services and health practices.

The health center has become involved in the community in other ways. Observing that many people in the area were struggling to get minimum food, clothing, and shelter and since these things are essential in promoting health, a cooperative farm and cooperative grocery and clothing outlets were developed.

Furthermore, the areawide health council has been involved in a water sanitation project, a housing program, and a project of patient transportation. These activities highlight the fact that it takes more than staff personnel to solve complex health problems.

Grant County in Oklahoma contrasts in many ways with the situation just described. It has the highest per capita income of any county in the State. Yet in the middle 1960's there were no physicians in the county with the exception of one elderly doctor. Wakita, one of the small towns in the county, became the location of a demonstration community health center of the University of Oklahoma School of Medicine. The purpose was to provide primary health care.

Funds were raised locally to build the center. It has rooms for three physicians, an emergency room, medical laboratories, x-ray facilities, and a pharmacy. It also has 29 hospital beds and 22 nursing home beds.

Illustrating the difficulty of staffing rural health facilities, the center—although dedicated in 1968—as of September 1970 had only one resident physician. Other physicians' services were being provided from Oklahoma University School of Medicine.

A number of models for delivery of health services are described in the publication, *Health Care Delivery in Rural Areas, Selected Models*, a publication of the Council on Rural Health of the American Medical Association. Among them are the programs in Lafayette County, Fla.; Torrance County, N. Mex.; and in Monterey County, Calif.

The situation as it exists and is developing is both a problem and a challenge for the public. It is not a question of whether the delivery of health services to people in rural areas will change, because it has changed and continues to change. The question is whether high-quality medical care can be provided to everyone regardless of isolation or other reasons.

Then there are the difficulties of overcoming established patterns both for the consumers and providers of health services. This requires understanding and support of sound innovations on the part of the public. It also calls for critical evaluation of new programs, because not all of them deserve support.

Also, when physicians and other facilities are some distance away there is greater need for the public to participate in delivering health services. This involves planning ahead to avoid emergencies when possible, and includes provisions for preventive measures and public health education. It may also mean participating in community activities to provide transportation or other assistance for those who need services.

The Cooperative Extension Service is one resource which should not be overlooked in health planning. It has a staff distributed throughout the country with experience in public education and community organization. These are elements needed to provide better health resources in rural areas.

Welfare Programs

HELEN W. JOHNSON and

BLANCHE D. COLL

IN ALL AGES and all societies, there have been individuals and groups who were not able to sustain themselves. Society has always accepted responsibility for taking care of those in need.

Historically, aid has been given to destitute persons—typically the aged, physically and mentally handicapped, the sick, the unemployed, women with young children who lack male support, and orphans. Over the years, assistance came largely from public sources, although voluntary and religious organizations also contributed funds and services.

Until the great depression of the 1930's, public assistance to the needy was financed and administered by State and local governments.

Beginning with the Federal Emergency Relief Act of 1933, the Federal Government began to grant large sums of money to the States for public assistance. The Social Security Act of 1935 established three categorical programs: Old-Age Assistance; Aid to Dependent Children (now Aid to Families with Dependent Children); and Aid to the Blind.

An additional category, Aid to the Permanently and Totally Disabled, was added in 1950. Through Medicaid, added in 1965, the Social Security Act authorizes use of funds for medical care of dependent persons and those unable to pay their medical bills.

Each of these programs is financed through a combination of Federal and State funds. They are administered at the Federal level by the Social and Rehabilitation Service, Department of Health, Education, and Welfare.

Besides groups aided under the Social Security Act, State and local funds are appropriated to assist other needy persons, for example, childless married couples in need (General Assistance).

Over the past 20 years, Old-Age Assistance has decreased due to more comprehensive coverage under Old Age, Survivors, and Disability Insurance (Social Security). The trend in Aid to the Needy Blind is also downward. While Aid to the Permanently and Totally Disabled has increased, this program accounts for a very small proportion of total persons receiving public assistance. General Assistance, also a small program, has remained almost constant in terms of numbers of recipients since the mid-1940's.

It is the Aid to Families With Dependent Children (AFDC) program which has shown a marked increase in the last 10 years. The ratio of children receiving AFDC payments per 1,000 population under age 18 rose from 34 in 1950 to 58 in 1968. In fiscal year 1969, total public assistance payments amounted to more than $10.5 billion. The AFDC program, together with medical assistance to families with children, accounted for more than $4.5 billion of this total.

About 50 percent of welfare costs are paid out of State and local funds. Increases in these costs have been accompanied by a decline in fiscal capability on the part of State and local governments. The rise in the amount of Federal grants to the States is also a matter of serious public concern.

The program which, more than any other, has brought the working of the present welfare system into question is Aid to Families With Dependent Children. Noncontroversial in the beginning, it was initiated to benefit

*

HELEN W. JOHNSON is Assistant to the Director, Economic Development Division, Economic Research Service.

BLANCHE D. COLL is an historian in the Social and Rehabilitation Service, Department of Health, Education, and Welfare.

Food stamps in hand, a mother shops in grocery store, above. Right, food stamps help this 83-year-old man and his wife stretch their income from Social Security.

primarily widows with dependent children. However, as pointed out earlier, the program has grown at a high rate, and also has changed in character and orientation. Divorce, desertion, and illegitimacy have replaced widowhood as the main cause of dependency.

Some criticism of the AFDC program has focused on administrative practices as well as rising costs. Because the program is operated differently in each State, there are great disparities in many aspects of its administration —in benefit levels, eligibility requirements, regulations, and procedures. In some States, for example, monthly welfare payments are less than a fifth as large per family as in other States.

Although regional differences would persist with a minimum income floor for all families with children, for example, a basic income payment would help to even out the present disparity among the States in levels of benefits to these families. Also, in many rural areas where per capita income is low, Federal guarantee of a minimum income, plus State supplementary pay-

ments of at least half their present levels, could significantly improve the status of many dependent families.

Inequity is seen in the current exclusion of poor families headed by males or females working full-time at low wages. This means that some families receiving welfare benefits can be better off financially than others whose breadwinners work full-time for low wages.

The AFDC program puts severe economic pressure on the already weakened social fabric of poverty families. The cause and effect relationship between AFDC and family breakup probably cannot be measured. But mothers with young children are frequently in better financial position on welfare than if the father remains at home working at low wages.

In 1969, 75 percent of the fathers of AFDC families were reported as "absent from home." This is clearly a social cost of the program, and unfair to families who stay together, attempting to work their own way out of poverty status.

In view of these facts, it is hardly

186

surprising that numerous proposals have been considered to reform the welfare system.

Differences of opinion on how best to accomplish reform evolve around such questions as income support—what level of income, who should be eligible, and how best to provide it—through an income floor, a negative income tax, income supplements, family or children's allowances.

Then there is the question of how to help people become self-supporting through the availability of new jobs and training in skills required, as well as by assuring equality of employment opportunity.

Questions also involve additional types of assistance, such as food stamps, health insurance, rent supplements, and supportive services while in training for employment.

Other issues focus on the cost of various proposals and the level of government that should bear the major share; and the question of establishing a national standard of eligibility for receiving welfare assistance.

These are difficult issues to resolve, and there is no national consensus on the "right" answers.

Among proposed amendments to Social Security legislation under consideration by Congress is the Family Assistance Plan which would replace the AFDC program. It would provide a guaranteed minimum income floor to families with children and would set uniform eligibility standards. Other changes in the present system would provide higher benefit payments for three adult categories—the aged, the blind, and the disabled.

Besides welfare assistance in the Social Security Act, programs for needy persons are carried out by State, county, and community departments of welfare.

Even when programs are administered by local agencies, access to them is sometimes complicated by the residential location of potential clients. For example, in many rural areas, the delivery of welfare services is hampered by physical and social isolation

of the needy poor. Often, they lack information about what help is available, how to become eligible for it, where and when to go to receive it. Transportation to the welfare office may not be available. Or poor persons may feel that applying for assistance is demeaning.

Inadequate information may also be a problem for welfare agencies charged with locating those in need and providing the kind of services they should have. Social services are difficult and costly to administer in sparsely settled and out-of-the-way rural areas. And yet, the needs are as real for these scattered populations as for the more visible and easier-to-reach people in urban centers.

Basic requirements of rural people for welfare assistance are the same as for people anywhere. Rural poor families and individuals need an income floor; they need food to combat hunger and malnutrition; they must have jobs and training to become self-supporting; their elderly, blind, handicapped, and dependent children deserve society's consideration of their particular circumstances.

In many rural areas where nonfarm jobs have not developed to compensate for the decline in agricultural employment, workers must obtain and be trained for alternative employment. This may mean going some distance from home for training facilities, job counseling, and placement.

If mothers of young children undertake training and/or employment, provision will have to be made for day-care centers. Again, this may involve traveling some distance. Innovative approaches to delivery of social services will be needed to make these services more effective in rural areas.

The objective of efforts to reform the present welfare system is to include all who are in need in a coordinated, comprehensive welfare program. Such a program will substantially increase the numbers on welfare rolls at least until collateral means are found, through training and job generation, to remove the need for the welfare assistance for all who can become self-supporting.

There is little reason to believe that the dimensions of public welfare responsibility will diminish in the near future in rural or urban America. If life expectancy continues to increase, more of our elderly people will live longer, and many of them characteristically choose rural areas and small towns as places of retirement. Also, due to the heavy urbanward migration of the younger age groups in the 1950's and 1960's, some rural areas have a disproportionately high percentage of population that is elderly.

Since families in rural parts of the country tend to have higher birth rates than do urban families—and generally less than average income—there will be more children of rural low-income families who will need welfare services of one kind or another. If, in addition, mothers of young children are encouraged to become breadwinners, there will be a vastly increased need for day-care facilities, public transportation systems, and income support during the job-training period.

In the end, the basic national goal is to enable all Americans who can become self-sustaining to do so, without welfare assistance. For those who cannot support themselves because they are too old or are handicapped, equity and humanity require an acceptable level and method of assistance. Improvement in the quality of life is important to both groups.

Concerning the poor and the near-poor, employed or unemployed, the need is to escape from poverty through work that is adequately compensated. To make this possible, it will be necessary in many cases to improve their chances of success through basic or remedial education, training in a marketable skill, comprehensive medical care, acceptable day care for children of employed parents, and public or private sector employment at satisfactory wage levels.

Communities, too, have a role to play in enhancing the quality of life. When families and individuals can support themselves with dependable employment, they will seek adequate housing, good schools for their children, accessible medical care, adequate transportation facilities, social and cultural amenities. A tax-paying citizenry can help support these community services. Communities without soaring welfare costs can provide the healthy environment in which all people can prosper.

Attributes of a healthy society which are of fundamental significance, in addition to material well-being, are equal opportunity and social justice. People who can lift themselves out of poverty and become self-supporting must have a truly equal opportunity to do so. For those who cannot sustain themselves, justice and humanity call for adequate assistance to be given without loss of their dignity.

Family Aide Services

HELEN D. TURNER

SNOW BEGAN FALLING when Caroline Morgan knocked at the door of the rundown house not far from her own home. Forty-five minutes went by as she stood in the snow explaining why she was there. The homemaker finally invited her to come inside. Now Caroline's work would begin. Homes such as this are her classroom. And Caroline is a most unusual and effective teacher.

Caroline Morgan is now a friend as well as a neighbor, but she is more than that—she and thousands like her are employed and trained for the work they do. Their job responsibilities vary, depending on the agency or organization they work for, and they are identified in a number of different

188

ways: as homemaker aides, homemaker-home health aides, program aides, health aides, Extension aides, nutrition aides, outreach workers, and community aides. They are part of a growing group of workers that includes teacher aides, dental assistants, paramedics, library assistants, and nurses aides.

Trained to work under direct supervision of the professional worker, aides perform tasks that relieve and extend the services of the professional. In this chapter we are concerned particularly with aides working in out-of-school educational programs and family-related services, especially those directed to the disadvantaged parts of the population.

The homemaker-home health aide is a member of a supportive health team that carries out a plan of care designed and supervised by professional health personnel. She provides for daily patient care needs and may maintain a home when the mother is hospitalized or disabled. Both public health services and welfare agencies employ homemaker aides.

Aides are also used by welfare offices to relieve professionals of some of the preliminary work in determining welfare applicant eligibility. Other welfare aides are trained to work as teaching aides who help families to better use available resources.

The aide employed by the Cooperative Extension Service has as her particular job teaching the knowledge and skills needed for improved family living. She works "with" rather than "for" the family—her goal is to bring about independent action. She, too, must be thoroughly informed about all the community resources to be able to guide a family to the appropriate solutions of problems not solvable within her role.

A South Dakota aide whose role was

*

HELEN D. TURNER retired in May 1971 as Deputy Assistant Administrator, Home Economics, Extension Service. She was responsible for the agency's expanded Food and Nutrition Education Program.

to help families achieve an adequate diet found a large family hungry and poorly nourished because they were too proud to ask for help in the form of food stamps. When the aide convinced them that using food stamps until the husband's earnings increased was not "accepting charity," they applied for and received the bonus stamps that made an adequate diet possible.

An aide in Arizona found a family with 10 children, a sick mother, no father in the home, and no one except teenage children to assume the burden of caring for the children, the sick mother, and the housekeeping responsibilities. The Extension aide recognized that there was a need for full-time homemaking and nursing care. Through her efforts, the services of a homemaker-home health aide were obtained. The two aides and their respective agencies cooperated in helping this large family deal with a crisis.

Aides are employed in largest numbers by public health services, welfare agencies, community action agencies, and the Cooperative Extension Service. They usually have had the same life experiences as the people with whom they work, and most often live in the same community.

More women than men are currently employed as aides, and the intimate working relationship between aide and homemaker almost dictates that this be so. However, there are successful male aides working with families on home sanitation, home gardening, and home repairs; as outreach workers and as community aides. A few are teaching low-income farmers agricultural know-how.

Usually there are few educational requirements, but aides must be able to read well enough to follow simple instructions and to write well enough to complete simple reports.

Aides must be able to communicate with the families they are to reach. They must have experienced or at least understand the problems of poverty and speak the language of the people. Perhaps most importantly, an aide must care about and have

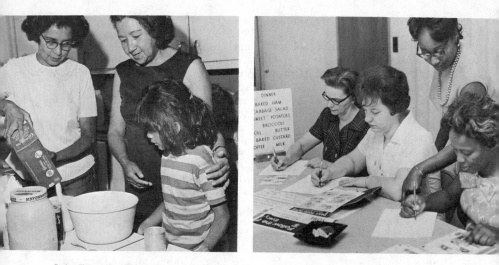

Left, Extension aide looks on as homemaker tries making inexpensive cocoa mix while daughter watches, on Tulalip Indian Reservation in Washington State. Right, aides undergo training.

sympathy for families, with the maturity to keep her from becoming too emotionally involved. (For example, new aides often have difficulty sleeping because they have not yet learned "to turn off" the problems of the families they work with during the day.)

Here is a case history about the importance of communication. A Puerto Rican mother of four—unable to read, write, or speak English—was left stranded by her husband in a large city. Frightened by the city and unable to get the help she needed to feed, clothe, and house her children, the young mother became desperate. The harder she tried, the more she ran into people who took advantage of her situation.

One day, a Spanish-speaking woman knocked at the Puerto Rican homemaker's door and said she had information that could help her. Suspicious at first, the homemaker refused to let her visitor in. The visitor was someone from the community who knew what poverty problems were and appreciated how difficult life was for someone who spoke no English. She was able to reach the young woman and help her solve some immediate problems by referring her to the proper agencies.

With the aide's encouragement, the family began drinking more milk and eating more fruits and vegetables. They cleared up a bill at a corner grocery store. And the young homemaker who had lost faith in people decided that someone did care, after all.

Aides acquire the families with whom they work by assignment— especially in the case of public health and welfare aides, by referral, and by knocking on doors. Community action agency aides and those employed by the Cooperative Extension Service most often use the knocking-on-doors technique, although Extension aides frequently call on families referred to them by another agency, a minister, school, or relative.

It takes perseverance, persuasiveness, and patience to be an aide. The clientele may view the aides with suspicion or even hostility.

One aide told about making five attempts to get beyond the porch to talk with a mother of five who was receiving welfare assistance. Because she knew the family was in need, she made the sixth call and was received with open arms. Credit at the grocery store had been cut off, there was little cash and little food to last until the

190

next check came. The aide was able to help the mother plan and shop so that the children were fed well balanced meals for the remainder of the month.

Aide recruitment is done through newspaper stories and classified ads, radio, and TV; other agencies; local employment services; churches; and by word of mouth.

Screening of the recruits and final selection is done against the criteria established by the employing agency, tempered by the interviewer's judgment. Final selection may be delayed until after the job candidates have completed their orientation training. Some aides recognize their own shortcomings and remove themselves from candidacy, while a few are referred by the employer to other job opportunities or job training.

In any case, the candidate's need for employment is not the deciding factor nor are premature judgments rendered as to the candidate's ability or lack of ability. Many applicants have little or no job related experiences and so must be trained in what it means to hold a job—any job—besides the knowledge and skills necessary to do this specific one.

If there is a single factor that determines how effective aides will be, it is the quality and relevance of the orientation and inservice training given aides. Professionals require special training and guidance to enable them to adapt subject matter and provide learning experiences for aides.

Even Cooperative Extension Service workers, who for many years have trained volunteers to teach others, find it difficult to use the simple, yet specific terms required to train those with limited schooling to teach others with still less knowledge and skill.

The situation is further complicated by the fact that aides must be able to respond to the immediate problem at hand. A Massachusetts aide on an initial visit to a home found a child in convulsions. Her knowledge of the medical resources available to the family made it possible to get immediate help for the child. Any agenda the

aide had for the visit was put aside for another time.

An Alabama aide planned to teach a young homemaker to prepare a baked casserole dish using foods the family received as participants in the U.S. Department of Agriculture food for needy families program. Upon her arrival, she found the gas cut off because the bill was unpaid. She could have made an appointment for a return visit after the gas was restored, but a fire in the fireplace—the source of heat for the home—inspired her to cook the casserole there.

Besides fulfilling the aide's teaching objective, this meant that the family had a hot meal that day and the young homemaker had a lesson in resourcefulness. The aide was also able to get help to restore gas to the home.

Aides must be prepared to initially use interest-getter activities, but they also must know when to move on to major objectives. Preparing a new recipe each visit may be fine for a start, but the real need might be to teach how to shop, plan meals, or handle money. Aides must be able to move from recipes to more complex learning experiences as rapidly as the homemaker appears ready. They must be trained as to what they can't do as well as what they can or should do. For example, an aide can't recommend a feeding formula for a new baby but she can help the mother learn to prepare the physician-recommended formula properly.

For the new learner—and aides are new learners—orientation training must be followed by repetitive learning. The challenge to the professional trainer is to create new learning situations based on the aide's work experience.

While aides must have specific training for the responsibilities they are assigned and to meet requirements of the agency or organization that employs them, there is emerging a body of knowledge needed by all. In the future this could be provided in formal academic credit situations in community colleges or in workshop training sessions provided by the agencies or organizations with aide positions.

Some multiple purpose training is developing, and agencies are, in a limited way, merging training programs. As the aide concept grows, this trend should be encouraged.

Many of the best qualified aides, at least among women, have had no previous employment. If they had job experience, it was in situations where tasks were routine and they were closely supervised.

Since much of the aide's work is planned and carried out in the field, it is important to know whether she is managing her time well, whether accurate information is given families, and whether the aide's own myths, misinformation, and folklore influence her work with families.

Many professional workers under whom aides work have had no training or experience in supervision. Well-planned supervisory tools and activities will give the professional an evaluation of how the aide is doing and, more importantly, indicate what additional training is needed to improve the quality and effectiveness of the aide's work.

Experience indicates that professionals must be taught to train and supervise aides. They must be helped to assign meaningful work experiences to aides and to consider aides an integral part of their staff.

The U.S. Department of Agriculture's Extension Service finds that if the professional is to continue with other job responsibilities, she can handle no more than three to five aides.

This number can be increased to 10 or 12 if one or two aides are trained to serve as supervisors. Where the sole responsibility of the professional is training and supervising aides, she can usually manage 15 to 20 successfully.

In one State, the Cooperative Extension Service assigns an Extension home economist to every 30 program aides, with a program assistant (supervisory aide) for each 10. The program assistant provides immediate supervision and some training. This plan seems to work well.

One critical aspect in training and supervising the aide is the number of aides who work for a brief period of time. Much of this is unavoidable and—indeed—it is often desirable, especially when aides are able to move into other more responsible jobs with better pay.

From the agency point of view, resignation may painlessly remove some of the less effective workers. On the other hand, rapid turnover compounds the problem of keeping a staff of well-trained workers by forcing the professional to spend too much time recruiting and training new aides. Work with families may be seriously disrupted by the time lag in getting a new aide and renewing family-aide rapport.

Good training, effective supervision, a feeling of being one of the team, opportunity to advance in salary, job responsibility, and adequate fringe benefits can help reduce turnover.

By using nonprofessionals, an agency or organization can sharply increase its working staff at less cost than would be true if only professionals were employed. This route seems to be part of the answer to meeting the needs of a rapidly expanding population of the seventies.

In most fields, it would not even be possible to find professionals in the numbers required to accomplish the one-to-one relationship needed with the bypassed disadvantaged without the added demands of the total population. In the properly recruited aide, the agency acquires skills which may not be available in its professional staff, such as language facility and intimate knowledge of the physical problems and psychological hangups of the audience.

Nonprofessionals benefit by acquiring job experience and job skills and training which are often of personal benefit to themselves and their families. Frequently the experience creates a desire for more education and/or training for a different job.

Many who have not completed high school have been encouraged to study for high school equivalency certificates. Such was the case of Mrs. Margy Rodgers in New Jersey. When she began working as an aide she had completed 10 years of schooling. She successfully completed her high school equivalency in 1969 and expressed a desire to take college courses at Rutgers-of-South-Jersey.

She began a special "college preparatory course" in January 1970 and enrolled for six credit hours in September 1970.

In Texas, a young Mexican-American homemaker was confined to her home, taking care of three small youngsters and trying to make her husband's meager salary meet the family's financial needs. Despondent over her problems, the young woman became overweight.

She was hired as an aide, and her training and work with families helped her solve some of her own money management problems. She also discovered how to lose weight through proper diet. She learned to sew, and the prospect of new clothes intensified her desire to lose weight.

Both husband and wife were so encouraged by the upturn in their lives that they began to plan a family vacation trip—something they had never thought possible.

Recruiting, selecting, training, and supervising the thousands of nonprofessionals for whom there are now funds tax the ingenuity of the professional workers and the agencies who employ them. Those who are deeply involved are excited about the challenge and the results. They feel their professional skills are being used to better advantage than ever before, and it is exciting and rewarding to see both aides and families take a new lease on life.

Professional workers recognize the value of this added staff dimension and are working hard to make the nonprofessional's job a permanent part of the staffing pattern of family centered organizations and agencies.

Management of Family Resources

RUTH E. DEACON

MOST PEOPLE think of money when they think about managing their resources, and specifically they think of current money income. Usually this does not match their level of wants. For example, family needs are highest in the early years of marriage when incomes are relatively low. At this time in life a broader view of resources and a longer view of what is important can be helpful in making satisfying choices.

Money management is a very personal responsibility—the business of each one. Success must be gaged in terms of the resources available, aspirations, and the conditions prevailing over time. Also, it is important to recognize the differences in family goals and the dominant expectations of society. USDA and State programs planned to help families become successful in their resource management may take the form of counsel, formal or informal teaching, and use of the mass media, with home economists giving particular leadership in these areas.

What do we know about families and their methods of resource management over a lifetime? A recent study undertaken by the Agricultural Experiment Stations in Nebraska, Missouri, and Indiana reported on major financial decisions and crises of families at different times during their years of marriage. An analysis of these life experiences suggests a pattern in financial decisions over the life span. Four economic phases were identified:

• In the "foundation" years of marriage (up to 5 years), goals are

193

formed. These are more definitive when both the husband and wife are employed or when there are children. Striving to provide the desired level of living is strong. Further educational or occupational decisions for the husband-wife team are made. Life style and management decisions are faced. And, health matters related to child care may be important.

• In the "developmental" period (up to 20 years of marriage), children's education and housing are important family considerations. Financial security questions including income and occupation continue to be faced, but these are related to earlier decisions which provided the direction for achieving family goals. Much emphasis is placed during these years upon fulfilling the possibilities initiated in the foundation years.

• From the 20th to the 40th year of marriage is a time for "assessment, achievement, and readjustment." Although some families continue to give attention to their children's education, meeting consumption goals and formulating retirement plans become important. Many wage-earning decisions at this time relate to the wife's employment, although major job decisions are more frequent when the husband's educational level is low. At higher income levels, decisions to strengthen financial security usually coincide with plans for retirement.

• After 40 years of marriage, the retirement period is at hand and resolutions of questions regarding housing and health become principal concerns. Goals are more likely to be reassessed by families with lower incomes than by those with higher incomes.

We are a mobile society, and about 20 percent of the population moves each year. This may come at any time for a given family, but moving

*

RUTH E. DEACON is Chairman of the Management, Housing and Equipment Division, School of Home Economics, Ohio State University.

brings in a unique set of financial considerations.

Younger families are more likely to move than older families. Those with lower income move more frequently than those of higher income. And, those with higher education move further and more frequently than those of lower education levels. Five out of six family moves occur within the State and one out of six is across State lines.

From these and other findings we see that families have varied financial demands over the years. Ways for meeting these demands obviously require different approaches. In order to succeed in coping with economic problems, family attitudes about meeting them and about getting ahead do make a difference. One important factor is to avoid the temptation to over-simplify problems.

What are the resources that make a difference to families? For most families, the basic resource around which planning evolves is the current money income. Unless changes in the pattern of earnings are anticipated, fluctuations may cause major financial problems. As an example, many young families can attest to difficulties in adjustments that arise when income from the wife's earnings is no longer available.

One of the most common adjustments that families make in trying to smooth out their consumption over the years is to find a way to supplement income from the husband's primary job. Outside employment of the wife is likely in the first months or years after marriage and then again after the children are established in school. The husband may take a second job, or the family may move to a new location to improve income potential.

Another important adjustment is to increase earning power through training, since new skills do have a direct bearing on the ability to earn.

Many efforts may be put forth by families over the years to increase or sustain their earnings. Even so, there are important approaches to handling earned income that can make long-run differences in life styles. These include use of credit, savings and investments, insurance, nonmoney income or unpaid production, wise purchases, use of public services, and responsible choices in relation to taxes.

Although a majority of families have participated in rising incomes and higher levels of living, there are still too many who have not. One, and often more than one, of the following conditions is likely to accompany lower income: Fewer years of schooling of earners; fewer earners or more dependents per earner; a younger, older, female, or unemployed family head; or lower expectations regarding income.

Credit offers an opportunity for families to adjust their incomes over time and provides for current needs and wants. The use of consumer credit seems to be responsive to income changes, according to studies of the Survey Research Center at Ann Arbor, Mich. Overall, more consumer debt is incurred as total income increases or decreases than when it stays the same.

This may indicate that in a relatively stable situation, we are not so inclined to use credit to change consumption. We respond optimistically to income increases by trying to improve our level of living. Through credit, we also try to maintain living patterns when income declines.

Frequently, younger families have some debt and a higher portion of income committed to payment of debts than do established families. Relatively more Negro families have some debt, but it tends to be a smaller amount than for white families.

Lower income families and those with a smaller amount of installment debt tend to get behind on payments. This becomes a circular and complex problem for which special counseling assistance is advisable.

When we look further we find that a number of factors appear to be related to credit problems, such as divorce, loss of spouse, low income, little education, youth or old age, having low savings, being underemployed or unemployed, not owning a home, or experiencing an income change.

No one of these conditions will necessarily contribute directly to credit problems, but they are conditions that may make it difficult to meet obligations—particularly if a number of them occur at the same time. These are the kinds of situations where sound counseling or advisory approaches can be most meaningful. Credit institutions are increasingly aware of the need to provide broad assistance in financial planning to promote successful use of credit by consumers.

Purchase of a car is the most frequent reason for consumer indebtedness. About one family in ten buys a new car each year, and twice as many purchase used cars. Other consumer durables such as appliances likewise may be purchased "on time" —most likely when the family head is under 35 or by those with higher incomes.

Studies of family assets show that equity in a home is the most important part of a family's net worth. Such equity not only represents security with respect to a family's financial status during the earlier years of marriage, but also is important as families look ahead to retirement.

Future directions in home ownership are not clear. If in the future more families are to rent throughout their married life, as some predict, alternative investment or savings plans need to be considered.

Families face a number of financial crises, including loss of income due to retirement, premature death, disability, and unemployment, plus major health and property loss expenses. Potential effects of these risks can be minimized, however, through private and public insurance plans. The important thing is to provide

An individual family may provide more or less in this way, depending upon its skills, desires and the value placed on alternative uses of time. The effects of augmenting money income through self-help should not be minimized.

Families can further extend their income through use of community resources like libraries, parks, adult classes. There are many publicly provided goods and services which offer an alternative to purchases.

Higher income families apparently take greater advantage of this opportunity than do lower income families. Any counseling or advisory program designed to improve the level of living can focus on this potential and expand on its possibilities.

Probably the best known opportunity to extend money income is through prudent expenditures. Foresight and planning in buying, and use of pertinent information in making financial decisions, can contribute significantly to consumer satisfactions.

Taxes are an added consideration in a family's financial management. Households both contribute to and receive benefits from taxation. Responsibility in this area includes a participation in decisions having the greatest potential for individual and community development in the use of tax monies as well as taking advantage of available allowances when

more adequately for the family in case that contingency arises.

Families that can afford to do so look over public or job associated insurance plans as a basis for building a private program that more nearly assures them of a continuing level of living in case of premature death or catastrophic medical costs. Insurance and other financial advisers can provide guidance in developing the kind of long range, flexible plans that are needed.

Since needs do change, protection plans should be reviewed periodically. The full responsibility for protection against property loss remains with the family, which thus can become another area for education and for counsel.

A far-reaching method to extend money income is through jobs that families perform for themselves and others without pay. Estimates regarding unpaid work, including homemaking and home maintenance, have been calculated by the Survey Research Center to add as much as 50 percent of their diposable money income to a family's total available goods and services.

Top, comparison shopping pays most on small items purchased regularly, or on infrequent purchases of large items. Right, ability to do major work on house, like painting, saves labor costs and helps maintain house's value.

paying income taxes. Public or private tax advisers are good sources of assistance.

Finally, when major changes in individual and family circumstances occur, or when income changes, special attention is needed to evaluate opportunities or control potential difficulties. As the family moves from one stage in the economic life cycle to another, it is time for making plans or receiving outside help.

In addition to good management in spending, achievement of family goals may come about through judicious use of credit, savings, insurance, home production, and public services. If families are to make the most of their economic opportunities, they must develop an ability to manage skillfully in a variety of situations. Education and service programs can augment personal decision-making by providing counsel, facts, and understanding.

The Aging: Needs and Services

E. GRANT YOUMANS

THE LARGE number of older persons in the United States—some 20 million aged 65 and over—is a relatively new phenomenon in society, and private and public programs are being developed to meet their needs.

In 1969, the Chairman of the Michigan Commission on Aging reported on hearings at which older citizens themselves came to tell about their problems. These meetings were attended by older Americans from large urban centers and from remote rural areas. According to the published hearing reports, the most common complaint was "inadequate income."

Many persons reported constant erosion of their fixed incomes in the face of rising costs of living, and complained of the additional economic burdens imposed by special assessments on their properties for such items as services, sidewalks, water systems, and paving.

The United States has a dual system of protection covering old-age incomes. One is the Federal Social Security program which aims to provide a basic level of living. The other system is that of private pensions and supplemental sources.

Inadequacy of these systems is illustrated by comparing the incomes of age groups in the United States. In 1969, according to figures compiled by the Administration on Aging, the median annual income of heads of families aged 65 and over was $4,803, only 47.6 percent of that of heads of families under age 65, whose median income was $10,085.

For unrelated individuals the incomes were markedly less and the disparity was even greater. In 1969, the median annual income of unrelated persons aged 65 and over was $1,855, or 43 percent of that of unrelated individuals from the time they entered the working force to age 64, whose median income was $4,314.

Median income figures, it should be noted, fail to reveal the sizable proportion of older people with very small incomes. These persons, who have had low incomes throughout their working lives and thus receive small benefits from public or private sources, find themselves in acute economic distress in their old age.

Experts on problems of the aged

*

E. GRANT YOUMANS is a Sociologist in the Economic Development Division, Economic Research Service, USDA, and Professor of Rural Sociology, University of Kentucky, Lexington.

have recommended amending both public and private pension systems to provide more adequate coverage for the aged.

The trend in the United States toward early retirement, according to a New York labor market analyst, aggravates the economic plight of many older persons. Early retirement reduces the size of social security benefits to the very persons who can ill afford a reduction.

More and more persons choose to apply for benefits before they reach age 65. In 1968, for example, of the men who started receiving social security benefits, about 54 percent were under 65 and therefore got reduced amounts. As might be expected, the average monthly benefit in December 1968 of $96 was substantially less than the $115 received by men who waited until 65 to retire.

This trend toward earlier retirement, according to the labor market analyst, is due to postwar industrial patterns in the United States and consequent amendment to the social security program permitting retirement of workers at age 62.

Between 1950 and 1960, employment in the Nation increased markedly in the newer and rapidly growing industries, which tended to hire young workers. During the same period there was a decline in employment in such fields as agriculture, mining, and railroads, where large numbers of older workers held jobs.

The difficulty of displaced older people in obtaining employment in newer expanding industries led them to elect to retire on reduced benefits.

Forced retirement from work, according to a practicing psychiatrist, has a deleterious effect upon many older Americans. Not only does this practice contribute to poverty among the elderly, but it also has profound psychological consequences.

Among the 20 million older Americans in the United States there are many who have the competence, the physical capacity, and the desire to work, but they can't find jobs.

Rejected in attempts to find socially useful work roles, many older persons experience loss of self-esteem, a condition that contributes to the rise in suicide rates with advancing age among men. In addition, according to the psychiatrist, involuntary retirement from work tends to bring physical inactivity and a deterioration in mental functioning.

A perplexing problem to many older persons is that of finding housing suitable to their needs and at prices they can afford.

As people grow old, it was reported at the hearings before the Subcommittee on Housing for the Elderly in 1969, their homes become more an integral part of their lives. Some older persons want smaller quarters, some want apartments, and some want to move to warmer climates.

The housing dilemma of many older Americans is aggravated by a chronic shortage of housing for the poor, and by their inability to maintain their homes in the face of increases in taxes. In some urban areas, they are forced to compete for the limited number of apartments available. This competition tends to cause increases in rentals, even though the buildings deteriorate.

Two cases illustrate the income and housing problems of the aged. "Mr. Evans, age 79, and Mrs. Evans, age 74, have a combined income of $2,250 a year. They paid $120 for prescriptions and $395 for their 1969 taxes on an antiquated house over 50 years old. They had $1,735 left for all other living expenses." "Mrs. Long is an 81-year old widow with a total income of $1,320. Her 1969 tax bill was $556, which was an increase of $161 over 1968. She lives in a substandard house over 50 years old. All she had left for living expenses was $764."

In 1970 an issue of the *Journal of Geriatrics* carried recommendations of a former Government official that a public corporation be established to buy, sell, rent, and renovate residential property for older people.

Such a corporation, it was suggested, could alleviate anxieties about financial transactions, and remove the fear of being defrauded. It could purchase the home of an aged person who is ill by paying him a monthly amount, which could be used for his health care.

A corporation might remodel large houses so that several older persons could live in them. It could advance down payments at a modest charge on the purchase of homes while the older person investigates the possibility of finding different quarters.

One of the most complex problems facing many older Americans is that of obtaining adequate health services. Their difficulties are aggravated by the prevalence of chronic disease, their reduced income, and the frequent lack of transportation for medical care.

After a struggle spanning three decades, health insurance for the elderly was provided in 1965 under Medicare. This program, along with Medicaid, was aimed at removing the financial barriers to health care. Rather brief experience with the programs has pointed up the need for improvements.

In 1969, testimony presented to the Subcommittee on the Health of the Elderly before the United States Senate called attention to both long- and short-range problems in delivery of health care to the aged.

Among those reported were delays in obtaining reimbursements, reluctance of some physicians to assign their bills to Medicare, prevailing shortages in auxiliary health personnel, and need to expand Medicare to give more adequate coverage to such items as prescription drugs, dental and foot care, eyeglasses, hearing aids, medical appliances, and annual health checkups.

Delivery of health services to the elderly, according to reports of the Special Committee on Aging, is further complicated by undesirable practices in American society. Frequently the aged person is adversely affected by complex drugs purchased in combinations, some of which are ineffective and others actually harmful.

The older person, it was alleged, is often obliged to buy brand name drugs at varying prices even though the wholesale costs are identical. He is often induced to buy patent medicines because of exaggerated claims that they relieve pain. And he is frequently victimized by worthless potions and devices.

Attitudes and behavior of older persons often handicap the delivery of health services. Physicians commonly report that many aged persons put off obtaining medical assistance until their ailments have reached a very advanced stage.

Many older people need special assistance in overcoming their inadequate diets. Some aged persons, according to social service workers, do not eat properly because they cannot afford to do so.

Others, who may have sufficient incomes, do not eat well because they lack skill in selecting and preparing nourishing and well-balanced meals. Some lack the means of transportation in order to shop for foods. A number lack the facilities to cook, or have feelings of rejection and loneliness which destroy the motivation to prepare and eat a meal alone.

These economic, social, and psychological factors often result in patterns of living that cause malnutrition and physical and mental deterioration.

About a third of the aged in the United States live in rural environments—in small towns, in open country, and on farms. It is often alleged that older rural people have the advantages of unpolluted air, abundant sunshine, lack of congestion, the simplicity of life moving at a slower pace, and the emotional supports of close family and friends.

Studies have raised serious questions about these notions. On every measure of well-being, the rural aged appear to be disadvantaged more than the urban aged.

Reports indicate that older rural persons, in comparison with the urban aged, have poorer physical and mental health, smaller incomes, poorer diets, more deteriorated housing, have fewer opportunities for satisfactory social relationships, and score lower on scales measuring happiness and morale.

In addition, many older persons on farms experience isolation because of inadequate transportation and because large numbers of rural young people migrate to urban centers to find jobs.

A publication by the Administration on Aging reports special need in rural areas of the United States for developing imaginative programs to provide services for the rural elderly.

Important to such programs are the cooperative efforts of Federal and State agencies, private institutions, voluntary organizations, various business and civic groups, and the involvement of older persons themselves.

Considerable public interest has been expressed about the welfare of older persons in the United States during the next few decades. Examination of some social and economic trends in the United States permits both positive and negative predictions concerning the aged.

On the positive side are the probable increases in pension benefits to retirees, the rising educational level of each age group as it enters the old age category, and the improved health status and physical vigor of older persons.

On the other hand, there are trends in the United States not so salutary to the aged population. An economist reporting on the aged and public policy maintains that employment opportunities for the aged probably will be less satisfactory from 1970 to 2000 than in 1960. He says inflationary trends probably will continue to erode the purchasing power of older persons, whether these flow from pensions, government bonds, annuities, or other fixed sources.

There are well-publicized predictions about the increase in population density in the United States, the continued rapid rate of technological change, and the continued increases in the mobility of younger persons. They suggest a widening of the "generation gap" and the greater estrangement and alienation of older persons from close social relationships.

A study by the Duke University School of Medicine forecasts that society of the future, even more than that of the present, will be one of secular values—of declining care by family members for the elderly and of increasing public care for the aged.

In such a society, this report points out, older people probably will develop more social organizations to exert greater pressures for increased benefits and for improved opportunities in employment and in performing other useful roles.

Local Level Community Development

DONALD E. RUNYON and
DONALD L. NELSON

MEANINGFUL community development must begin on the local level, with local people at the helm. Who better than they know their own community, its needs, problems, resources, and potential?

Once a comprehensive plan is formulated, the local leaders should look for all the financial and technical help they can get from whatever sources. This includes State and Federal assistance.

Community development programs in Alabama and Texas are excellent examples of what local people can do with a little help. Perhaps you'll find some ideas from these examples on how to get a project "on the road" in your community.

The Four Winds Industrial Foundation, Inc., Quanah, Tex., tackled an enormous task and then reached out in all directions for help big enough to match its ideas. Representing a new concept in economic development, the foundation welded four counties into a team—counties which formerly had competed on every front.

Prospects seemed dim at the outset. The farm-oriented economy which supported their core communities had been depressed by mechanization, a drop in farm employment, the sale or loss of family-run farms. As trade decreased, more businesses closed their doors permanently—resulting in a weakening overall economy.

Economic stagnation was becoming a widespread problem in Childress, Foard, Hardeman, and Cottle Counties. Many rural north Texas communities faced a dim future. Ninety percent of area high school graduates moved away to find jobs elsewhere.

This depressed economy had to be revitalized if the steady outmigration of people to the cities was to be stopped and, if possible, reversed.

These goals could be accomplished only if the four counties joined in a unified regional development program. This effort would demand the support of all local governments, businesses, and people.

The base of the area economy had to be broadened by attracting new industries and payrolls, strengthening and expanding remaining small businesses, and arranging for location of government facilities in the area. Potentials for tourism and commercial recreational facilities had to be ex-

*

DONALD E. RUNYON is Chief, Current Information Branch in the Rural Electrification Administration.

DONALD L. NELSON is an information specialist with the Extension Service.

ploited. New methods for attracting income-making projects had to be created.

The Four Winds Industrial Foundation was organized to:

• Help develop and finance area businesses and industries;

• Speed up cooperation between public and private agencies;

• Involve the wholehearted commitment of area people at all levels.

Plans of the foundation included expansion of existing industry and obtaining new industry. Among the goals were reviewing land use, seeking an industrial water supply, surveying area recreational possibilities, and establishing financing sources—public and private. Other objectives included developing a regional information and marketing service system, expanding water and sewer systems, improving and broadening vocational training, providing facilities for higher education, and improving transportation facilities. Developing a program for repair and construction of housing was another target.

R. A. Yarbrough was elected executive director of the foundation. He is manager of the Gate City Electric Cooperative, a Rural Electrification Administration borrower, in Childress.

He is also field coordinator for the NorTex Regional Planning Commission; a member of the Reclamation, Conservation and Development Board; and serves on the Governor's Economy Task Force: "Goals for Texas."

The Gate City co-op encourages board and staff members to take active roles in local development programs. For example, O. T. Holmes, president of the co-op board of directors, works with soil conservationists and is active in building rural water systems.

The Foundation was chartered in 1967 as a nonprofit organization. It depends solely on donations from citizens and businesses within the four-county area for its support.

Programs of the Four Winds Industrial Foundation are directed and managed by a 16-member board of directors. Four directors are elected from each of the four counties.

The group conducted educational meetings in each of the area communities. Once they obtained temporary financing and informed the public of their aims and purposes, the Foundation reached out for the support of private industry and private groups. The West Texas Utilities Company, Lone Star Gas, Frisco Railroad, Southwestern Bell Telephone, the Burlington Railroad, local banks, and the West Texas Chamber of Commerce joined actively in the program.

The Foundation now reached out to State and national legislators for support. Further widening their aim, they obtained assistance from REA and other agencies of the Department of Agriculture, from the Department of Housing and Urban Development, and the Small Business Administration.

They made use of the Office of Economic Opportunity Job Corps training programs. They received the cooperation of the Texas Highway Department, the Greenbelt Water Authority, the Red River Authority, the Texas Water Quality Control Board, the Texas Employment Commission, and the Texas Pollution Control Board.

Washington-level coordination of the program is handled by the Community Development staff of REA. Technical assistance is provided on the spot by Extension Service and other USDA field personnel in the project areas.

The Foundation compiled and printed industrial data and statistics concerning the four-county region. These booklets are presented to industries and businesses interested in locating in north Texas.

Industrial parks on selected sites are in the works. The Foundation is working with the Farmers Home Administration on an adequate water supply for the region.

The foundation has attracted industries difficult to locate because of odors, such as tanneries, to take advantage of hides and byproducts from feedlots and packing houses. A project involving Federal funds and research is underway to eradicate the mesquite which infests the area.

The foundation has a forward-moving program with the Farmers Home Administration on promotion of housing projects for low-income families, for community buildings, and sewage plants.

Results of the combined efforts steadily and continually accrued as the Foundation entered the decade of the 1970's.

A large mobile home manufacturer opened a factory near Childress, employing more than 100 semi-skilled local workers. A water conservation program, the Thirsty Water System, is in operation. Other projects, the Readi-Rain Water System and the North Wichita River Water Association, have Farmers Home Administration approval and aid. Labor and health surveys have been conducted through the four counties.

The foundation is proceeding with its work with cooperation of the Texas Industrial Commission in contacting, informing, and attracting industry.

The St. Clair County, Ala., Resource Development Committee also took a look at its own community. Like the Four Winds Industrial Foundation, members saw many needs and problems. They also saw local resources and the potential for a better life for all county residents.

The group was wise enough to know they couldn't "go it alone." Besides a united community effort, St. Clair County would need outside help to revitalize the local economy and society.

The county was classified as "severely depressed" in 1960.

Springville was typical of the small communities in this north central Alabama county. It was increasingly difficult for Springville to provide services to its citizens. Nearby coal mines had been worked out and then abandoned. Farm income had dwindled.

Some townspeople commuted to nearby Birmingham to work. Many of the young people had moved away. Relief rolls were swelling.

The Resource Development Committee wanted adequate schools and educational programs, including training for unskilled and uneducated adults. Committee members also saw a need for better transportation and communication networks. Other priorities included safe water supplies and improved sewage and garbage disposal, additional power and fuel sources, housing improvement programs, and attractive recreation facilities. Perhaps most important were the goals of more jobs and convenient and modern health services.

None of these things was going to spring magically into being. Organization, effort, and assistance were needed.

St. Clair's resource development program got started when 75 county leaders, representing all interest groups, responded to the call of Probate Judge Hoyt B. Hamilton and County Extension Chairman H. L. Eubanks. Judge Hamilton, also chairman of the Court of County Commissioners, was named chairman of the RD Committee and Eubanks as executive secretary.

The committee has 117 members, each assigned to one of these subcommittees:

1. Agriculture and forestry, 2. commerce and industry, 3. public facilities and services, 4. tourism and recreation, 5. training and retraining.

These citizens represent more than 50 different organizations, communities, and other groups in St. Clair County.

An executive committee of 16 members serves as the catalyst for an active, on-going development program. The committee has as its mission community and rural development. It receives support from the Alabama-USDA Rural Development Council, and the Alabama Resource Development Committee. These organizations make it possible for a citizen group to get assistance from a number of Federal and State sources without having to contact individual government agencies. You might call it "one-stop shopping for assistance."

The committee first studied local problems, inventoried resources, set goals, and developed a plan of action. Specialists from State and Federal agencies and private organizations helped the committee put together an Overall Economic Development Program for St. Clair County. In all, the RD committee has drawn on the program resources of more than 20 Federal, State, and regional bodies to achieve its development goals.

At the time the fledgling county RD committee was testing its wings, the 822 residents of Springville were watching sticks and leaves blow about the doorways of abandoned store buildings. But that was before plastic pipe and lowboys.

Through efforts of the county RD committee, the Springville Development Corporation was formed. More than one in seven of the townspeople bought stock in the corporation. The community began to stir.

Employing realistic planning, the group used resources of the Small Business Administration, the Farmers Home Administration, the Economic Development Administration, Department of Housing and Urban Development, and other agencies.

Springville planned each step of its development in advance. Goals were: to have several small industries rather than a single dominant one; to diversify industries, avoiding peaks and valleys of employment; to provide jobs for women as well as men; to develop industrial sites prior to need; and to organize financing in all ways possible.

Springville's careful planning has paid off. In 1970, it could boast of new and expanded industries with combined payrolls of $4 million a year. The town is in the enviable

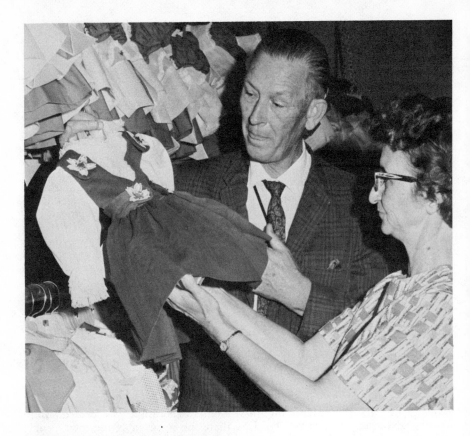

Community development pays off in St. Clair County, Ala.: Above, industry producing children's dresses has expanded. Left, new plant makes woven baskets.

position of being able to select from applicants wanting to locate in its industrial parks. The population has grown.

The industries turn out a variety of products. The two expanded industries produce book binders and covers and children's dresses. The new plants turn out metal cabinets; plumbing fixtures; trailers, including lowboys for transporting heavy equipment; woven baskets; lumber; and plastic products.

Of the National Cabinet Company's 141 employees, 67 percent were once on the county's relief rolls.

The Birmingham Manufacturing

204

Company's lowboys are used at Cape Kennedy to move rockets to launch pads. Springville's newest industry, American Plastics Corporation, makes plastic pipe, which is fast capturing a growing share of the construction market.

Under the leadership of Corporation President Archie Jones and Mayor Marcus Pearson, careful planning and hard work spurred the economic revitalization of Springville. Jones doubles as chairman of the county RD executive committee.

Springville is not alone in its efforts to create the "good life" for local citizens. All over the county—in towns like Pell City, Steele, Ashville, Ragland and the Odenville-Moody-White's Chapel-Margaret area, and in the open country as well—development projects are moving full steam ahead.

The St. Clair County Hospital, modern in every way, was built with the assistance of a Hill-Burton grant and a special county tax.

A county water system is planned. A Farmers Home Administration study laid the groundwork; the county water authority and State-Federal funds will carry it out.

On the "fun front," the St. Clair County Association for Tourism and Recreation (SCAT) has joined forces with a 17-county recreation and tourism development group.

Private interests are active, too. Many farmers have quit trying to eke a living out of the thin soil and are converting their farms to recreation uses. "Horse Pens 40" is the colorful name for a scenic area which attracts thousands to its weekend folk festivals and art shows. It is estimated that tourism has generated $18 million more business for the county as a result of the new 15,000-acre Logan Martin Lake on the Coosa River.

Improving services at the county airport is a Commissioners Court project.

In agriculture, money from the Farmers Market Authority and other sources helped to establish a new $200,000 tomato market on Chandler Mountain. About 75 farmers sell quality produce there.

Odenville walked off with top prize among six communities participating in a community improvement contest. The contest was sponsored by the county and State chambers of commerce, the Cooperative Extension Service of Auburn University, and Liberty National Life Insurance Company.

Projects underway include irrigation and drainage systems, assistance to meat and poultry processing plants, establishing of catfish processing and marketing facilities, a county fire control plan, public and private housing for low and medium income families, a new vocational-technical training high school, civic centers, and a county library building.

As Executive Secretary Eubanks of the RD Committee says, much has been done, but much needs doing. Schools, water, the job situation and many other things still have room for improvement.

For instance, 2,028 new jobs have been created. The combined county payroll has increased $27 million. Numerous projects for better living, working, and recreation conditions have been completed.

But plant modernization eliminated jobs in some industries. Continued outmigration from agriculture and mining has meant some other job losses. Total employment hasn't changed much. The county gained more than 1,000 people during the 1960's. Housing improvement, though accelerated, can't keep pace with the increasing demand.

Citizen involvement continues to be the keystone for success. Helping hands from those in government and private agencies sustain the effort.

The Four Winds and St. Clair development programs continue to be geared toward a better life for all people concerned. Where the need exists, and with a little help, any community can do the same.

Youths Pitch In for a Better America

DALLAS K. FERRY,

J. DAN LEHMANN, and

STEVE WETZEL

YOUNG PEOPLE in America do have something to say, and they are serious about it. They mean business. They are backing up their words with action.

Their voices ring out—hundreds of thousands strong:

"Learning to Do. Doing to Learn. Earning to Live. Living to Serve."

"Be Prepared." Yes. The Boy Scouts of America. Busy today learning how to live tomorrow.

These are the slogans of a few of the youth organizations in America which are dedicated to changing the face of America, through positive and constructive efforts.

The 4-H clubs, the Future Farmers of America, the Boy Scouts, Key Clubs International, and many other organizations, large and small, are meeting the challenge of today and of the future. Not by rioting, not by tearing down the establishment, not by protesting and demonstrating, but by working, by building on the foundations of our society, and by cooperation.

Our young people are vitally concerned with the complex problems associated with the Nation's growth —population, jobs, homes, pollution, recreation, and generally, improving the quality of living.

To get some idea of the strength and vigor directed to solving our problems, multiply 536,000 youths in high school vocational agriculture classes times 15 hours a day of youthful energy and love of life. It's a powerful force, and it's making itself known.

Young people know the gloomy picture too frequently painted of rural America. Families have been drawn to the urban areas leaving few behind to buy food, clothes, and services of rural businesses.

As demand for goods and services decreases, fewer people are required to supply them. The drain of economic life makes it more difficult to support and improve schools, churches, and housing. Pride for the community fades.

This economic whirlpool has left rural America with a third of the Nation's population but with half of the poor housing and more than half the poverty.

Two main tasks are required for rural development: 1. improving the quality of rural life by providing recreational programs and community facilities, community safety and health care, beautification and rehabilitation projects, and 2. expanding occupational opportunities to keep young and aggressive men and women in rural areas.

Rural youth can work in both these areas as individuals and as groups.

An individual must have personal initiative to make his community a better place to live and work in. It is not enough to beautify his own home and its surroundings; a young person must avoid littering or polluting the environment. And because economic vigor is important to a community, he should patronize local stores and shops when they offer goods and services at comparable prices. He must pass this interest and energy to his neighbors.

Naturally, some rural development

*

DALLAS K. FERRY is an Information Specialist, Farmers Home Administration.

J. DAN LEHMANN of Pleasant Plains, Ill., is 1971 National President, Future Farmers of America.

STEVE WETZEL of Pocatello, Idaho, was the 1970 National 4-H Club Reporter.

jobs are too large for individuals to handle and this is where the youth organizations come in. The Future Farmers of America (FFA), the youth action and leadership development arm of vocational agriculture, has originated a community development program called "Building Our American Communities," or "BOAC."

BOAC resulted from the cooperative efforts of the FFA and Vocational Agriculture, both a part of the Office of Education of the Department of Health, Education, and Welfare; the Farmers Home Administration of the U.S. Department of Agriculture; and the Lilly Endowment, Inc.

"Building Our American Communities" is a study action program. The vocational agriculture classroom is the study site and the community itself is the laboratory and workshop. A study guide prepared by the Farmers Home Administration helps the instructor teach community development. It only remains for each FFA chapter to discover community weaknesses and then to develop a positive program to overcome them.

Through BOAC, FFA members are helped to:

• Understand the dynamics of local community development.

• Analyze population problems, depletion of resources, economic stability, and environment conservation.

• Initiate constructive projects which use the fundamentals of community development.

• Inform the whole community of these efforts and obtain its support.

Efforts to improve the quality of rural living are underway in many communities and planned for others.

FFA's role in these endeavors are visible and tangible. But the task of expanding occupational opportunities will be more difficult for youth. Their greatest contribution may be to provide a highly trained, well-educated corps of workers who can attract industry and business to rural areas.

Training and education of rural youths is available through vocational agriculture in the public schools.

Farming, agriculture, and related fields are taught to help prepare rural young people for occupations including agriculture supply and services; agriculture mechanics; forestry; ornamental horticulture; air, water, and land management; and safety.

The Future Farmers of America is an integral part of the instructional program, and helps to develop well-rounded persons with experience in leadership, citizenship development, and cooperation with others.

The goal of Vo-Ag and FFA working together is to train productive, concerned, and involved rural Americans. Building rural America provides great challenge as well as opportunity for the imaginative minds of our young people.

Another nationwide youth organization also is involved in the constructive job of helping communities—the 4-H clubs. Improving the quality of life is the objective of each and every Head-Heart-Hands-Health member. Nearly 2.4 million 9- to 19-year-olds belong to about 92,500 clubs coast to coast.

The Cooperative Extension Service—which conducts the 4-H program—helps another million young people in schools, other youth-serving agencies, and elsewhere "learn by doing," and about half a million boys and girls are enrolled in 4-H by television.

In answering the call to be involved, 4-H'ers everywhere have developed programs to fight pollution, erosion, and whatever else degrades the environment. In 1970, 4-H'ers in every State—and nearly every county in the United States—have had projects to help preserve and improve the quality of life.

The 4-H motto "To Make the Best Better" has always served to challenge members to conserve and develop further the natural resources of our country.

The challenge in the future is greater and emphasis, methods, and techniques must be different. 4-H programs vary in different States and communities, depending upon the

FFA chapter at Northfield, Minn., collected and sold donated corn to send handicapped children to Camp Courage. Below, counselor giving camper a lift, and two busy cooks. Left, boy camper takes speech therapy.

need, but the goals are all the same: better communities to live in.

Some of the programs operate on a massive scale, as in Clinton County, Mich. In Operation Clean-up, 425 youths and adults gathered some 65 truckloads of trash from 200 miles of roadsides.

In a smaller but very significant activity, Massachusetts 4-H'ers demonstrated their concern for senior citizens by landscaping a recently constructed nursing home. Teenagers helping octogenarians—and not a generation gap to be seen!

In the far west, Community Pride, a program sponsored by Standard Oil Company of California, provides encouragement and recognition for groups which make constructive contributions to their communities. Through PRIDE, 4-H members Plan, Renew, Improve, Develop, and Enrich their communities to help make them better places to live.

Young 4-H'ers are also active in preserving another resource of America—our youth. A young woman 4-H'er from Indiana worked with 12 mentally retarded children to give

them meaning and purpose in their lives.

In Idaho the 4-H Booster Club conducted a "Special Camp for Special People." The camp provided a weeklong treat for kids from low-income families. It enabled them to share in something others take for granted.

What is the aim of 4-H activities? It is community harmony, fighting pollution, protecting the quality of life, helping others, and learning to get along with people. It is learning about community problems and how to solve them.

A powerful force for good in this country for 60 years, the Boy Scouts have been an important part of American life because they have remained relevant. In Scouting, young people contribute to our nation's future by developing leadership and good citizenship qualities through constructive projects.

Scouts across the Nation also are becoming involved in conservation projects. The purpose is to help Scouts realize the importance of natural resources to the future of our country. They will be involved in environmental protection projects of nearly every description.

The Scouts' primary goal is to produce men with leadership ability, so it was almost inevitable that they should combat the greatest threat to a man's potential—drugs.

The Boy Scouts of America decided to find out why young people turn to drugs. After a year of careful study they found that young people who become involved with drugs feel a lack of underlying things which other people think they have.

These fundamental things are:

—Good friends who care about them.

—Warm and open relations with their parents.

—Being a part of something larger than oneself.

—Genuine "highs" in their lives which make artificial "highs" unnecessary.

"Operation Reach," a program undertaken on a limited basis in four pilot areas, will focus on these underlying factors with the view that drug abuse is symptomatic. Scouts will be challenged to reach for these things and engage other young people in the same effort. Results of the new program will be carefully monitored and evaluated before a national project is set up.

The Nation's young people, with confidence, spirit, and energy, are searching for answers to the problems of tomorrow that they will share with each other.

Key Clubs International is another youth organization involved in constructively improving local communities. From Florida to the Yukon, Key Clubs are bringing about change through positive means.

Community development went international when the Monrovia (Calif.) Key Club traveled to San Vicente, Mexico. There they put on a roof, installed gas fixtures and drains for sinks, and painted an agricultural training school for the Mexican people.

Up in Maine, skiers mean money. A local ski resort faced closing because of dangerous runs and outdated facilities. The Maine Central Key Club worked more than 1,400 hours painting, cutting new trails and slopes, and installing a new lift. The resort is now operating and provides winter recreation and income for the local economy.

In Columbia, Mo., the Hickman Key Club showed its concern about the community's disadvantaged citizens. The Club restored and painted an old building to house a disadvantaged family.

A newer addition to the organized groups of young people is the "Teen Corps." Robert Benedict of Bloomington, Minn., was deeply moved and concerned over the poverty and despair he saw on a trip to Appalachia. He and his friends organized the Teen Corps to help the people of that depressed area.

The Teen Corps, with picks, shovels and bare hands, persisted in road building until embarrassed county officials sent bulldozers to finish the 6 miles of road that provided access to distant jobs and schools for 1,500 Kentuckians living along its path.

Outmigration of educated people and knowledgeable leadership has cost rural America clearly in potential growth. In Appalachia more than 70 percent of new teachers leave within 4 years. To build new citizenship, to involve young people, and to create opportunities, a new Youth Leadership Development program has been established by the Appalachian Regional Commission.

There are three basic features in the plan.

First, County Youth Development Councils—made up of young people interested in responsible community development—were organized. Their purpose is to coordinate and support youth programs and provide an organized voice for the young, including dropouts and low-income youth.

Second, Youth Involvement Seminars are developed to supply information about the needs and problems of community development. In these seminars, participants learn about local resources and community needs, and how they can be brought together. They also learn to be involved with the community development process.

Third, an Intern Apprentice program lets the leadership trainees work with community leaders to practice what they have learned in the Councils and Seminars.

America has always belonged to the young. Young people founded it, they nurtured it, sustained it, and developed it. They are still working today to make our great nation even greater.

They work as individuals, each doing what he can. And when it's a job that's too big for one person, they join forces. It may be a local club with a dozen members, or an inter-national organization with hundreds of thousands of members. Whatever it takes—one person, one group, or one Nation—whatever, the youth of America is ready to give.

Energy Sources for the Future

DONALD E. RUNYON

DICTIONARIES define energy as the capacity for doing work—and work is defined as the expenditure of energy. Which means that the energy we've expended right here thus far has brought us around in a neat little circle.

Energy sources range from muscles used in brushing teeth, digging in the earth with a trowel, or writing with a pencil, to an avalanche, the sun, a tidal wave, a space ship's rocket thrust.

In every kind of work, some sort of energy transformation has taken place, and man is not always aware of it. For example, energy given off in radioactive elements (like radium and uranium) took place for millions of years outside the span of man's knowledge. Powerful surges of energy sweep through the outer galaxies, as yet beyond man's understanding.

As Einstein predicted in 1916, magnetic fields are wave phenomena (with crests 100 miles apart), much like light and electricity.

The Milky Way, with its 100 billion stars acting as molecules, may form a lens which focuses magnetic energy from an unknown source "out there." There are no instruments yet to detect the source of these pulsations, nor is there any statement of the theoretical basis for them.

Many of the forms of energy that man uses today were virtually unknown 150 years ago. They were not "invented"; they were discovered. These discoveries were the result of a heightened awareness on the part of a few gifted men, aided by increasingly sensitive instruments which revealed to them changes previously unnoticed. Only recently in man's history have such forms of energy as cosmic rays, television waves, and x-rays been detected by man.

Elting E. Morison wrote in *Men, Machines and Modern Times* (1966): "All earlier history had been determined by the fact that the capacity of man had always been limited to his own strength and that of the men and animals he could control. But, beginning with the nineteenth century, the situation had changed. His capacity is no longer so limited; man has now learned to manufacture power and with the manufacture of power a new epoch began."

Or to quote from an Atlantic Refining Company brochure, "A century after Colonel Drake's invention of the first successful oil well, only one percent of America's physical work is done by man himself. The rest is done by machines."

With the transformation of "energy" into "work" for man, his rapid advances began in all the sciences.

But even with our advances we have only begun to tap the unlimited resources available to us. The sun, the winds, the tides—we do not yet use them to any great degree or try to harness their awesome power.

The most enormous source of energy of all is the sun. Solar energy has been streaming in upon the earth since the birth of the planet. Sunlight provides in the United States every two days enough energy to outlast all our known remaining fossil-fuel reserves.

*

DONALD E. RUNYON is Chief, Current Information Branch, with the Rural Electrification Administration.

Perhaps this energy could be transformed to electricity on a commercial scale if the techniques for doing it were known.

Geothermal power is being tried as an electric energy source in northern California. Geothermal power (heat from within the earth) is formed by steam spewed from within the earth's 20-mile-thick outer crust. By drilling through this crust, man is able to release steam from seepage water heated over molten rocks to 2000° Fahrenheit.

The wind was among the first of the nonbiological sources of energy to be used by man. It drove his ships and windmills, lifted his water, ground his grain, aired his mines.

Harnessing the wind provides a source of energy which is free. It exhausts no natural resources, and it produces no pollution. As long as the earth turns, it will be available.

Ocean tides may serve as important sources of electrical energy. They are another inexhaustible natural resource waiting to be harnessed. They are predictable and produce no pollution. But cost and efficiency must wait on technological advances.

Nuclear energy is another source of power. Even though its use has been slowed by man's fears, most of the electric generating plants planned are nuclear.

We live in an energy-oriented society. We don't hesitate to use it abundantly. Many forms of energy, like electricity, have been controlled, at least partially, for the uses of man.

We accept lighting, heating, cooling, and even entertainment at the touch of a switch. In fact, adequate and dependable supplies of energy are demanded, and expected, for all kinds of uses in all kinds of places.

Overall energy demand in the United States grew at an annual rate of 2¾ percent from the end of World War II until 1964. Since then it has averaged nearly 5 percent annually.

Use of electricity alone has been growing at a rate of 7 percent per

211

year with a rising trend to 9 percent annually in 1968 and 1969. This kind of growth can be better understood in terms of the estimated need for 250 new electric power plants of 1 million to 4 million kilowatt capacity by 1990.

Generating and transmitting this additional power raises important considerations. The environment rates high among them.

While incredible amounts of power must be produced, there is a need at the same time for a rational environmental protection approach to every development. For example, at the beginning of the 1970's, 3,600 electric utilities in the United States operated more than 300,000 miles of overhead electric transmission lines, pre-empting nearly 4 million acres of right-of-way.

We see, therefore, that the very look of the landscape becomes a serious consideration. The seriousness will increase in proportion to power demands in the years ahead. And it is estimated that during each of the remaining decades in this century 100,000 miles of new transmission lines will be built upon 1½ million acres of right-of-way.

To 20 million Americans the rural electric cooperative is the source of the power they need on their farms, in their rural homes and businesses. In fiscal year 1969, the cooperatives used 68.7 billion kilowatthours of electric energy to supply the demands of the rural people they serve. By the year 2000, the demand is expected to exceed 470 billion kilowatthours.

This is only a part of the total. Total electric energy production by the utility industry in the United States in 1969 exceeded 1.6 trillion kilowatthours.

Many other forms of energy, especially heat, are used in numerous industrial processes. Transportation of people and movement of material on land, and in the air, eat up enormous amounts of energy, most of it applied from internal combustion engines without conversion to electricity.

Consumption of natural gas in the United States in 1969 was reported by the Independent Natural Gas Association at 20 trillion cubic feet. This is estimated to grow to 40.1 trillion cubic feet by 1989.

The National Coal Association reported 507,275,000 tons of coal used in our Nation during 1969. The Bureau of Mines estimates 737 million tons of coal will be required for 1980.

The National Oil Fuel Institute estimates all petroleum used in the United States during 1970 at 14.8 million barrels a day. By 1980, estimates call for from 21 to 22 million barrels a day.

Thus the urgency for research toward new or better ways of using existing energy supplies. Examples of this are projects of the Basin Electric Power Cooperative, United Power Association, and Minnkota Power Cooperative. During the late 1960's, these electric cooperatives, with financing from the Rural Electrification Administration, built large generating units in the lignite coal fields of North Dakota.

The units are three times as large as any previously designed to burn this low-grade coal.

Boldness of the concept involved in installing the units has paid off for rural users since the plants are among the lowest cost producers of electric power in the country.

In fact, in 1968 the Basin plant achieved the lowest total unit production cost of any generating plant in the United States. And fueling the plants has given new vitality to an otherwise decaying local mining industry.

As a result of existence of these plants, problems inherent in burning lignite in large units have been subject to study on a scale never before possible. Major problems have been solved. Many other problems as yet unsolved are becoming more clearly understood.

Production of energy is almost

212

Wires strung through air detract from neighborhood appearance. Utilities financed by Rural Electrification Administration advocate putting wires underground. Surroundings look better, there is less chance for service outages due to storms, and property values are enhanced.

always accompanied by residue, waste, or refuse which can result in pollution. The extent this continues depends on the degree to which we exert our capabilities for doing something about it, while at the same time providing the additional energy we must have.

We are capable of neutralizing, changing, recovering, converting, and using wastes which now pile up and cause us the anguish of increasing pollution. We need only to direct our intellects and our energies toward solving these problems. This effort simply must become a priority—in money and in direction.

But solutions should not be pursued from a rigid utopian-like point of view. There is no such place as utopia—that's what the Greek stem word means, "no such place."

Even though man may never be able to achieve the imaginary perfection of a utopian state, he can strive toward reason in the ecology control and power supply confrontations. The simple truth remains—to live, to grow, even to die—are in themselves pollutants.

Human needs cannot and will not be denied. But they do not have to be filled with disregard for environmental effects. Therefore, careful planning and coordinated regulation are essential if our Nation's present and future energy requirements are to be met while at the same time achieving a clean, healthy environment. We must find the best means acceptable, in line with reasonable cost, for accomplishing these goals.

Perhaps a model utility environment protection act is an answer. A single agency might be charged with full responsibility for coordinating the location of new electric generating plants and gas and electric transmission lines and their construction and operation.

213

Insatiable demands of the American people for energy in all forms to support an ever-increasing effortless living situation, combined with an extraordinary growth in population, resulted in the energy crisis which achieved national attention in 1970. The problems of developing present and future energy sources, coupled with the questions of suitable environmental control of energy production and application, present exciting challenges.

We are finally waking to the fact that the primary energy sources upon which we have been drawing so heavily in the past 30 years—oil, natural gas, and high quality coal—are in limited supply.

Many gasoline companies by mid-1970 were reminding their customers: "The United States is using oil at an increasingly rapid rate. In the next 10 years, we are expected to consume almost as much oil as has been produced in the United States in the past 100 years."

A conference was sponsored in the summer of 1970 by the International Atomic Energy Commission, at the invitation of Dr. Glenn T. Seaborg, chairman of the U.S. Atomic Energy Commission (AEC). It reported that by the year 2000 the world would be getting about half its electricity from nuclear power plants, including "breeder" types. The AEC defines a "breeder" as a type of reactor with the potential for producing more nuclear fuel than it consumes.

At the National Press Club in Washington, D.C., on August 10, 1970, the Chairman of the Federal Power Commission, John N. Nassikas, discussed "The National Energy Crisis." He said:

"Currently 21 percent of our energy requirements are supplied by coal; 43 percent by crude oil, its products, and natural gas liquids; and one-third by natural gas. The remainder is divided between electricity developed from hydro and nuclear resources.

"Over the next decade the principal reliance of the electric industry for its base load generation will be fossil fuels, with nuclear generation becoming increasingly important in 1980–1990."

A solution to the problem of critical energy sources and supply will require changes in a number of crucial areas. For instance:

• We must find ways to guide material growth and energy consumption, making them compatible with the preservation of environmental values and simultaneously improving the quality of living in America.

• We must develop new ways to facilitate the day-to-day decisions of individuals, industry and government concerning the development of energy sources, facilities and locations.

• We must decide where and in what direction our efforts and our money can best be used to accelerate basic research on energy production in relation to environmental values in the 1970's and beyond.

These issues involve every American. They should stimulate our thoughts and concerns.

Buckminster Fuller wrote in *The World Game:* "I find man utterly unaware of what his wealth is, or his fundamental capability is. He says time and again, 'We can't afford it.' For instance, we are saying that we can't afford to do anything about pollution, but after the costs of not doing something about pollution have multiplied many fold beyond what it would cost to correct it now, we will spend many fold what it would cost us now to correct it."

The best hope for the future lies in new technology in the fields of energy sources and applications. Vastly expanded efforts sponsored by both government and private enterprise will be required to produce commercially applicable techniques to develop these energy sources and applications.

Numerous research and development projects are being pursued, among them the development of new automobile power systems, solar power, geothermal resources, new systems to transport oil and gas from the Arctic, oil shale recovery, and new power plant siting concepts.

The most promising and pressing fields for research and development are:

—Development and application of the nuclear breeder. The United States and other nations are currently supporting large efforts on the liquid metal fast breeder, but much additional work remains before the system is commercial. The molten salt and fast gas concepts offer alternative approaches should it become desirable or necessary to expand the program.

—Development of a low-cost underground high-voltage transmission technology. Recent work on electric facility location problems showed that getting electricity to the customer frequently raises as many environmental problems as generating it. Underground transmission offers a means of reducing the land required and eliminating much of the opposition if technical and economic problems can be overcome.

—Development of the fuel cell as a source of low pollution energy. The potential efficiency of fuel cells at low unit sizes offers real advantages in certain locations because of their portability and light weight. They have no moving parts and produce low-voltage electricity from chemical reactions similar to a battery.

—Development of better cooling towers and other methods for disposing of waste heat. Dry cooling seems to pose the fewest environmental problems, so it deserves particular attention.

—Research and development on thermonuclear fusion. Although there are many scientific problems still to overcome and a long period of engineering development ahead, fusion seems particularly attractive because of fuel availability and environmental compatibility.

The imagination and ingenuity of a Jules Verne, combined with the practical, persevering genius of a Thomas A. Edison, may be required to resolve the energy dilemma of the future. Such imagination, ingenuity, practicality, perseverance, genius are at hand today.

Satisfactory means and methods to produce and apply energy for all reasonable purposes are achievable in the next few decades. We in America can have the best of all possible quality of living without destroying ourselves or the environment which sustains us. We looked at the moon and went there. We certainly should be capable of maintaining ourselves happily on earth.

Communication, Bridge to a Better World

GORDON WEBB

WE HAVE the knowledge and the resources to make ours the best of worlds. The bridge between knowing and achieving is communication, which motivates as well as enables.

This is no new role for communication, nor for the communicator. From folk tale to satellite, civilization moves forward on the creation, storage, dissemination, and practical use of knowledge.

Today's flow of knowledge from basic and applied research shocks this layman's imagination. Even more amazing are the means for electronic storage, retrieval, review, and analysis of new information as well as the old.

"One commercial integrated circuit computer can execute 12 million instructions per second... experts predict that by the early 1970's the memory (of computers) will hold 4 billion characters, and external storage as many as 3 billion."

So wrote Thomas L. Whisler of the University of Chicago in his book, "Information Technology and Organizational Change."

Even obscurely reported research can come to light when the computer is put to work; witness a 1970 press report of efforts to find ways to reduce or eliminate mercury contamination of the environment. A computer search "of all data published about mercury compounds," according to the news report, "discovered" the work of Japanese scientists. They had reported in an "obscure journal" the ability of a strain of bacteria to thrive on mercury compounds, then to release the mercury in a volatile form in which the gas could be trapped in a filter.

Television cameras and satellites bring to our homes "live" the *moment's* great events of history, sports, and entertainment from around the world, or from the moon.

With instant replay, we can decide for ourselves whether the referee's call of "pass interference" against our team was correct. We're not likely to change the referee's decision.

Television, which brought the Vietnamese war into our homes daily, undoubtedly did influence public opinion regarding Southeast Asia.

Whether our field of interest is improved agriculture, better nutrition, breaking the poverty cycle, population growth and distribution, or education in the arts and sciences, the new electronic technology is the communicator's tool. And knowledge, however old or new, remains the lode he mines and refines.

But communication that motivates

*

GORDON WEBB retired in 1970 as Deputy Director of Information, U.S. Department of Agriculture.

216

depends on much more than the mere availability of useful and needed information and on faster, or even better means, of disseminating it.

"Few of us believe," wrote Whisler, "that man will ever devise machines or systems that will take over the function of creation and invention. In all our theories and philosophies of social development we see the need for the maverick—the innovator in the organization, the unconventional politician, the controversial writer, the entrepreneur."

The innovator has his role in communications.

Indeed, imagination, creativity, and innovation have been hallmarks of communications work by the land-grant university–U.S. Department of Agriculture team.

Consider radio and television.

Two land-grant universities, Nebraska and Arkansas, were among the first four American institutions of higher learning to start radio communication work prior to 1900. At Nebraska, experimentation with radio started soon after the first Marconi announcements in 1895. By 1916 the university was sending out, using a spark transmitter, regular reports on markets and the weather and road conditions.

One of the early problems, Robert A. Jarnagin of North Dakota State University noted without specifying institution or individual, was "the refusal on the part of many professors to speak over the radio because they thought it was 'undignified.' "

Farm and home communicators also were quick to put to work the new and vital dimensions of television.

Cornell University's first TV program was over a commercial station at Schenectady in 1946. The first TV station owned by an educational institution was WOI at Iowa State University. Broadcasting from Ames began in February 1950. The FCC permit was for a commercial station; noncommercial licenses were not being issued then.

But ingenuity and creativity were

by no means limited to the broadcast media; they encompassed press, publications, visuals (for example, the pioneering work of the Motion Picture Service in USDA's Office of Information), and every other medium and method of conveying ideas.

Many large, commercial farmers and livestock producers go directly to agri-business sources with their production and marketing problems. These sources include farm supply and marketing industries, and perhaps a marketing cooperative.

A great number of farmers are regular clients of the county agricultural agents and other agricultural specialists, including those in agricultural foundations. They attend experiment station field days. They also may go to the stations at almost any time of year to look at experimental plots, check on livestock research, or seek a solution to a new problem. They know and use the services of their State Departments of Agriculture and USDA.

Most farmers keep abreast with farm and other developments through the mass media—the newspaper farm pages, the farm magazines, radio market news broadcasts, and television farm programs. They have the information services of their general farm organizations, their commodity and breed associations, and their cooperatives.

Commercial farmers also have a good idea of their research needs, and they are articulate in expressing them, both individually and through their organizations.

Increasing and maintaining farm income will continue to be a matter of importance in agriculture. Research findings that increase farm income—by reduced unit costs, quality control, lower marketing charges, or by whatever means—will hold top interest among farmers and, therefore, the careful attention of communicators.

Aside from income problems related to supply and demand, to the cost-price squeeze, and to public support for adequate farm programs, farmers and livestock producers-feeders find themselves in a new ballgame called environmental protection.

For decades, farmers and ranchers have been outstanding conservationists of soil, water, forests, and wildlife. They were protectors of the environment long before environmental protection became household words. Now, some of the more effective chemicals for increasing production and reducing farm costs are under attack. A few pesticides have been restricted in use or banned. Others may also be restricted or banned.

Until research comes through with equally effective alternate means of pest control (and I am confident it will do so), farm costs stand to rise by tens of millions of dollars annually. Pollution control may and likely will increase operating costs of some feedlots and some plants processing agricultural products. Less well understood, at least by the general public, is the probability of higher food costs to the consumer.

Few issues have gripped public attention more tightly than that of environmental protection. It is an emotion-packed area requiring the best communication we're capable of providing, not only to the farmer, the rancher, the feeder, and the woodland owner, but also to an equally concerned general public.

The best communication of the future will continue to be the "packaged" combination which involves balanced use of all media and methods. We gain information from many sources, and may not recall which source finally motivated us to action. Hence, no single means of communication is likely to be as effective as the planned, simultaneous use of all media and methods.

The information "package" will have many segments—oral, visual, and written, for example. Each segment should seek to gain to the extent possible the advantages of man's oldest and most effective means of communication—person-to-person, face-to-face exchange. We are influenced by many

217

Above, *peach shipment marketing research is subject of videotape for TV. Below left, dairy specialist studies computer printout. Below right, closed circuit TV carries figures from electronic price board at Chicago Board of Trade, as part of a grain futures brokerage service for farmers.*

different stimuli. All the senses and emotions are involved in communication. For those reasons, communication is more productive when carried out where the new information or new methods are needed—in the pasture, the feedlot, the field, the woodlot, the home.

Even the best-written, best-illustrated, and most creatively designed publication will never equal person-to-person exchange. As part of a package, however, it will reinforce other elements of the total information effort; and, depending on the reader's prior knowledge of the subject, it could well provide all the additional facts needed for decision and action.

Person-to-person communication is a key factor in making U.S. agriculture the most productive in the world. It is largely responsible for outstanding youth training through 4-H Clubs and the Future Farmers and Homemakers

218

of America, and for the "extra lifting power" of supervised credit from the Farmers Home Administration.

Soil and water conservation progress leaped forward after the Soil Conservation Service was created to offer on-the-ground help to landowners specifically for making and carrying out individual conservation programs.

The newer but already successful Expanded Food and Nutrition Education Program of the Cooperative Extension Service is proving anew the value of in-the-home communication. In this program, nutrition aides—recruited from low income communities —are trained to work directly with homemakers and youth to improve the nutrition and health of the needy.

The telephone and the broadcast media seem to offer the best hope of mass communications while retaining much of the personal touch and the stimuli of give-and-take discussion between specialist and producer, homemaker, or club member. Use of these media will continue to be important parts of the comprehensive information package.

For years, the telephone has been a vital extension of the voice. On the farm, it is both a business instrument and a form of social activity. In 1970, the Rural Electrification Administration estimated, 82 percent of the Nation's farms had telephone service. REA itself had helped commercial companies and cooperatives to finance telephone facilities serving nearly 2.5 million rural subscribers.

With the upgrading of telephone equipment, the "party line" largely faded into history.

But the University of Wisconsin Extension Service has given the "party line" new life and a new turn.

Through use of the University Extension's Educational Telephone Network, specialists in their offices in Madison can meet with farmers in locations throughout the State. Each installation out in the State has a telephone with an amplifier-speaker which allows a roomful of people to hear the telephone transmission. At any time, a listener at a receiving point can speak into the system, with his voice heard throughout the network.

Conference use of the telephone is made more effective because it is part of a larger communication package which includes visuals and publications. They are made available at each conference location well ahead of the telephone "party line" meeting.

Two-way radio, often teamed with the telephone, increasingly is providing person-to-person contact among Extension county agents, the people they serve, and area and State specialists.

In the tradition of its early pioneering with radio, the University of Nebraska is establishing a statewide, two-way radio communication system for agricultural extension work.

The Nebraska system, first of its type in the Nation, was started in 1967, and uses master microwave towers of the State's emergency communications network.

By mid-1970, all or a portion of 50 of Nebraska's 93 counties had radio communications network availability; but, for lack of funds, the system had not then been implemented in a majority of the counties. However, the system had been expanded to include base radio stations or control links in five agricultural departments and the Extension administration headquarters at the College of Agriculture and Home Economics in Lincoln.

Five mobile radio units were located at the university campus, and the radio network had been connected to the university telephone switchboard for radio-to-telephone as well as radio-to-radio communication.

In an evaluation of the network's operation in the 12-county pilot area, Donald W. Swoboda of Nebraska's Cooperative Extension Service noted:

"County staff mentioned two unique features: 1. the ability to get immediate answers from area staff, even when area staff were in their autos, and 2. the ability to bring a specialist into a conversation with a client in the agent's office.

"In addition, the ready access of

the system and the 'party line' feature that allowed multiparty conferences for program planning were important time-savers."

Extension Director John L. Adams, who conceived the radio network idea, reported in late 1970 that two additional transmitters had been financed. "These two transmitters," Adams said, "will effectively double the area covered by two-way radio in Nebraska and will service a large, very sparsely settled area where communication by more conventional means is particularly a problem."

Cable antenna television (CATV) systems are opening a completely new door to communicators.

At the beginning of 1970, Broadcasting magazine estimated that 2,385 cable systems were in operation, serving 4.5 million people. The Federal Communications Commission ordered, effective in January 1971, that CATV systems with 3,500 or more subscribers originate their own programs. The FCC directive, I believe, will increase very greatly the use of public service material on CATV.

Many agricultural and home economics communicators already are taking advantage of this additional in-the-home outlet.

J. Cordell Hatch of Pennsylvania State University has reported that home economists in Montour, Northumberland, Snyder, and Union Counties in January 1970 started a weekly series, "The Open Door," on the Shamokin, Pa., CATV system. The 10-minute programs, at 5:20 p.m. each Thursday, were oriented to low-income families. In June of 1970 the same counties started a weekly program on the Mount Carmel system and had plans for another over the Danville system.

Although farm programs sponsored by advertising have never survived for long on TV networks, local commercial television stations have been generous in public service and sponsored news time made available to farm and home communicators.

An excellent example is the long-standing cooperation from NBC's WRC-TV in Washington, D.C., which telecasts "Across the Fence," produced in the station's studios by USDA's Office of Information. This weekly, 30-minute program is videotaped and, at the beginning of 1971, was being seen on 111 different stations throughout the country.

In addition the networks provide occasional public service time for "spot" announcements, such as the excellent and timely filmed "spots" produced by the Office of Information to emphasize safety with pesticides.

The more ambitious uses of educational television (ETV) and telephone include the "electronic teach-ins" produced with great imagination by the University of Vermont Extension Service.

Facilities of Vermont Educational Television were combined with a special telephone hookup to offer programs on subjects as diverse as winter feeding of dairy cattle, taxes, and nutrition.

The dairy cattle feeding program was a live, 60-minute presentation from the ETV studio. At 16 simultaneous county meetings, held in schools, 265 farmers viewed the program on the schools' sets and, by telephone, asked questions of the panel in the ETV studio. An undetermined number of other farmers saw the program in their homes.

The program itself was part of a larger package. This included publication of a special winter feeding issue of Green Mountain Dairying summarizing information presented by the ETV panel and answering questions the dairymen had asked. The publication went to 7,000 dairymen.

Tom McCormick, Vermont's Associate Extension Editor, was asked to evaluate the "electronic teach-ins."

"I would say," McCormick replied, "the jury is still out. A new program goes pretty well with extensive promotion. But part of this is due to novelty and possibly loyalty to the agent by his farmers. After that, a program is on its own.

"We're finding it increasingly difficult to get people out for meetings. We would assume that this would happen with TV submeetings if we put on very many.

"This seems to say that the future is in the home."

Karin Kristiansson, producer of the teach-ins, also emphasized the home.

"Electronic teach-in via television seems to be most effective if you do extensive promotion and encourage people to view at home," she said.

Perhaps one of the more effective efforts dealt with nutrition. Home visits and special packets of literature added impact. Nutrition aides, trained in advance, visited homes before and after the telecast.

If asked for a definitive statement of the future in electronic communications, I would repeat Tom McCormick's words: "The jury is still out." Undoubtedly the opportunities are great—almost unlimited. Surely, farm and home communicators will find even better ways to use them.

In the meantime, let's overlook none of the opportunities of other mass media and methods. Mrs. Sally Ebling didn't. As a County Extension agent in home economics at Cleveland, Ohio, Mrs. Ebling developed a six-lesson home study course and offered it via a metropolitan newspaper.

More than 3,200 Cleveland homemakers enrolled and completed Mrs. Ebling's course on food buying and meal management.

Mrs. Ebling next turned to television. Working with the Extension specialists at Ohio State University, she created a 26-part television series on family living.

The half-hour programs were supplemented with small group meetings of leaders, who, in turn, taught local groups of young homemakers with preschool children.

For using mass media communications uniquely to bridge the gap to better living, Mrs. Ebling earned the USDA's Superior Service Award.

There are untold other gaps to bridge, and plaudits to be earned.

Our Fragmented Transportation

DAVID C. NELSON

TRANSPORTATION plays a big part in our daily lives. It can provide us with the opportunity to live, work, and play as we wish. To the extent that reduction in the time and cost of overcoming space is important, transportation becomes very significant indeed.

Society is beset and concerned with a battery of problems of unprecedented magnitude and complexity. As these growing problems should remind us, a maturing economy demands more complex and better services from the many parts of the system. The parts which attempt to bring more and better services to producers and consumers are both public and private.

On the one hand, society, through its government sector, attempts to provide a bundle of services for which there is a direct need. Such things as national defense, education, housing, police protection, health, recreation, and communication are part of this bundle of services which are tied together by the transportation system and made available to large numbers of people.

On the other hand, society through its business sector attempts to provide producers with the material necessary to produce goods and services for consumption. Again, the transportation system makes the raw materials and the goods and services available to producers and consumers by establishing a network which is traversed by autos, trucks, buses, railroads, airplanes, barges, steamships, etc.

*

DAVID C. NELSON is Director, Upper Great Plains Transportation Institute, and Associate Professor of Agricultural Economics, North Dakota State University, Fargo.

221

Obviously, the ability of a political economy (government)-business partnership to deliver a high level of living to all of its people is highly dependent upon a good transportation system. Whether or not it is or will be a good or poor system is pretty much left to the private business sector.

It is true, of course, that there are many kinds and amounts of subsidies to each of the modes of transportation. However, the primary sources of these funds—user taxes paid on gasoline used by auto owners, for example—go into the national highway trust fund which in turn is used to build highways. Thus they can't really be considered true subsidies.

But even with user subsidies, the private business sector makes the final decision to provide or not to provide transportation services. Owners of trucks are not obligated to go into the commercial transport business and within limitations the service provided can be as good or as poor as the owner wishes it to be.

Putting it another way, transportation services will only exist in the United States when there is sufficient need for the services. If California oranges are needed in North Dakota, a way will be found to deliver them there at a final price North Dakota consumers are willing to pay. On the other hand, there is no need for California-grown durum in North Dakota and no one is concerned about transporting it there.

The demand for transportation, therefore, is *derived from* the demand for the goods and services producers and consumers use. In other words, goods and services have value only if they can be moved or made available to those places where people wish to consume them.

This also means that the transportation system can play an important role in creating demand for a good or service. This is particularly true where the good or product involved is low in value per unit (as with most agricultural products) and producers are located great distances from potential consumers.

If the product is low in value and has to be hauled long distances, transportation costs will be a high proportion of the final value. Any downward adjustment in transportation costs then has the effect of making it easier for distant users of the good or service to acquire it.

To the extent that it becomes a lower cost than some previously used product or service, a new demand is created for that product or service and producers are called upon to expand production of the product or provide more services. For example, if the freight rates on bricks were low

Copter leased by Illinois Department of Agriculture flies grain inspectors to barges moving down the Mississippi, so they can get grain samples for grading without need for tieup.

enough, they could be substituted for lumber in homebuilding. This would act to call forth more production of bricks (and perhaps reduced production of lumber).

A problem arises in an economy which is not growing (where a new market is not developing). When the distribution cost for a good or service is reduced and it becomes substituted by a distant user for a previously used good or service, then the total economy does not gain—one area of the country gains at the expense of another. In this case, brick manufacturers would gain additional business and lumber processors would experience reduced business.

If the demand for both bricks and lumber is expanding (if the economy is expanding), then both suppliers can share in the expanding market. That is, without a transport rate adjustment, brick processors might not gain any of the new growth in the economy—but with sufficient reduction they share in the growth with lumber processors. But this is only possible if the railroad serving each supplier pays close attention to the relationship between prices on bricks and lumber and helps maintain a position in the market for its shippers.

Thus the transportation industry can and does play an important role in answering the economic questions of what is to be produced, how much is to be produced, for whom it is to be produced, and by whom it is to be produced. It can, in fact, play a very important role in determining what, how much, and where resources (land, labor, capital, management) will be used and who will get to use them.

The transportation system plays other roles also. For example, it can cause changes in the social structure of society. To the extent that it can make people and other resources more mobile, more labor, capital, and enterprise can be employed in production. These factors can be used in more combinations also. This means more people can share in more of the benefits of technology (new machines,

chemicals, power, and ideas) and consequently improve their standard of living.

Transportation can unlock isolated communities, regions, or countries. When this occurs, it affects the breaking down of sectionalized prejudices and of basic differences in religion and other cultural traits.

Transportation systems tend to establish commercial routes. Since population tends to concentrate along commercial routes (primarily where resources exist) transportation can play an important role in the socio-economic pattern of a society.

Transportation influences the physical pattern of a community or a town. Each community or town seems to expand along the routes which facilitate both economic and social activity. Thus communities or towns become shaped like stars, fans, circles, squares, rectangles, triangles, etc., depending upon the existing location of transport facilities (primarily streets).

Transportation can even affect the nature of a political system. That is, the ability of a country's political, economic, and social institutions may depend highly upon the effectiveness of the transport system. In fact, a convincing case can be made that the solidarity of the Union was maintained because of a strong transportation system in the North during the Civil War.

The pattern of development of a political economy then results from those forces inherent in the transportation industry itself and from the nature of public policy related to transportation. The partnership approach to development through improvement in transportation is going to have to become more important in the United States.

It is not likely that the forces inherent in the transportation system itself are likely to seriously change the patterns of production, consumption, and other conditions. The primary motive in the private business sector—to secure sufficient profits to maintain its own existence—is not very often overwhelmed by welfare motives. In other words, transport routes and application of new power sources are not likely to change to the extent that existing population patterns will be much affected.

The major role of transportation from its point of view as an enterprise whose major responsibility is to stockholders will likely be one of supplying food to consumers who will continue to be located in highly concentrated groups.

This may be accomplished through creation of new agricultural supply areas by adjusting transport costs downward on products produced on land not now under cultivation. It implies that the existing transportation system would be expected to absorb an increasing volume of tonnage.

The latter assumption may not be realistic and may, in fact, dictate a much different approach. The problem in expecting the existing system to haul many multiples of the existing tonnage is that it simply is not capable of meeting the challenge.

The private transport system is incapable of commanding capital of the magnitude needed to feed, clothe, house, and entertain up to 100 million more people expected by the turn of the century. The system is very fragmented—the parts of it rarely agree on how to solve problems of the economy, let alone their own.

This means there is really no such thing as a "national boxcar fleet," a "national truck fleet," a "national airplane fleet," etc. Further, there is no such thing as a transportation company. We have railroads, airlines, truck lines, and water carriers—none of whom may work jointly with another mode.

As long as it is composed of lumpy parts, the industry will always seriously lag behind expansion in the economy. For example, it is highly unlikely that the Nation's railroads can, year-in and year-out, effectively move the grain production of the country. That is, the transportation industry cannot now and will not improve its ability to supply the necessary capacity to the shippers at the time they desire it.

This inability to supply shipping capacity will obviously become more serious as the need to locate food, textiles, lumber, etc., becomes more serious with up to 100 million more Americans three decades from now.

It is likely then that the manner in which the transport system will satisfy the needs of this population upsurge will probably be determined largely by decisions made by public agencies in concert with the private firms in the transportation industry.

This will probably mean emphasis on building new systems which can move large volumes of products and large numbers of people at low cost. Even though railroads will become the beneficiary of some of the attention, river systems not now developed will probably become navigable, new highway networks will be constructed, and airports will receive increased public development.

There are many good examples of how the public satisfied these needs. The interstate highway system was partly financed through monies from each of the States. Construction of this system means people have easier access to recreation and food and other goods. The interstate system should create demand for many other services including both recreation (campgrounds, marinas) and industry.

Probably the most exciting new idea in freight transport is the lightweight container. The idea started with the notion of putting truck trailers on flatcars and hauling the commodity in the trailer with the tractors permanently stationed at destinations. This brought about reduced costs as well as handling and warehousing changes.

Of course it wasn't long before someone had the bright idea that the truck wheels needn't be hauled either. This then led to the container which can be easily handled by barges, new ocean ships, motortrucks, and railroads. As airplanes become larger, they too will be capable of handling the same container as the other modes.

This will mean that we will have the basis for a true department store type of transport system. That is, we should be able to buy container service from any mode of transport, and the management of the mode serving that shipper can worry how it gets from one place to another. Rate systems could be greatly simplified because generally each mode would be hauling a "container" rather than commodities.

It would seem that public investment in facilities related to containers would have much greater payoff for a broader spectrum of the population than in such transport ideas like the supersonic transport (SST). Heavy investments are going to be required in "container ports," in "container ships," and in the containers themselves. One can imagine that with the proper kind of public "help," the freight car supply problem might be solved through greater dependence on low-cost containers.

Part of the interjection of public agencies into the problem of 100 million more Americans may result in deterrents to continued expansion of existing population centers.

For example, one could project quite safely that development of the Arkansas-Verdigris River to Tulsa, Okla., will provide an economic base for accelerated growth in northeastern Oklahoma. Through more and higher levels of income plus improvement in water facilities, the entire quality of life should be improved in that area. It certainly will deter export of population and should create a base for importing people from other parts of the country.

Federally financed experiments, then, may help determine the best approach to correcting imperfections in the use of resources in the transport system.

Public intervention can duplicate the trial and error system of the private sector and identify the most effective methods for deterring population concentration.

It is highly likely that the direction taken by public agencies in determin-ing transportation policy will be highly influenced by those with the greatest voting power. In other words, the needs of rural areas may become secondary issues and this includes the problems of the rural poor. Urban votes may command that primary emphasis be placed upon feeding the urban masses.

The expanded demand for food, clothing, and housing products will mean expanded economic activity in existing agricultural production areas.

In any case, it appears that transportation will play a primary role of supplying the material and recreation needs of the population in the year 2000. It will play a secondary role in determining which agricultural production areas will benefit primarily from the increased needs in supplying the expanding population. By itself it will play a minor role in relocating people by the year 2000.

However, with carefully planned "trial and error" experiments, the transport system may be employed to emphasize nonagricultural development of predominantly agricultural areas.

Water Systems and Sewerage

ELMER E. JONES and
THOMAS F. HADY

WATER is a basic necessity of life. Water is also a source of many pleasures in modern living. As the population increases and the available water supply per person declines, much of rural America should enjoy the advantage of having fresher, higher quality water than the downstream metropolitan areas.

Left, Pennsylvania home with no water supply. Above, privy at edge of North Carolina mountain stream.

Increasing concern from the cities for rural environmental quality may be expected.

The cities, in effect, will be asking "What are you doing to 'our' water?" For the Nation's water, like its food, comes largely from rural areas.

Today, however, much of the rural population does not enjoy the quality of water service provided by the larger cities.

The impact of this is not solely upon rural residents, for 140 million urban residents use the rural water supplies and sanitary waste disposal facilities as they travel and spend time in rural areas.

The 1969 Community Water Supply Study by the U.S. Public Health Service revealed that major deficiencies in water system facilities increased as the population served decreased. Inadequate protection of the source of supply was a major factor. Only 10 percent of the systems met the

*

ELMER E. JONES is Agricultural Engineer, Farmstead Water Systems Research, Agricultural Engineering Research Division, Agricultural Research Service.

THOMAS F. HADY is Chief, Community Facilities Branch, Economic Development Division, Economic Research Service.

226

bacteriological surveillance criteria, most often due to inadequate sampling frequency and records rather than findings of contamination.

Significant improvement can be made with these problems by education, good engineering, and adequate financial support.

Between 1946 and 1960 there were 158 outbreaks of waterborne disease reported, with 6,056 individual cases, stemming from private or semi-public water supplies. Over half of these were attributed to untreated ground water. It is possible to have safe sanitary wells in most areas, yet many wells were constructed with little regard for sanitary protection. Some wells in use are older than the Nation.

Seventy outbreaks of waterborne disease, with 19,928 cases, were traced to public utility water systems between 1946 and 1960.

In 1960, the last year for which census data were available at the time this was written, more than half of all rural housing units obtained their water from individual wells and about a third were connected to central water systems. Public sewers were less common in rural areas than were public water systems; only 14 percent of all rural houses were connected to public sewer systems in 1960.

Regional variations in sewer and water sources are due to incomes, residence patterns, geology of the area, or other reasons. For example, a 1966 study in Tennessee found that only 11 percent of the rural houses studied had public water systems. Two-thirds had an individual well. Nearly a quarter relied on springs, cisterns, ponds, or other sources.

Another study found that in the Mississippi River Delta region in 1966, 45 percent of the rural houses had neither a public sewer nor a septic tank or cesspool.

These data suggest there are many instances in rural America in which the water supply and waste disposal methods leave a potential for water-borne infections or are otherwise less than adequate.

Some 33,000 communities, about 60 percent of the communities in the United States with populations over 25 persons, are without public water facilities. Most of these communities contain fewer than 1,000 residents— but a few have populations over 5,500.

Forty-three thousand communities lack public sewers. Again, most are small, but more than 100 have populations over 5,500.

Data are not available to estimate how many of these communities need central systems in order to provide safe water economically. Under many circumstances, individual wells and septic tanks may be satisfactory and considerably more economical than public facilities.

The automatic electric individual water system has made it possible for many rural residents to have excellent water service. Many well-designed systems can deliver 1,000 gallons of water with less than a nickel's worth of electricity.

In some areas it is not possible to develop a good water supply at reasonable cost. Ground water quality may be poor. Or the water table may be quite deep, making the initial cost too high for low volume users.

In "hard rock" areas, where the rock is essentially impermeable, water is obtained from cracks and crevices. The water may have excellent quality but the uncertainty of obtaining a productive well may be sufficient to prevent some people from obtaining an adequate supply of good water.

Many communities need central water systems now, and the need will increase with time and population.

Rural water systems normally serve fewer people spread over a larger area and sell a smaller volume of water. As a result, they are likely to have higher average costs per gallon delivered.

In considering a new water system, the cost of building the desired facility seems most important. Capital costs can be a major part of the total budget. But once the system is installed, its ability to provide the desired services at a reasonable cost is the measure of success.

It is extremely important to understand how planning decisions will affect long range operating expenses in order to avoid the false economy of substituting excessively high operating expenses for slightly reduced initial cost.

Initial cost of the system can be divided into two parts, the waterworks and the distribution system. Engineering and construction costs of the waterworks, excluding long transmission lines, are not greatly affected by capacity. Doubling the capacity of the wells, pumps, treatment facilities, and storage probably would increase costs less than 30 percent. Costs of the transmission lines and distribution system are closely related to their length.

Many small rural communities of less than 1,000 population have core areas as densely populated as larger cities. It is the fringe areas that reduce the average density. An area with 80-foot-wide lots would have over 100 families per mile, about 50 feet of main per lot.

It appears quite obvious that the more families served by the waterworks, the smaller share of its cost each family must pay.

But when the distribution system costs more than the waterworks, it is important to consider the effect of each additional family on total system costs, average cost per family, and operating costs.

Operating costs can be divided into management services and production costs. Management services include management, records, plant supervision and maintenance, and quality control.

Some of these costs vary with the number of customers, but others do not. For example, a 10-percent increase in the number of customers is not likely to have much effect on the costs of supervising the plant. Production costs include the costs of pumping and treating the water, and are fairly constant per 1,000 gallons at a given capacity.

For a local situation, production costs are almost entirely determined in design or planning. The location of facilities, selection of pumping equipment, pipe size, and type and size of storage facilities must be carefully considered. Differences in elevation should not be ignored. Water will run downhill but must be pumped uphill, thus each foot of difference in elevation either reduces or increases pumping costs.

It is very easy for an engineer to select pipe size to move so many gallons per minute with energy cost of, for example, 1 cent per 1,000 gallons per mile. But designing a water system involves much more difficult decisions than that. For example, the relationship between the average flow and the capacity of the system (engineers divide total flow by capacity and term it the "use factor") is important in overall costs. Pipe sizes, pumping rates, and other factors must be balanced in order to design a system that will minimize the cost of delivering water to the consumer.

The problem is particularly complicated by the fact that we lack perfect knowledge of today's demands, and our ability to predict future demands is even more limited.

The costs of being wrong can be high. Within limits, it is possible to deliver more water by pumping it faster through the same size pipe. But for a given pipe size and length, friction loss increases about as the square of the flow rate, and the power required to overcome that loss increases as the cube of the flow rate.

With initial costs of 1 cent per 1,000 gallons per mile, doubling the flow rate raises pumping costs to 8 cents per 1,000 gallons. Tripling the flow rate would skyrocket costs to 27 cents per 1,000 gallons per mile.

Pumping costs could be reduced by installing larger pipe. They could also be reduced by installing storage tanks, so that peak flows can be accommodated from stored water that was pumped at lower rates of flow.

No water system is leak free. The difference between water produced and water sold or accounted for is termed unaccounted loss. The cost of producing this water must be paid for by the consumer.

Great improvements have been made recently in piping and joints. But some leakage should be anticipated and it is usually uneconomical to find and repair small leaks. In large systems, daily leakage of 2,000 gallons per mile is acceptable, and unaccounted losses will be less than 10 percent of production. In some rural systems this could be over 50 percent.

In considering whether to extend mains to additional customers, then, one ought to consider more than just the fact that fixed costs can be spread over more customers. The length of the mains needed to serve them will directly affect pumping costs, and, of course, building those mains costs money.

Pumping costs will be affected more if the new customers substantially increase peak loads than if their demand is largely concentrated in off-peak times. This is one reason rates should be kept low enough to encourage use of water for sprinkling lawns and gardens.

Water systems have to be designed

to deliver adequately during periods of peak use. Because sprinkling has long periods of water use, it improves the use factor—the level of average water use, relative to peak capacity—and makes it possible to deliver water at lower average costs.

The cost of piping water to widely scattered dwellings can be quite high—$10,000 per mile is not an unusual cost of installing pipe. If the amount of water used is no more than average household consumption, it is entirely possible that it may be cheaper to haul water.

An optimal system, under these circumstances, might have transmission lines terminating at points where average use would fall below 10,000 gallons per day, with 3,000-gallon tankers hauling from storage tanks at the end of the water line to 5,000-gallon tanks at rural homes.

Most water used in modern homes is disposed of as sanitary waste or sewage. Two of the greatest inventions of the 19th century were trapped and vented sanitary drainage systems and the septic tank-soil disposal system. It was the septic tank that brought the convenience of the indoor toilet to rural America.

A properly functioning, properly located septic tank-soil disposal system can be a very efficient way of disposing of sewage. The soil disposal system (drainfield) actually performs most of the treatment. Discharge from the septic tank is black, odorous, and heavily laden with suspended solids. Soil bacteria and fungi which reduce the suspended solids and filtration through the soil should produce a clear, sparkling, bacteria-free and odor-free effluent. Most septic system failures occur in the soil disposal field.

Unfortunately, too many septic tank systems do not work properly. Such systems are a serious threat to health and environmental quality.

Many small towns or suburban areas served by septic tanks should have central sewer systems and more will be needed as the rural population grows.

In some cases, soil conditions dictate a need for large disposal fields, and housing is dense enough so that municipal sewers are less expensive. In other instances, the ratio of ground water recharge from septic tanks to natural rainfall is high, and ground water quality would be degraded. Even removing sludge from septic tanks in densely populated areas can be a nuisance and hazard.

Development in many existing communities did not occur with sewerage costs in mind. A cost-conscious modern land developer will carefully consider the cost of sewerage. Many existing rural communities present real challenges in planning economical sewerage for the existing development and topography.

Sanitary sewers normally have gravity flow; to be satisfactory they must be self-cleaning. For a given sewage flow, a certain combination of pipe size and grade is required. While water mains are normally installed just below the frost line, gravity flow requirements will often cause sewers to be buried over 6 feet deep.

When a sewer becomes too deep, a lift station is required. Lift stations are quite expensive. An alternative to lift stations may be serving groups of homes with a septic tank and pumping the effluent away for disposal. This would require much smaller pumps and pipe sizes.

The aerobic lagoon is now recognized as one of the least expensive means of treating domestic waste. This is a small manmade pond or lake so designed that the sewage loading does not consume all of the oxygen in the water, permitting most of the degradation to take place by aerobic organisms —minimizing odors and environmental degradation.

Properly designed lagoons require a minimum of supervision and operating costs. However, the lagoon has a high land area requirement per person. Depending on the climate and other considerations, some lagoons will have to dispose of waste effluent while some will require additional water to give adequate treatment.

229

Some communities will find it desirable to use conventional primary (sedimentation) and secondary (biological utilization of organic matter) treatment. Some will use an aeration process known as extended aeration. These plants will have to dispose of effluent (treated waste water) and sludge.

Availability of cropland will greatly reduce the sludge disposal problem. The effluent will normally have to comply with either State or interstate standards.

The value of sludge as a soil conditioner is much greater than its equivalent fertilizer value because of trace minerals and organic matter. Benefits obtained from sludge on some problem soils are very great.

Each community provides a different problem for sewage collection and treatment. Each will have several possible solutions.

Careful analysis of the problems of rural communities and community leadership willing to accept innovations can be expected to make significant progress in reducing the cost of sewage service.

With increasing concern about development of rural areas and about the quality of our environment, communities wanting to improve their sewer and water systems are likely to find it much easier to get help than a few years ago.

Since these programs change, we have not tried to summarize them here.

Communities contemplating improvements can get help in finding out about available programs from a number of sources.

Perhaps the best place to start is with the local office of the Farmers Home Administration and with local representatives of the Cooperative Extension Service.

Communities should also be sure to consult the State agencies having advisory or regulatory control of public water systems, such as the State Health Department or the State fire marshal's office.

230

The Battle for Better Fire Control

E. M. BACON

WENATCHEE, WASH., Sept. 1: 14,000 men mobilized, 100 aircraft in action, 80 bulldozers clearing roads and trails and constructing frontline defenses.

Sounds like a war bulletin? It was war all right—all out war in 1970.

No, the Nation was not being invaded by sea or across our northern border. The enemy was fire—wildfire —unleashed, uncontrolled, and running free.

Striking in hundreds of different places across the Northwest, dry lightning storms touched off a series of holocausts that were to blacken more than 100,000 acres, destroy scores of buildings, cost millions of dollars to suppress, cause resource damage estimated in the hundreds of millions, and necessitate the expenditure of more millions for rehabilitation.

Fifty years ago, the fires might well have blackened millions of acres rather than the 100,000-plus acres that they did.

But these fires were bad enough. Firefighters and other personnel were brought in from all over the United States. There were crews from the Army, National Guard, U.S. Forest Service, Bureau of Land Management, State forestry agencies, local fire departments, forest industries, and other sources. They all worked together as a team to get the job done.

An even worse disaster than the Washington fires hit southern California the last part of September and

*

E. M. BACON is Deputy Chief for Cooperative State and Private Forestry, Forest Service.

Above, fresh fire crew on the way in. Right, bulldozer builds fire line. Below, equipment at fire camp site waiting to be put into use.

the first part of October in 1970. From Sept. 25 to Oct. 3, some 56 major fires and many smaller ones burned over half a million acres of rural and suburban lands. Eight lives were lost, including five persons who died in a helicopter crash. The largest single fire seared an estimated 187,000 acres.

The California fires burned forests, watersheds, farm and ranch lands, and many rural and suburban homes and businesses as well. The Small Business Administration estimated that 1,500 homes, businesses, or other buildings were destroyed or damaged.

Fire loss on these buildings was put at $175 million. In the three hardest

hit counties, 424 families were left homeless because of the fires.

Despite progress made in fire protection, wildfires still cost the Nation many millions of dollars every year for prevention, preparedness, suppression, rehabilitation, and resource damage.

The California fires might well serve as an example of what we can expect in many more areas in the future. Southern California presents a special fire hazard condition, compounded by the density of its population. To accommodate a rapid influx of people, many homes and even whole communities have been built in large, nearly unbroken, areas of brush and forest lands.

The greater number of people increases the chances of fires being started, and the many more buildings and other improvements along with rising land values make losses from fire far more costly. Similar conditions may be expected in other areas as our population grows.

One thing is certain—like death and taxes, wildfires will always be with us. In 1969, there were 113,351 reported wildfires in the United States.

Nearly 1,000 rural people lose their lives to fire each year, and total farm fire losses in the United States in 1969 amounted to $227 million. These tragic losses could be reduced by adequately trained and equipped rural fire fighting forces.

Who is responsible for fighting wildfires? Under Civil Defense, the Secretary of Agriculture was assigned fire defense responsibility for all rural areas. In practice, Federal wildlands are protected by the Federal agencies which administer them.

State and privately-owned forest and watershed lands are protected by the States with assistance from the Federal Government through the Clarke-McNary program for Federal-State cooperation in fire protection. Nearly a half billion acres of other rural land, including small communities and farm and ranch homes, fall under the jurisdiction of a multiplicity of local governmental units (townships, municipalities, fire districts, etc.) for fire protection, which in too many places is inadequate or totally lacking.

Let's look briefly at the development of organized fire protection for rural lands in the United States. Up to 1911, the States had made little effort or progress in protecting privately-owned forestlands from fire.

Only 16 States had forest fire organizations which were headed by either a State forester or a chief fire warden. It was estimated that only about 60 million acres were receiving some degree of fire protection.

The Weeks Law of 1911 introduced a new and—until then—untried national policy of cooperation with the States to control forest fires on State- and privately-owned lands. One provision of the law allowed the Federal Government to assist the States financially in fire control activities. It was, however, limited to "forested watersheds of navigable streams."

Cooperative fire control provisions of the Weeks Law were administered by the Forest Service under written agreements between the Secretary of Agriculture and the States.

Federal-State cooperation for forest fire prevention and control was expanded under the Clarke-McNary Act of 1924. Federal cooperation was extended to "any timbered or forest producing lands, other than those in Federal ownership."

In 1925, the Clarke-McNary Act was amended to include nontimbered "watersheds from which water is secured for domestic use or irrigation." This was needed in order to extend fire protection to large areas of brush and grasslands, mainly in the western half of the Nation. Especially vulnerable were the chaparral covered slopes in southern California.

The 81st Congress passed legislation in 1948 enabling States to form mutual assistance compacts for the better coordination of firefighting forces. By January 1950, six New England States and New York had ratified a mutual assistance agreement. This is known as the Northeastern Compact. The 82nd

Congress passed supplemental legislation to permit Canadian provinces adjacent to member States to participate in such compacts.

The Province of Quebec joined the Northeastern Compact in 1969, followed by New Brunswick in 1970. A Southeastern Compact with 10 member States and a South Central Compact with five were organized in 1954. A Middle Atlantic Compact involving six States was authorized in 1956. It became operational in 1965.

In 1964 the Army, Office of Civil Defense, and the Department of Agriculture's Forest Service established five test projects—one in each of the States of Colorado, Florida, Kentucky, Missouri, and Oregon.

Object of the tests was to develop appropriate training materials and to organize, train, and assist volunteer groups and individuals to adequately equip themselves for the fire control job. Direct supervision of the project was provided by State foresters of the States involved.

Federal financial participation ended in 1966. However, the States, recognizing the need for the test projects, are continuing the effort with very limited resources. Cooperation and acceptance by local officials and the public has been enthusiastic and the results are considered as highly successful.

Federal and State agencies have adequately trained forces and sufficient equipment to protect the Nation's public lands from fire in all but extreme situations. The same cannot be said for most local firefighting forces and for much of the Nation's privately-owned rural lands.

Fire insurance premiums are commonly much higher in areas where protection is inadequate. Many rural families are discouraged from carrying sufficient insurance to cover losses when fires occur. Improved organized protection would reduce both the losses and the insurance costs.

In 1942, a national fire prevention campaign was launched and has been gathering momentum ever since. The campaign is a cooperative effort of the Advertising Council, the U.S. Forest Service, and the State forestry agencies. Free "public service" advertising time and space donated by radio, television, transit companies, outdoor advertisers, magazines, and newspapers carry the fire prevention message into practically every home in America.

The symbol of forest fire prevention and the central figure in the national campaign since 1945 has been Smokey the Bear. Smokey's success is evidenced by a study completed in 1968 in which 98 percent of all children, 95 percent of all teenagers, and 89 percent of all adults in the area covered identified Smokey correctly. His popularity with children exceeded that of Bullwinkle, Pinocchio, Tony the Tiger, and the Jolly Green Giant.

In 1959, a special "Southern Cooperative Forest Fire Prevention" campaign was initiated. Its primary objective is to curb incendiarism and debris-burning which constitute a special fire prevention problem in the Southern States. The campaign uses a more adult approach and supplements the national campaign. It is headquartered in Atlanta, Ga.

What of the future? Will we be able to eliminate wildfire on rural lands? Not very likely! We will continue to have fires until we can control human carelessness, incendiarism, and dry lightning storms. Our best prevention efforts can only reduce the number—not eliminate them.

Since we will have fires, the challenge then is to keep them small. The way to keep them small is through preparedness, early detection, and speedy attack. If we can hit them soon enough and hard enough, we can keep the costs and the resource damage to a minimum.

The key to successful fire prevention and control is good land management planning. A great deal of "built in" fire protection can be provided through proper planning. For instance, the hazard created by large unbroken blocks of fuel can be reduced through the placement of roads, tree plantations, and green crops such as clover and some types of grass. Fire breaks can be established and maintained with advance planning. In areas of mixed ownership a great deal of coordination will be needed.

Research and development have given us many new and improved tools and techniques. Some projects now in progress that seem to hold promise include missiles that "home in" on fires carrying fire retardant chemicals, and weather modification. If it becomes possible to modify the weather on a large scale, we may be able to cut the number and size of wildfires quite dramatically.

Rapid changes in land-use patterns, along with soaring resource and improvement values, have increased the need for adequate fire protection.

Rural fire protection is important to all Americans. If it is effective it will help us to maintain and improve the quality of our environment, to obtain the products and benefits we desire, to protect the lives and homes of rural residents, and to pass on the heritage of our natural resources to succeeding generations.

Shopping Centers, Where the Action Is

RAYMOND W. HOECKER

CONSUMERISM is winning the day. The emphasis on consumerism and on the more concentrated use of land is producing shopping centers with the cultural, educational, community, and civic facilities of the downtown center.

Developers soon will be answering such questions as "Why isn't there a museum in your shopping center?"

The Urban Land Institute defines the shopping center as: "A group of commercial establishments, planned, developed, owned, and managed as a unit, with off-street parking provided on the property and related in location, size, and types of shops to the trade area that the unit serves—generally in an outlying or suburban territory."

The experts classify shopping centers into as many as eight types. But in this chapter I will talk about the larger, regional centers and the smaller secondary centers which are so familiar to all of us. It is here that the action is.

Early in 1970, it was estimated that the tight money situation would be eased sufficiently to start construction during 1970 on 1,100 to 1,200 new and remodeled shopping centers. A spokesman for the International Council of Shopping Centers said the number of shopping complexes would double within the next 10 years, from 12,000 to 24,000. The shopper of the 1970's is in for many new shopping experiences.

When it comes to buying in shopping centers, I find that my wife, Betty, is an "average" consumer. She gives most of her patronage to one large center, one small center, and a free standing supermarket chain store.

The closest large center is 5 miles from home. It has plenty of free parking, with a minimum of automobile traffic, stop lights, and pedestrian traffic to interfere with her trip. And the center boasts two outlets of the dominant department store chains, a large supermarket, and over 60 national regional chains and strong independents.

Betty doesn't buy our food at the supermarket in the large shopping center. She favors the free standing supermarket, because it is only two blocks from home; and the supermarket in the small shopping center,

*

RAYMOND W. HOECKER is assistant director of the Transportation and Facilities Research Division, Agricultural Research Service.

which is only 1 mile from home, because it gives her what she considers the best buys and service. Features of a shopping center that count with my wife and others like her are convenience, price, selection, service, comfort.

Betty's 2-to-3-hour shopping trips to the favorite regional center contrast sharply with her all-day, 12-mile trips to downtown Washington for shopping before the center was built.

Of course, the big difference between the two is convenience of location and comfort. She still makes the trip to the central business district occasionally. But I find that as the regional center meets more and more of her needs, the downtown shopping trips become increasingly fewer.

When our regional shopping center was planned 10 years ago, it had everything. It was one of the best. Since then, with rapid expansion of the population and with new concepts of service and comfort, it is no longer one of the very best.

The center's occupants find that their customers' concepts of convenience, price, selection, service, and comfort are highly relative and that they must pursue an imaginative program of expansion and change to remain No. 1 with their shoppers.

Leaders of my community are eager to keep customers like my wife shopping in their city and are thinking about constructing, within a half mile of our home, the "most" modern shopping center. These leaders recognize that a modern, attractive center can be a source of pride and profit to the city and can materially boost the quality of community life.

A new, modern center will attract most of the shoppers in our city because it can have everything the older, competing centers have, plus a great deal more convenience and comfort.

Additional benefits are expected. Modern stores require alert, resourceful, imaginative managers to operate them—just the kind of individuals needed to become active in local civic affairs. Further, modern stores stimulate development of the community. Convenience in local shopping makes the community attractive to builders and home buyers.

Availability of this convenience for their employees enhances the area's appeal to prospective industries when they are deciding on plant locations.

A large, central shopping center contains nearly 100 stores of all types. Employment opportunities for city residents can be most attractive. Tax revenue generated by such a center can help materially to balance our city's budget.

Another real plus for my city would be the replanning that must accompany such an undertaking. I think we can learn from the experience of Chicago's Englewood area. In recent years, the area had become rundown. Stores were boarded up, chain stores moved to the suburbs and to modern shopping centers, and crime increased. Blight was invited and it stuck.

Then the shopping concourse was reorganized. As a result, two large chain department stores moved in, plus 127 other tenants. Last year the center had a sales volume of $78 million, an increase of $13 million over the annual volume before the reorganization. Bank officials involved in financing the concourse reorganization said the declining trend was reversed through a change of attitude within the community.

If our city officials decide to go ahead with their planning, one of the first things they will recognize is that developing a center is a complex job and that they will need the help of experts to make a thorough market analysis. Such an analysis will involve a determination of the sales potential from both the existing trading area and the future trading area which will be developed in part by the facility to be constructed.

The market analysis will consider several factors:

Population—Size of the population and its density, dispersion, growth trend, and characteristics are all major factors in site selection.

235

Income and stability—Fundamental to a sound analysis is a study of the income of the area, distribution of that income, the source that provides the income, and relative economic stability of the area.

Competition—Both the quantity and quality of competition in and near the proposed center must be thoroughly investigated.

Community Character—A great deal of emphasis is placed on progressiveness of the community, as evidenced by modern schools, new construction, active civic groups, adequate parks and playgrounds, and strong and active churches.

Site—Vital to the success of any center is the site's accessibility to customers.

Highways and mass transit systems adequate to serve present or potential traffic needs are most important. The site must be large enough to provide adequate space for buildings and for free parking, and must not be too costly to develop.

The center of tomorrow will be a multilevel and multifunctional complex that will be accessible by car and by mass transit systems. Centers are encouraged to go up and not out by rising land costs, larger stores in greater numbers, nonretail activities, and customer convenience requirements.

"Shopping" will be dropped from the term shopping center because centers will house not only stores of every description, but also offices, movie houses, live theater, sporting events, concerts, lectures, schools, and churches. Events will be scheduled to balance traffic and increase use of parking facilities.

Retailer occupants of such high-density centers will benefit from the increased traffic of area residents, office workers, visitors, and participants in various functions of the center, and from the center's almost continuous use during the entire day —most of the night—on weekends and holidays.

Design of the center of tomorrow will make comparison shopping easier despite the greater number of items offered. Three-dimensional viewing screens will be used to show the shopper available merchandise in her size, price range, and style. This technique will greatly speed up the customer's shopping and reduce the labor needed for selling.

Moving sidewalks, moving chairs, and moving displays will be provided to minimize the need for walking. Floors in the centers will slope at a slight angle and move customers from one floor to another without their being aware of it.

Cars will be parked in multilevel

All season iceskating rink at Lloyd Center, Portland, Ore.

garages, both above and below ground. In some instances, center structures will be built on stilts so cars can go underneath, out of the way and out of the weather. Computers will be used to control parking. As each car comes into the center it will be directed to a vacant space by signs and flashing arrows. When the car leaves, the computer will again direct the way to the preferred exit, or detour the car if these exits are overloaded.

For some of us the future is the present. For example: A two-level mall is in use in the Washington, D.C., area. A shopping center has been built on stilts in Belgium; carpeted malls replace terrazzo floors. An instant stage is enabling a South Florida center to put on numerous small-scale attractions; art exhibits of local talent are being held. In Alexandria, Va., a center has a 20,000-square-foot ministry which provides hourly child care, counseling, worship, theater-in-the-round, and consumer education.

Our Cultural Needs, to Add Zest to Life

DAVID E. LINDSTROM

PROSPECTS for as many as 25 million more families in the United States by the year 2000 are real and disturbing.

Disturbing because the children and youth of today will be the parents in 10 to 30 years. Where and how will they live?

With the core of the cities already painfully overcrowded, the fastest growing section of the population is the suburbs—which cannot keep up with demands for cultural facilities.

Prospects of a rise in the population to over 300 million at the turn of the century are the most disturbing when you consider that all cultural facilities will need expansion, especially in rural areas.

We know that with adequate planning and execution, rural America can become the more desired place in which to live and rear a family. Many attractions denied city dwellers can now be found there, and rural people can avail themselves of modern cultural facilities once limited to city dwellers. This is possible with modern roads, modern modes of travel, and modern forms of mass media.

The fact that 40 percent of the Nation's poor live in rural areas only aggravates the situation. People have continued to move to the cities and the suburbs where they hope to find better opportunities for making a living. Many of those banking on this hope move back home again.

For example, one of the surprising facts revealed in discussions at the Appalachia Conference on Research in Poverty and Development held at the Virginia Polytechnic Institute in Blacksburg, Va., in July of 1968 was that 60 percent of those having moved to the city came back to their home communities.

As population surges upward in the next 30 years, rural areas must be prepared to adjust to the inevitable ruralward flight of frustrated people.

Not the least important of efforts to make adjustments are those relating to cultural facilities like schools, churches, libraries, arts, crafts, and similar facilities. These are the cultural forms that help make the countryside a more attractive and desirable place to live.

This type of effort is already well started in many country and small town areas under the impetus of the U.S. Department of Agriculture, the State Cooperative Extension Services, and other community development movements.

*

DAVID E. LINDSTROM is Professor Emeritus of Rural Sociology, University of Illinois, Urbana.

237

Looking over books in library at Morgantown, Ky., that doubles as a community center.

The period of the Seventies and the decades that follow therefore will see the necessity for bridging the gap between technological developments and their effect on man.

Researchers stress the importance of looking at man's place in the total environment that will provide not only productive human beings but also a desirable quality of life over a certain span of years. One of the proposed lines of investigation is to "Identify people's beliefs, values, and attitudes concerning the natural environment as it relates to the home, neighborhood, and city," as a basis for developing educational and action programs that will attack poverty of land, man, mind, and spirit.

Cultural forms develop in any civilization because they are ways in which living together becomes more worthwhile, interesting, and enjoyable. They are a means of personal growth and fulfillment and serve to dispel loneliness and despair.

Cultural facilities arise from the needs and desires of people. As time

goes on, both private and State interests become involved. When people find it difficult to adequately meet their cultural needs, they may turn to government. It is best when the initiative comes from the people with the full participation of the people, their leaders and groups.

Growth and development must then inevitably take place. Farmers of the Nation, for example, have made extensive use of government services and facilities. At first these were limited largely to facilities that have to do with earning a living by increasing productivity on the farm and in the home. More recently they have been broadened to facilitate enrichment of life in the home and community.

The church, as one of these facilities, has often been the center holding the people together. It has given the majority of the rural people of the Nation hope, faith in the future, and a sense of security in a world of strife and uncertainty.

For many, the church still is the center where people gain a sense of togetherness. You have doubtless heard that the church is fading away in a culture of technology and a loosening of ties. Often this has been the case, but the church nevertheless remains a strong and basic voluntary force.

There have been ups and downs. A Missouri study by Hassinger and Holik, on the membership changes from 1952 to 1967 in various types of churches in places under 2,500 popuation, shows there was relatively little change. Losses were largest in the well established churches, where there was a 7.4 percent membership drop. Gains (4.9 percent) were in the most rapidly changing sect-type churches. Ability of these churches to maintain their groups intact was remarkable, according to the authors.

Churches in the best agricultural areas, especially the smaller churches lacking adequately trained leaders, can no longer provide the religious nurture required by an increasingly complex technical society. Fewer and

238

larger farms and smaller families on the land also have had their effect.

A significant move, taking place all over rural America, is the holding of interdenominational conferences and training schools to provide better trained pastors who can serve more effectively in a rural culture. Colleges of agriculture and their extension services have been called on to help plan and hold many of those types of meetings.

One purpose of these pastor-lay training schools is to orient young pastors, many from cities, to work and live in rural areas and to help these pastors understand the unique problems of farmers.

Training schools on such cooperative bases are numerous all over the countryside.

The future of the rural church lies in change—in programs emanating from the church and carried out in the life of the community, enlisting young people in the programs. The enlivened churches are becoming more concerned with conflict, tension, poverty, racism, and many other problems besetting people as they face into the seventies: problems of relevance to today's world.

This has given impetus to ecumenism—the coming together of denominations and to what is termed church renewal.

Among the numerous facilities enriching rural life, none seems more on the move than the library. The time is coming, perhaps in the decade of the seventies, when we can say, "None of the people in rural areas are without library service." The goal, widely accepted by librarians, is to provide library service for every citizen and child, no matter where they live.

This goal is being attained more rapidly in the inner city than in rural areas. Even in so rich a State as Illinois as late as 1963, over 21 percent of the people—mostly rural—had no access to public library service. The situation is more acute in depressed areas.

Librarians over the Nation can tell you the answer is Library Systems Development. This plan is being carried out in a dozen States spread over the Nation. The basic unit is the community library, with its facilities reaching out to the remotest parts and the basic service linked to county, regional, State, and national libraries.

National libraries—the Library of Congress, the National Library of Medicine, and USDA's National Agricultural Library—cooperate with the systems libraries. Grants from the Federal Government for development are quite usual.

Through this linkage system reference materials, good books, pamphlets and periodicals, government documents, and other library services once limited to the city dweller can be made available through inter-library loans, facsimile transmission, and other modern means of communication.

Bookmobiles are out in the country reaching villages on back roads, in the hills and the hollows and on the plains. No one will be missed.

Good librarianship is part of the plan. Both professionals and volunteer workers are being trained so they can study community needs, give guidance in selection of materials, and help groups plan programs to meet needs and problems.

Library facilities, under the systems plan, can enhance the services of the agricultural and home economics extension services. Library resources of schools can be supplemented by putting much used public library resources on reserve. Adult educational facilities—visual and audio—can be furnished to planning councils and local government bodies. Group and community meeting places are now available in many libraries.

The systems library is a tremendous future development, filling the gaps now left vacant. Its development will doubtless extend well into the seventies, providing an important part in cultural advance.

Art forms of a culture may characterize its quality. Rural areas have always been a birthplace of many cultural facilities: folk music, drama, crafts, literature, and all those fine things of esthetic creation that help make life joyous and worth living.

Rural cultural arts have taken many forms: town and country art shows, celebrations of historic significance, family reunions, gatherings related to the growing of specialized crops, music, drama, and dance festivals. Together they give zest to life in the country. My first agricultural extension activities related partly to promoting farm people's music and drama tournaments in Wisconsin and Illinois.

The Nebraska State Arts Council provided help in 1970 with music, exhibitions, special events, opera, and dance to 150 participating communities. Illinois has its annual Town and Country Art Show. The Wisconsin University Extension Office of Community Arts Development reports that 600 arts councils have been organized throughout the country. This type of activity will doubtless spread.

Many schools have included music, art and drama in their curricula. County and State fairs have exhibits of farm, home, and community arts which delight the eye and create a friendly atmosphere of competition.

The revival of crafts has not been restricted to areas of economic distress or as a means for increasing incomes. Crafts, rather, have been a significant way to satisfy esthetic yearnings, as well as to increase income. Some of the major forms have been textiles, woodworking, ceramics, basketry, landscaping, and many other forms of creative endeavor and of making home and landscape more beautiful.

An example in the landscape field is a county 4-H project to beautify grounds for a new hospital in Douglas County, Ill. Initiated by the county 4-H Federation, what the young people considered a huge project was launched—taking 4 months for planning and marshalling human and natural resources. The actual job of planting was finished within 4 hours. A $2,000 project actually cost little because human and material resources were practically all contributed.

Involved were the 4-H leaders and members, Extension advisers, the Extension landscape specialist from the university, and hearty approval and help of the hospital administration, along with contributions of materials and supervision by representatives of area nurseries. Four-H'ers did much of the work—300 of them from 33 clubs in the county, all of whom can look back on this professional job and say proudly, "I helped!"

The Outdoors: Recreation and Responsibility

R. M. HOUSLEY, JR.

IF YOU are like many Americans today, you expect more from your outdoor recreation than just a change of scene and activity. You want to learn from your experience as well.

In fact, more and more outdoor recreation visitors are convinced they have a personal responsibility to understand their recreation environment. This understanding can enable them to use that environment without destroying it, while providing the basis for the individual to relate to his own environment, whether at work or play.

How well we learn these lessons in ecology will determine what kind of outdoor recreational opportunities Americans will have by the turn of the century.

Whether outdoor recreation takes place in a city park or a National Forest, the first step in studying the environment is to read about it.

Books from your local library and publications from Government sources can get you started on your orientation to a specific area. From these, you will begin to see how soil, plants, animals, water, air, and shape of the land interact to form the ecosystems of which we are a part. ("Ecosystem" means the interrelated inhabitants of an environment and the life-support elements it contains. The planet Earth is itself a tremendous ecosystem comprised of many smaller ones.)

Once outdoors, you may seek visitor centers, interpretive signs, and nature trails as the next step in developing greater awareness of your surroundings. These aids are increasingly provided by the Forest Service and other land-managing agencies at every level of Government in response to demand.

Thus equipped with background, you can add exploration and discovery to your recreation activity as you see for yourself evidence of the interdependence of living things and their life-support systems. From this first-hand knowledge will stem your ability to use a lake or stream, a mountain or forest, a beach or prairie, without damaging its values so that others can also use it now and in the future.

Beyond learning how to live with a recreation environment, there are discoveries waiting for us in terms of new places and new kinds of recreation activity.

Many are satisfied to perfect skills already acquired and to use them in familiar surroundings. But the more adventurous—those who want to broaden their experience—can choose from a whole spectrum of outdoor opportunities.

For those who seek solitude and demanding physical activity, there is wilderness and "back country" set in often spectacular surroundings. On the other end of the scale is driving for pleasure to enjoy scenery or a change of locale, without the physical demands of backpacking or horsemanship.

*

R. M. HOUSLEY, JR., is Director, Division of Recreation, Forest Service.

Once basic skills are mastered, some find that traveling and camping amid natural surroundings are only the means, however enjoyable, to the pursuit of other recreation activities.

Hunting and fishing are traditional outdoor activities. Photography and nature study continue to gain in popularity. Horseback riding, rock climbing, skin diving, floating, canoeing, and winter sports offer physical challenges and require varying skills. Because they put the visitor in close touch with his environment, they help him to learn about it.

The snowmobile explosion has opened up the winter landscape as rugged scooters and 4-wheel vehicles make rough back country roads usable. Ecologists worry, not without cause, that burgeoning cross-country vehicle use will upset environmental balances.

Concern for winter elk and deer herds which may be unintentionally harassed or even moved by snowmobile travelers points to the need for these users to develop environmental sensitivity. Motorcyclists and ATV (all-terrain vehicle) drivers also need to be aware that misuse of their mechanical steeds can carve into the protective vegetation which keeps soil from eroding into streams and lakes, with results that may alter the fish environments.

Another ecological lesson to be learned is in the environmental impacts that occur when visitors come in large groups—whether by bus, on horseback, in caravans of cars and trailers, or in fleets of boats. A site that can safely accommodate 10 people for 100 days during a season might well be destroyed if 100 people used it for 10 days, or if 1,000 people came in 1 day.

Landowners and land managers can control this kind of overuse by regulation. But the groups who organize outings should recognize this ecological fact in their own publications and through programs at their meetings.

Movies and speakers are available

Top left, hiking in a National Forest. Above, "Touch and See Nature Trail" for blind at National Arboretum, Washington, D.C. Left, and below, stream profile chamber and animal life display at National Forest visitor centers. Lower left, trailer campers.

from U.S. Department of Agriculture agency offices in most counties to help groups recognize the physical and ecological capacity of a vista point, a beach, a trail, or a picnic area. Other Federal agencies and private conservation organizations can provide similar assistance.

Recognizing the more abstract psychological capacity of a recreation environment is more difficult because people have different tolerances toward proximity of others, and that tolerance varies by activities.

For some, a wilderness experience is ruined if they see more than three or four other individuals, even at a distance. In some campgrounds, on the other hand, observers found that isolated, well-screened spots were the last to be chosen.

The point is that an individual planning for recreation needs to recognize this aspect of human ecology, and allow for it in deciding what to do and where to do it.

The way that recreationists use natural resources today will help shape the opportunities that their descendants will have in the year 2000. Other steps we take today will have just as much bearing on whether there will be enough open space and attractive rural environments to support outdoor recreation as we know it.

Planned expansion of urban areas, or establishment of new ones, ranks high as a key to tomorrow's outdoor recreation potential. Planning for use and production must be done to assure that the basic resources of space and soil are not impaired in their role as continuous suppliers of our physical and esthetic needs.

Several USDA agencies are engaged in this kind of planning assistance for recreation on rural private lands.

The Soil Conservation Service works in connection with farm and ranch planning. State foresters work with private forest lands. Cost-sharing programs of the Agricultural Stabilization and Conservation Service, and the loan programs of the Farmers Home Administration and the Rural Electrification Administration provide the financial incentives.

Recreation research programs of the Forest Service, Economic Research Service, and Agricultural Research Service help to lay the foundation for planning.

This planning and research must take into account tomorrow's citizens —their needs and expectations. Recreation users in the year 2000 will be more numerous. If today's trends continue, they will be more affluent, with more disposable income. They will have more leisure as the result of increased productivity.

They will have a keener awareness of surroundings and their relationship to them or they will not have survived that long. And they will be possessed of greater intellectual curiosity and knowledge. If you doubt that, compare today's state of knowledge and technological advancement with that of 30 years ago!

What can an outdoor recreation seeker expect to find when he leaves his urban habitat 30 years hence? At best, he can expect to share recreation opportunities with more people, or perhaps to wait longer to enjoy them.

Experts predict that reservations will be required for most popular parks and recreation areas, particularly those where heavy demand is coupled with low physical or psychological carrying capacity.

Once he arrives, the outdoor visitor of the year 2000 will likely find he is subject to more regulation than he is today.

Controls to protect site values and even visitors will become increasingly necessary, unless the recreationist does an exceptional job of self-regulation based on his sophisticated ecological knowledge. Professionals in land management hope more regulation won't be necessary. "It's up to the users," they say.

In any case, recreation users are entitled to better planned, more intensive recreation developments for their use. And along with these will inevitably come innovations in transportation to replace much automotive travel. These will include rapid mass transit to reach outdoor recreation areas as well as trams, lifts, monorails, or even yet-to-be-conceived transportation within recreation areas.

The ecologically sophisticated visitor of the year 2000 will demand and get more interpretive services designed to enrich his recreation experience.

By the end of the century, recreation facilities for limited or exclusive individual use will have decreased in favor of facilities or opportunities for the general public's use of the most desirable sites.

To the extent that anyone can see into the future of outdoor recreation, the picture is a mixture of good news and bad. The proportions of both will be determined by how well we plan as a nation, and on the kind of priority we give to financing and carrying out these plans. They will also be determined by our individual actions today in learning how to use the recreation environment without destroying it.

How Communities Can Cut Costs by Changing Size

EBER ELDRIDGE

A N EAST COAST suburbanite begins his early morning journey toward the cluster of tall buildings 40 miles away, not yet visible through the city haze. He'll spend an hour and a half each morning and evening, if bad weather doesn't slow traffic for him and thousands of his fellow commuters. He spends 15 hours a week so he and his family can have the best of two worlds—urban and suburban.

He has time to observe the miles of developments, apartments, and large industrial plants that have attracted millions of people. "Attracted?" Well, at least the jobs represented by the industries brought the people here.

Later that morning a machinist begins his 15-minute drive across town to the small factory where he works in a medium size community far to the west. But his thoughts are not on this pleasant community where there's less pressure on people and on the land. He thinks of a farm 30 miles away that once was his "job".

However, only the machinist's thoughts return there—he no longer drives past the "home place". The sight is too depressing. The house stands vacant and in disrepair. The large area of trees, grass, and flowerbeds around the house is gone. The only foundation plantings now are the corn and soybean stalks planted by a former neighbor.

At the same time, a small town merchant walks to his business, past the vacant stores on the block, to serve customers who seem to be growing fewer every day. Nearby is lots of space, clean air, and the greenery people say they want. But the people aren't there.

The merchant's own son moved to the city a few years ago. "There's not much future here, Pop," his son said. Now "Pop" wonders if there's enough future for him to stay.

These stories, with minor variations, are repeated thousands of times across the nation. And all these people are affected by the same set of social and economic forces that are reshaping the profile of America. Creating problems in both urban and rural areas, the forces stem from successful use of four types of technology—in farming, manufacturing, transportation, and services and institutions.

*

EBER ELDRIDGE is a professor of economics and extension economist at Iowa State University, Ames.

The technology of farming has improved productivity, enabling one man to operate more acres, like the small town machinist's former neighbor. Consequently, many farmers, farmworkers, and their families were eliminated from the rural economic base. Farm population has fallen from 30.5 million in 1940 to 10 million in 1969. Most of these former farm people have taken jobs in the larger population centers as did the machinist.

Some rural people think the migration from farm to city will soon stop or be reversed. But the forces at work indicate this is wishful thinking. Many small farms still remain in the rural areas and there's much more technology to be applied. This suggests the number of farm families will continue to decrease rapidly in the next 20 to 30 years.

In manufacturing, nonfarm technology is creating new jobs at a rapid rate. Here, there's more wishful thinking that new plants and industries will rush to rural areas away from the city congestion. Although some plants are locating outside the congested areas, most are on the periphery of the large industrial complexes, not out in the sparsely populated rural areas.

A study in the Southeastern United States showed employment in rural communities is increasing more rapidly than in the standard metropolitan statistical areas—the large counties. But counties with increasing employment, though rural, are within commuting distance of the large cities.

A 1966 study by the Federal Reserve Bank of five States around Chicago indicates the larger areas are getting larger and smaller areas are getting smaller in terms of employment. This is generally true throughout the Midwest and western part of the United States. Most jobs are still being created in congested areas and are inducing workers to leave the rural areas.

Transportation technology is the third factor affecting rural and urban America. Changes in both the highway and the vehicle make it possible for rural consumers to patronize larger retail centers within a reasonable driving time.

As the rural consumer seeks wider selection in quality, price, or style, he bypasses the "home town," driving to an area retail center as much as 50 to 60 miles away. No longer does the retailer in the small town have his "captive" customers. This increasing retail leakage from the small town has caused many towns to disappear in a functional retail sense.

Retail sales records show that 706 rural Iowa communities under 1,000 population had only 3.9 percent of the consumers' retail dollar in 1968. Yet these communities had 12 percent of the State's population, plus a number of farm people in their trade territory.

The growing tendency of major railroads to discontinue low-volume lines also is penalizing the small community. Rail service is gone from many small towns, and more will lose it. This often raises costs for local merchants, making them even less competitive in relation to the larger central city businesses.

Meanwhile, citizen demands and other forces require rural communities to stay up-to-date. High schools must add new courses or laboratories; special medical clinics have replaced the general practitioner; the rural stores have to add credit card convenience. Each new service takes additional capital. To keep per capita costs down with these new services, the number of clientele or the economic base must be enlarged.

Three of the four applications of technology—farming, manufacturing, and transportation—essentially are reducing the economic base in the rural community. The fourth application—services and institutions—is pressing for a constantly larger base.

Many rural leaders are finally realizing that the employment base of most rural communities is getting smaller, while the demand for higher quality services and institutions is growing. The idea that institutions and services cannot be duplicated in every

245

rural community without either exorbitant costs or reduced quality is gaining acceptance.

Rural leaders are accepting the difficult conclusion that the answer to rural problems does not exist within the boundaries of the traditional community. The answer can be found only when the economic base is large enough to permit high quality services and institutions with a reasonable cost.

Many rural people accept the fact that most of their communities are too small, but they wonder about the economies that are associated with increasing size.

Underlying all the discussion is an elusive idea about the "optimum" or "right" size for a community.

The idea of optimum size has its origin in economic theory on economies of scale. The principle of economies of size assumes that each business, service, or institution has a long-run U-shaped cost curve (see illustration). Though the curve for each organization may vary, the basic shape is presumed to exist. The "right" or optimum size is at the point where the cost line dips closest to the base line of size, or point Y in the illustration.

Communities are presumed to have a similar cost curve for all their goods and services, but are operating short of the least-cost point. In other words, rural communities are too small to provide quality services and institutions at the least cost. At the same time, large metro-communities are operating beyond that point—they're too large to supply goods and services at the lowest cost.

Discussion of economies of size, along with its implications, becomes emotionally charged when applied to a specific community. For this reason, many leaders have avoided the issue. But avoiding issues can only delay the time when rural areas can enjoy high quality institutions and services at the lowest possible cost.

Rural people tend to resist the idea of a "central city," particularly if the city is one they have always regarded as a competitor. Rural people fear the loss of local control in government or business decisions to be made on an expanded economic or geographic basis. Observing the problems generated by growth in the cities, many have not accepted the idea that the larger community can offer more benefits than now exist.

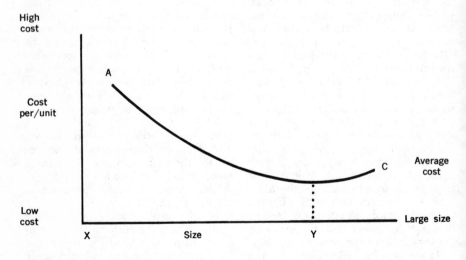

Note: The horizontal axis indicates size or volume of firm or institution. The vertical axis indicates the cost of producing each unit of product or service.

246

Growth of Regional Agencies

Type of agency	1954	1968	1969
Council of Governments	1	100	175
Economic Development Districts	—	84	109
Regional Planning Commissions	45	276	274
Other	—	15	18
Total	46	475	576

A number of groups have made recommendations indicating that economies can be attained if the rural communities increase their size. The Committee for Economic Development in 1966 recommended:

• Consolidation of the present 2,700 rural counties into not over 500.

• Abolition of townships not suited to incorporation as full municipalities.

• Disincorporation of most non-metropolitan villages with less than 2,500 residents.

• Abolition of self-governing special districts.

• Continuation of school consolidation until every system has at least 1,500 students.

The National Service to Regional Councils (NSRC) in its 1970 Regional Committee Report also endorsed the concept of economies of size for rural communities. The report said:

"The concept of 'regionalism', however one defines it, is intimately tied in today with one of our great domestic problems—demographic imbalance. This imbalance threatens to grow worse as we seek living space for another hundred million citizens by the end of the century. So far the great bulk of the new citizens seem destined for the large cities of the Nation.

"Traditional disparities in the amenities of life between the metropolis and the countryside have to be overcome if any resettlement policies are to succeed. Yet, most existing governmental units appear too small to achieve economies of scale that can cut cost and raise quality. It seems likely that regionalism may be able to do jointly in this regard what individual units cannot do singly."

The regional concept that depends primarily upon "economies of community size" is being increasingly accepted. Significant growth in the number of multi-jurisdictional regional agencies in recent years was reported in tabular form in another NSRC report. See table.

Recognition of the insufficiency of many existing rural communities is spreading, as is the acceptance of the multi-county base for rural institutions and services. However, the exact description of this larger community base has not yet been fully accepted.

Dr. Karl Fox, Iowa State University economist, has described the kind of grouping of small communities in rural areas that will be necessary. He terms it a "functional economic area," although it might be called a labor market area, expanded rural-city, functional sociological area, or a multi-county community.

The functional economic area might be visualized as a large city of more than 100,000 population spread over an extensive land area of several rural counties. The area would have a sufficient base to provide commercial and institutional services of high quality at low cost. All commercial or institutional services would be within an hour's driving time for any resident of the functional economic area.

In geographic terms, the functional economic area of rural America would consist of a central city (wholesale center) of at least 25,000 population. The area also would include several retail centers (county seat towns) and numerous villages and farms over about 10 counties. The exact

247

geographical area would be determined by local population density and transportation conditions.

Nearly three-fourths of the incorporated towns in rural America are under 1,000 population. Many are relics of "horse and buggy days." A number have lost—or will lose—their economic reason for existence. As they do, the people will need to learn to accept the new economic area as "their community."

Certainly if people are to become actively involved in community improvement or economic development, they must first accept the geographic area as their community.

Though the economic function of an area can be documented, social and political behavior is much less certain. Sociologists say the functional economic area is not a social system. Perhaps area delineation can eliminate some confusion, and acceptance of the larger communities will help formation of a true social system.

Theory and logic indicate economies of size do exist in rural areas. But people are not always convinced by theory and logic. They want to know the gains, costs, and drawbacks.

These questions require some research. Unfortunately, research in this area is time consuming, costly, and somewhat imprecise. Consequently, little has been done. So it's almost impossible to tell any rural community that the consolidations, mergers, etc., will produce specific gains in terms of cost or performance. But there are a few pieces of evidence that support the theory of economies of size. Here are some illustrations:

• In 1963 Harvey Shapiro grouped the counties of each State by population and analyzed the average of local government expenditure per capita in each group. He found a cost curve similar to the first illustration in this chapter. In 20 States, the largest average per capita expenditures occurred in counties with populations of less than 5,000 (see table). In 10 States, the largest expenditures were in counties of more than 250,000 population.

• In an Iowa study, Marvin Julius produced a formula for county government costs by selecting county functions that are similar in all Iowa counties and relating the costs of these functions to county population. He found county government costs were equal to $175,000 plus $31.27 multiplied by the county population.

This formula proved more than 95 percent accurate when applied to Iowa counties. The $175,000 can be interpreted as the fixed cost of running a county government. This is the amount that might be saved if two county governments were consolidated to operate from one existing courthouse with no duplication of services.

Total per Capita Expenditures of Local Governments by County Population Size Group, 1957

County population	Distribution of States with highest and lowest expenditure		
	Highest	:	Lowest
	Number		*Number*
Less than 5,000	20		1
5,000 to 9,999	7		1
10,000 to 14,999	2		3
15,000 to 19,999	3		4
20,000 to 24,999	1		8
25,000 to 49,999	2		7
50,000 to 99,999	0		15
100,000 to 249,999	3		9
More than 250,000	10		0
Total	48		48

248

The Iowa analysis does not show specific savings such as personnel, machinery, or equipment. But it does indicate, based on actual tax askings, that an average county of 20,000 population operated its county government in 1970 for $175,000 less than the combined cost of two average 10,000 population counties.

If the $175,000 is accepted as an estimate of 1970 county government fixed cost, then if all of Iowa's 99 counties were consolidated into 16 super-county or regional units, savings would total $14.5 million.

• Robert Wessel concluded in a Minnesota study that some of that State's counties cannot continue to operate with their small economic base. "Alteration of the administrative structure will not increase local resources for county funds. Some counties face dilemmas of a valuation so low they cannot indefinitely continue their present government.

Consolidation of county governments into regional units, operating from one courthouse, has been proposed to maintain or improve governmental services at less cost.

Enrollment by school size	Pupil-teacher ratio Elementary	Senior high school	Cost per pupil	High school units offered
200– 499	18.5	12.2	852	34
500– 749	20.0	14.7	789	39
750– 999	20.8	16.1	727	40
1,000–1,499	22.5	17.3	728	44
1,500–1,999	22.3	17.1	704	51
2,000–2,999	23.4	18.6	680	54
3,000 & over	25.5	19.6	693	79
State average 1,446	22.9	16.8	718	43

"The basic alternatives open to these counties," Wessel asserts, "are either consolidation—assuming that another county will take over one that cannot finance itself—or additional aid from State and Federal sources. The number of Minnesota counties in this predicament is small. But as rural areas decline in population, as cost of existing services rise, and if valuations remain constant, more counties will be added to the list."

• In a study of 109 high schools (not districts), John Riew found a significant relationship between per pupil operating expenditures and the average daily attendance. Costs declined rapidly as school size increased, until an enrollment of 1,675 pupils was reached. Then costs rose. Increasing the enrollment from 500 to 1,000 pupils cut costs by $111 per pupil.

• Nels W. Hanson, studying school districts and not individual schools, found evidence of a cost curve similar to this chapter's first illustration. Optimum school district sizes varied, however, from 20,000 pupils in Nebraska to 160,000 in New York. Changing from 1,500 pupils to 20,000 in Nebraska saved only $15 per pupil; but changing from 1,500 to 100,000 in New York saved $96 per pupil.

• An Iowa analysis by Wallace E. Ogg shows that per pupil costs decrease until school enrollment reaches 3,000. After that point, per pupil costs seem to increase (see table). This study also indicates that the pupil-

teacher ratio did not change greatly and the larger schools had more course selection.

These and other examples support the logic of economies of scale. They suggest rural areas can gain by reorganizing services on a larger economic base.

There is just enough evidence to create interest in the possibilities, but not enough to provide the certainty most decision makers desire. Clearly, more information is needed before community leaders and legislators have the base they need for decision making.

But economies of scale appear to offer a promising route to examine for the dilemma of many rural counties. Further research could provide material for sound decision making in this direction and also should indicate the type of economic organization necessary for success. For perhaps the frustrations in rural America today are partly due to the recognition that the old community is gone—or going— and the new community is yet unclear.

More and better information is needed to guide the "development through adjustment" efforts in rural areas, but the information gatherer faces difficult obstacles.

An Illinois farmer or a Detroit automaker can measure the quantity and quality of his output. Therefore he can determine the precise cost of each unit of output. But how does one measure the output of a school—or a local government? How can educational quality be measured? What is the quantity of county government that each citizen receives? Until these questions are answered, the information on economics of communities will be inadequate.

But the answers are needed. Local government officials, State legislatures, and Congress will need these kind of answers if the problem of population redistribution is to be solved. This neglected area of research is vital to some of our most pressing national problems. It can be understood only if substantially more resources are devoted to study and analysis of this elusive question.

"Main Street's Too Narrow"

RICHARD J. EDWARDS

THE MAYOR had heard it all many times. "Main Street's too narrow." "If we ever faced a big fire, I don't believe we would have enough water to fight it." "I hope the State doesn't check our sewer plant, we only half process the stuff." "Premier Manufacturing considered putting a new plant here, but they said our town was behind the times." "All we've been doing for 80 years is patching up this town."

The Mayor had some comfort in the fact that not everyone was dissatisfied. A number of people liked a quiet town. They considered themselves lucky that they don't have a lot of new people moving in. New schoolhouses are nice but cost money without any promise of a better education. The "best" educated move away anyhow.

Then too there is the landmark question. Widening Main Street would probably mean that the old hotel, scene of every big banquet since 1853, would have to come down. Is expansion worth the loss?

A town renewal discussion carries with it many hot arguments. On the one hand, unless modernization is done, ours will be a ghost town. But on the other hand, think of all the money it will cost to rebuild streets, the sewage system, the school, the hospital, downtown, and just about everything. If growth doesn't take place after spending all that money, we won't even have the joy of a graceful retirement.

The Mayor was faced with a dilemma. How can we reach a decision about recommending some sort of physical renewal? The feelings for and against any idea are emotional. In his search for answers, the Mayor turned to an acquaintance at State University, who worked with community development problems of towns throughout the State. They talked about many things ranging from how the town got in the condition it is in, to the things that should be looked at in making renewal decisions. Some of what they discussed follows.

Like all towns and cities, ours had its day as a boom town. When it was named, it was a crossroads and little else. It was located on a favorable transportation path and became the major market of the surrounding area. Each year, things looked ever more prosperous. New homes, stores, repair shops and even an implement manufacturing plant were built, providing work for the sons who didn't stay on farms.

Each new addition made something older look out of place. Frame and clapboard replaced log and plank; brick and mortar replaced frame. Water was piped in where wells had done the job. In a few years the

*

RICHARD J. EDWARDS is an Agricultural Economist in the Community Facilities Branch, Economic Development Division, Economic Research Service.

waterworks was replaced with a new one and many mains had to be dug up because everything was too small. Each time a street was ripped up, it was replaced with a more solid material. The physical structure of the town became more and more firm and difficult to change.

Among the improvements our Nation experienced was an improved transportation system. The markets for some towns grew ever larger while others, like ours, seemed to reach out less every year. For several years our town has not grown—comfortably holding its own. It has stayed comfortable for more than a generation. Now, will some of the additional 100 million or so people expected by the turn of the century decide that our town is for them? Most townsfolk realize that few new people will settle here unless some modernization occurs.

The townspeople also understand—whatever change is proposed has both benefits and costs to be considered. A listing of possible alternatives, together with the associated costs and benefits of each, will greatly improve the decision making process.

Whenever possible, these costs and benefits should be given in dollar terms. Many important factors cannot be valued in dollars and cents, but they should be listed so the people can place their own importance on them. There are many groups of items that planners will consider in preparing such a report.

First, there is the broad category of better use of the community's resources. Well built modern schools and public buildings add greatly to a town's value. Not only do they add value in themselves, but they also enhance the value of the private property of a city. All neighboring property is increased in value by replacement of an obsolete structure with a new building.

Public buildings, streets, and utilities have a tendency to set the stage for private development. Few people are encouraged by the prospect of

building or remodeling next to an unkempt, 19th century courthouse or on a location serviced by poorly designed streets. Most citizens are proud of streets on which the traffic flows at a rapid pace, and proud of modern new public buildings. Private construction is encouraged in such an atmosphere.

Public revenue receipts should begin rising. The new buildings are worth more and local business should increase.

A renovated city has an advantage in attracting new business and industry. Most businessmen prefer to locate in areas that have adequate public facilities and services that show indications of vitality.

Per capita costs of operation should decline for some areas of municipal services. Well designed streets offer greater ease and efficiency in providing police protection. Fire departments should receive major benefits with the replacement of older structures and elimination of fire hazards. Maintenance costs of new utilities are lower than those replaced.

Savings to citizens in the operation of their private business and in their social life can be an additional benefit. A decrease in insurance rates and more efficient transportation are but two areas of decline in private expenses resulting from public action.

Another group of benefits are the social improvements that can accompany renewal. Redesigning the highways results in a decline of driver frustration at having to wait long periods of time in traffic clogged streets. The knowledge that an adequate supply of pure water is readily available gives security and peace of mind to all citizens.

The beauty and esthetic value of a planned new development add to the quality of life in the community. The level of housing in the city is improved. Areas of the city which are thought undesirable begin to diminish in number and size.

All of these items are difficult to total up in dollars and cents, but they can be among the most important additions to a community's life.

Balanced against the gains are many cost areas. First, there is the big area of demolition costs and the loss of value of the old structures removed. Survey and planning costs are highly visible but valuable necessities. Largest single item is the cost of new public improvements. All of these are easily valued in dollars and are usually published.

A second area of costs is hard to estimate. Occasionally an improvement of generally broad-based benefit will actually cause a decline in value of some land. An expressway through part of a well-to-do residential area can have this effect.

Many times, items of historic interest are in danger of being lost or drastically changed. Their preservation may add greatly to costs of the renovation. The community is then faced with the difficult decision of appraising a part of its heritage.

Old neighborhoods often will be split or completely disrupted, changing established living patterns. City renewal can and has resulted in such major and expensive building in private construction that housing for lower income families is eliminated. The omission can lead to the additional cost of guaranteeing housing these families can afford.

Much of the value of the benefits, and weighing of the social costs, depends on expectations for the future. If a city still has good location advantages or some particular natural resource, it can expect renovation to encourage growth and activity. But if whatever advantages the city once had are no longer important, then first consideration must be given to changing this condition. Renewal of the physical plant of a town will provide greater benefits than the costs only if increased activity occurs.

With all the problems and pros and cons about renewal, why not forget the old places and build new towns? New towns *will* be created but not for the population increases America

is expecting. We already have a big investment in the existing towns and cities and it's less expensive to add to the plant in operation.

Most areas of the Nation already have a city or town located in them. Any new town proposal would likely have to be connected with an existing city. The task of organizing all the operations of a city—the amount of housing necessary, the shops, and the jobs—is enormous.

At the same time, older cities of all sizes are having problems with their physical plant. The saying, "Our town is just like New York only the buildings are not as tall," has some merit. New York City has circulation problems—a hardening of the arteries. Movement of people to and from work and shopping is a major problem. The people are struggling with the threat of a power shortage and the counter threat of major air pollution if some of the power plant proposals are followed.

Many other cities are faced with large parts of the city's structure being out of date. The new subway construction in San Francisco is but one example of attempts being made to tackle problems that have beset older cities for years.

Towns and cities across the land are continuing to look at themselves and plan for change.

Ava, Mo., is an example of a town of 2,000 people that was faced with many of the problems we have discussed. Factory owners looked at the town and decided against locating here. In the late 1950's, after a major effort, the main highway to the town was reconstructed. The new highway was straighter and it was three miles less to the next largest city.

When a new industry was seriously considering the town as a site, expansion and updating of Ava's water and sewage facilities were undertaken.

Within 3 years, two sizable new industries had located in the town with the aid of a local development corporation. Population of the town increased by 400. Property valuation rose almost two-thirds and the tax rate declined a fifth.

The people in Ava were fortunate. They had sufficient advantages to continue to grow once the city's physical structure was modernized. In cooperation with the county government, they undertook some advanced planning. Renovation was not done too far in advance of prospective growth of a type which would help pay the bills. They had not financed frills. They did build a revitalized town.

Our Mayor and his friend said goodbye. It had been a big afternoon.

On the way home, the Mayor thought over all that had been discussed. He was convinced our town had a future as part of the growth America would experience. But what he and the town needed were facts.

The next few months would be busy. We need facts and planning to decide if Main Street really is too narrow.

What and Where of Community Services

E. J. NIEDERFRANK.

COMMUNITY services—who needs them? We all do! But they occur and thrive or not according to demand. And demand for services varies depending on numbers of people and economic development.

It takes more than a lovely view or clean roadways to attract new people to a rural area. If community services, public and private, are lacking or inadequate, prospective new citizens may never arrive and native young people will not stay.

Viable communities nice to live in are those that contain an adequate mix of satisfying services and employment opportunities compatible with the size of the community and the characteristics of the residents. Where the community structure and population composition are constantly changing, the problem of providing an adequate mix of services becomes very serious. Useful services can be adequately provided only where there is a good base for their support.

When planning for development, there is a tendency to concentrate mainly on ways to attract new industry and retail business and thus create a flourishing community. This course, however, often bypasses the very important assessment of community services which will be needed by a more sizable population with progressive ideas.

New citizens in a town expect the schools to be good enough to prepare their children for college. They take it for granted that a good library will be close by. They expect adequate police and fire protection and good streets. They assume that the services of health facilities, hospitals, and doctors are conveniently available for them and their families.

But some of these community services are the very ones that are most deficient in rural areas. And a community cannot hope to draw and hold new people if it lacks any of these amenities of community life.

Community services are a function of two factors—population and economics. And even these factors are interrelated because you generally find population increases where the economic situation is favorable compared to other places. For where the economic base is small or shrinking, the population tends also to decline and community services become less and less in quantity and quality.

*

E. J. NIEDERFRANK is a rural sociologist in the Extension Service.

254

So population and economics—which is the chicken and which the egg? The crucial matter is not one of finding the final answer to this question, but of understanding the situation of your local community and surrounding area and bringing about changes that are necessary.

What is happening in terms of important trends, and why? What services are we now supporting adequately and can we continue to do so; and what services are in the immediate surrounding economic area? What services are we likely to lose? What changes will the people need to make in order to keep such services, or go to them in nearby places?

Or shall we improve transportation and communication with the service firms and agencies in the larger surrounding towns? This will mean locating and getting acquainted with another doctor and dentist, another post office, another bank, another school system. Studies show that small grocery stores are the last to leave declining communities.

A study reported in 1964 by Dr. Robert Saunders of West Virginia University for the Appalachian Regional Commission shows that some industries and services have a high "location quotient," meaning there is enough support for them, while others have a low quotient, therefore are less than self-sufficient and would not survive. He also found that local industries, business establishments, and public services tend to concentrate according to the demands for their goods or services.

All this means that much careful attention should be given to planning development so that adequate services can be economically provided by public agencies and private firms and conveniently used by the people.

Furthermore, this kind of planning has to be done on time. All too often some new industry or government installation comes in without giving the area enough lead time and helping it make plans for developing the additions to services which will be needed by the expanding community.

Community services range between two general types as to requirements for support. At one extreme are *local microtype* services which can thrive on relatively small volumes of use and are needed near at hand. Examples are the post office, gasoline stations, churches, elementary school, barbershop, small bank, and one or more stores selling basic groceries, household and farm items. Generally lacking in places like these are adequate health facilities and services, advanced educational opportunities, and waste disposal systems.

At the other end of the scale are *area macrotype* services of a county, multicounty, or regional nature. These include physicians and dentists, hospital, specialized health services, high school, vocational school and possibly a community or junior college, several banks, sizable specialized stores, legal services, finance and credit services, building and plumbing tradesmen, theaters, an attractive library, cultural art programs, agricultural industries, outdoor park recreation areas, extensive public water and sewerage systems, the offices of government agencies, modern trash collection, main highway access and bus services, perhaps rail and airline services.

The above lists of examples represent both public and private community services. Both have to be considered in community or area development. Both require adequate volumes of business to warrant being established and maintained. Both are affected by population and economic changes. Both benefit from sound development planning.

The Economic Research Service of the U. S. Department of Agriculture, in a series of articles in *The Farm Index*, August to November 1970, briefly summarizes the basic requirements of various kinds of community services and related conditions affecting rural America. Certain services cost much more than others per thousand population.

Because some people need certain services close at hand or with convenient access, regardless of where they live, usually service agencies and business firms work out plans for providing these services through field workers, transportation service, part-time services and the like.

But the additional costs of such provisions can be held to a minimum and better service provided if housing and economic changes are guided by proper development and land use planning coupled with good zoning.

Social scientists for years have pointed out that the major reason people migrate from outlying rural communities to the larger towns and cities is because the additional facilities and services found there mean more opportunities for employment, cultural activities, and other satisfactions of living. Migration causes problems in both the places of decline and the places of growth. But specific adjustments can and are being worked out in both places to reduce the effects of such change.

Studies made during the early 1960's by Charles Press and Clarence J. Hein in Michigan, Daryl K. Heasley in Pennsylvania, and Sheridan Maitland in Maryland indicate that people differ in what they think about community services. Longer resident rural people tend to be more conservative than the suburban-type newcomers about seeing the need for certain services, although suburban people tend to become more conservative in this regard after 10 or 15 years in the community.

Rural residents tend to hold back on new methods to meet community problems. Persons with only rural experience were found to be most opposed to changes such as new street lights, zoning, police protection, expanded public health services, and school changes, and most critical of new taxes necessary for improved services. They were less aware of what was actually happening in their communities and what effects this might have on the community.

Arthur Walrath in Virginia found that the adjustment situations which pertain to schools, health services, and similar changes are aggravated by the time lag between the influx of people and the collection of more taxes based upon the values of new property and improvements made.

Modern transportation and communication have contributed greatly to the development of commercial and social service centers based on larger geographic areas than formerly. As the larger county seat towns and surrounding cities grow, various businesses and services tend to concentrate in them. But when this kind of development goes on unplanned, it causes problems and inconveniences to people both in the growing cities and in the small communities which are losing these services.

I have observed many cases of haphazard suburban development and unwise location of new industries which were made with no reference whatever to any overall development or land use plan, or because one was not adequately followed. Such unwise development often makes it impossible to economically provide public services like power, water, and school systems, besides creating lags in other services which not only cause many inconveniences but also added economic and social costs.

Some towns undoubtedly will dry up despite the strong attachments of people to them and what they may try to do to assure stability. Many others a little more favorably situated, and with leaders favorable to bringing about needed adjustments and improvements, are surviving and will grow.

Rural people must realize that the future of their small communities is inextricably a part of the surrounding larger urban-centered community and must make efforts to plan for developments accordingly.

Problems of location, availability, and accessibility of services may be expected to become even more difficult in the years ahead as populations increase and the ecology of communities change. Especially must ways be found to help residents of small towns and sparsely settled areas to obtain trade, business, and public services at costs comparable to similar services in densely settled areas.

One way is through cooperation between two or more towns or counties. For years some towns of New England have cooperated with one another to provide fire protection, library service, health clinics, or special school programs. The cases of cooperation are increasing among Midwest counties to jointly provide certain public services in preference to outright consolidation of counties.

Good examples are the TENCO (ten counties) and NIAD (Northern Iowa Area Development) projects in Iowa; also the Syracuse, N.Y., rural-urban program.

The idea of development districts enacted and supported by the State governments is taking hold in Virginia, Georgia, Kentucky, Missouri, and several other States. The U. S. Department of Commerce and the U. S. Department of Housing and Urban Development have programs of planning and funding to help foster this kind of development based on area growth centers.

Similar efforts for improving health services in rural areas are being undertaken by the Comprehensive Health Planning and Regional Medical programs of the Department of Health, Education, and Welfare in cooperation with State governments. Especially noteworthy is the Appalachian program of coordinated health facilities which includes such cases as the Hazard, Ky., regional hospital, clinics in outlying places, and outpatient services.

Another type of adjustment is Metro development, in which metropolitan commissions or authorities are established to work out systems for providing certain services cooperatively between central cities and their widening rings of suburban counties, sometimes even crossing State lines. This is providing such services as extended rapid transit, extended water systems, extended health services, and cooperative educational programs. A program of this type is underway in the Washington, D. C., area; Atlanta, Ga.; Minneapolis, Minn.; and several other places.

Private businesses of cities, often led by a newspaper or broadcasting station, also are taking greater responsibilities for more adequately servicing surrounding areas beyond the city line.

Part-time and once-a-week services, such as health clinics and employment service contacts, are being used in some States to provide at least limited service to very sparsely settled areas.

New ambulance service, including emergency training for drivers, is being provided in Colorado in cooperation with medical associations

An airport usually serves several counties or is regional in nature.

and public health departments. In such cases it is believed that proper emergency treatment and rapid transportation to an adequate central hospital is preferable to trying to build and maintain small, inadequate hospitals in the rural areas. Some Western places are even trying helicopter ambulance service. A study made in 1968 by Leland Bierman and Mark J. Powers of South Dakota State University compares the costs of different types of rural ambulance services operating in a 16-county area of northwest South Dakota.

Since 1950 I also have seen community improvement clubs and county development associations in some Southern States being instrumental in bringing about improvements in community services and environment, through community-wide cooperation, joint efforts between small communities, and by initiating communication with agencies for receiving special assistance from them. 4-H and FFA programs in several States also have begun giving increased attention to community study and action by youth.

Finally, it seems to me the greatest need for change in order to bring about desirable adjustments for providing effective, efficient community services is *change in the attitudes of people*, based on greater understanding of the economic and social facts of life affecting their areas.

Leaders in both rural and urban communities, along with officials of planning and development agencies, must recognize this need for strategies which will develop greater understanding and constructive actions among the people for a sound and orderly area development.

This is the key to adequate community services.

production resources for living

The Task Ahead For Food And Fiber

REX F. DALY and
MARGUERITE C. BURK

FARMERS in most of today's world still wonder if they can win the food-population race. They keep producing more food with better seed and chemicals. But each year, people multiply so fast that gains are literally eaten up.

American farmers wonder how much food and fiber they will need to produce to meet the added demands of more Americans. And they wonder, too, about the future of world markets which take an important part of our farm output. The pace of the green revolution in world grain production, and the growing number of increasingly affluent consumers in many nations, will strongly affect how much food we export.

We cannot predict just how much the U.S. population will grow, or how global food needs will affect our foreign sales. But we can make some rough projections based on trends and economic relationships.

At the outset we assert that American farmers probably can provide added food and fiber needs during the next 30 years without great pressure of resources available. More capital equipment, chemicals, land, and know-how will be needed, but most analyses indicate that these resources will be available.

Farmers are less certain about what commodities will be demanded by a growing number of increasingly affluent consumers. They wonder, too, along with the food industry and housewives, how food technology and nutritional science will transform our daily diets during the next 30 years.

Our incomes, our tastes, and our style of living will continue to change. They will change in ways that will affect the demand for individual food and fiber products. The appearance, quality, and convenience of what we eat will change dramatically in the years ahead. And tomorrow's farmer will have to tailor the variety and amount of food he grows to meet these changes in demand.

First, take a look ahead at trends in population, incomes, and food preferences and the outlook for our net foreign trade balance in agricultural products. These are the influences that will basically determine the level of demand for the produce from our farms for the next three decades.

Then, venture a little into the remarkable changes in food technology and nutrition that will affect both the food and fiber you use and the farmer produces.

U.S. population growth, creating more mouths to feed and more bodies to clothe, will be the main force expanding food and fiber demand in the next 30 years. Growth in domestic markets for food and fiber closely parallels population growth.

Actually our longer-run population outlook is very uncertain. Until a few years ago, population experts assumed that the growth of the 1950's and early 1960's would continue. By this reasoning, another 100 million Americans would be here before the year 2000. But new forces and issues are at work. Americans are worrying as never before about the strain that a continued high level of population increase would place on world food supplies, pollution control, waste disposal, and the general quality of life.

*

REX F. DALY is Director, Economic and Statistical Analysis Division, Economic Research Service.

MARGUERITE C. BURK is an Economist in the Consumer and Food Economic Research Division, Agricultural Research Service.

These new concerns could have a big effect; many experts foresee slower population growth for the decades ahead. The Census Bureau Series D projection calls for 281 million people by 2000. And growth could fall short of this if young families embrace the zero population growth idea. The recent Census Bureau "X" projection assumes a low birth rate and no immigration, resulting in a population of around 250 million by the year 2000. In fact, under these assumptions the population would level off at about 275 million during 2035–2040.

Slower population growth is a real possibility. But attitudes toward population planning are also tied up with religion, folklore, and politics and they usually change slowly. So a U.S. population around 280 million by 2000 seems a reasonable basis for projecting food and fiber demand. This means a population increase of about 35 percent in the next three decades.

Undoubtedly, even more people will live in urban areas, and the age composition of the population will change during these decades. But these changes in locale and age may be largely offsetting in their effect on total food and fiber demand. Impacts of the rural-urban shift on our diets will slow, especially if cultural changes among today's youth encourage renewed emphasis on subsistence production of food.

As Americans grow more numerous in the next three decades, they will also grow more affluent. During the last 30 years the real buying power of each consumer doubled. This gain had a big impact on the demand for individual foods, boosting purchases of preferred and often higher priced items among the meats, fruits, vegetables, and most convenience foods. These changes contributed to reduced buying of grain products, fruits, some high energy vegetables, and potatoes for fresh use.

Once again, during the next three decades, the real buying power of each consumer will at least double. People will be able to spend more money on the foods and fibers that they consider most desirable and most convenient.

Besides the anticipated impact of population and income growth on consumer purchases of food and fiber, farmers are concerned about the competition of substitute products. They are also concerned about many developments in technology affecting food and fiber which will influence markets for farm products.

The new Americans born in the next three decades will expect more of their food than the most jaded epicure of Ancient Rome ever dared dream of. They will insist on food that is:

Available when they want it, in or out of season,

Tasting as it did when it was picked,

In a "grade AA" state of wholesomeness,

Providing a full measure of nutritional value,

Ready to fix with little or no fuss.

And amazingly enough, the new Americans are very likely to get food that meets these standards.

During the last 30 years food technologists began the task. Their creations included frozen foods, fortified foods, year-round produce, and "instant" beverages and food mixes.

In the next 30 years, new advances on the horizon in the way food is grown, processed, transported, and prepared will make recent innovations look quite old-fashioned.

Even meat, a major source of income to American farmers, will be challenged during the next three decades.

Scientists discovered that the soybean, a legume which is about a third vegetable protein, can be processed and transformed into meatlike products. These products look and taste much like some popular meat and poultry items and come close to "the real thing" in protein and vitamin content.

Vegetable proteins which imitate

261

steak, ham or chicken haven't gained widespread popularity because they offer few price incentives over real meat products. Consumers are basically conservative about such changes. They may be slow to change as long as good quality beef, bacon and poultry are available at relatively moderate prices.

On the other hand, substitution of lower priced vegetable proteins, such as those made from soybeans, will increase as an extender in many processed meat items: hot dogs, meat patties, sausages, and luncheon meats. Looks and taste of these foods disguise the exact ingredients. Moreover, they are easy to blend and generally less expensive than meat protein.

For many years, consumers have extensively switched to soybean and other vegetable oils away from animal fats. Substitution of margarine which is made from vegetable oils for butter and of nondairy creamers for other high-fat dairy products— table cream, evaporated and condensed milk—has restricted the market for milkfat. Although the trend toward use of vegetable oils in filled milk and frozen desserts has slowed, the potential exists for further inroads into the traditional markets for milk products.

The competition between soybean products and animal fats as well as some meat products is of great interest to both soybean farmers and livestock producers. It makes the future of their products extremely difficult to foresee.

The same uncertainty prevails among many other farm commodities for which science has developed substitutes. The popular synthetic drinks and sweeteners, the manmade fibers, and leather-like products come from the factory, not the farm.

Use of synthetic fibers has risen dramatically in the past two decades. They have cut deeply into markets for cotton and wool fibers. Currently manmade fibers make up almost half of total domestic use of broadwoven goods.

The citrus industry faces growing competition from synthetic drinks. And synthetics have materially reduced traditional markets for fats and oils in the manufacture of soap, paints, and varnishes.

New processes also change the forms in which foods are offered for sale. Processors are testing improved methods of freezing, radiation, dehydration, chemical preservation, use of antibiotics, and sterilization. An important aim is to find processes for each food that will retain the qualities of the fresh product, increase the ease of use, and reduce marketing costs.

Remember the advent of frozen juice concentrates? The potential for sterilized and dehydrated foods is equally dazzling.

Sterilized foods packaged under sterile conditions by an aseptic canning procedure retain a high level of nutrient quality, palatability, color, and texture. The process is very effective for preserving low-acid fruits and vegetables such as applesauce and sweet corn and for heat-sensitive dairy products like whole milk, whipping cream, and eggnog.

Another process arousing much interest is a form of dehydration called reverse osmosis. Liquid food products are put under pressure in a membrane that forces out water or other small molecule products and leaves a concentration of solids. This relatively inexpensive process is already in limited use.

A number of other approaches will help maintain the quality of food products between the processor and the consumer:

• New types of refrigeration equipment are being developed to protect food from deteriorating during storage.

• Edible coatings are being tested for meats, vegetables, and fruits.

• New knowledge of microbiology and biochemistry is being applied to maintain shelf life of processed foods and to control the atmosphere of perishable foods.

• The flying freight cars of tomorrow will bring a great variety of tropical fruits and vegetables to metropolitan distribution centers.

• We can eventually expect the underground delivery of food to neighborhood pickup points from area distribution centers on orders from the household computer.

Food scientists have a variety of ways for changing the attributes of agricultural commodities to match consumer wants. Examples are meat which is enzyme-tenderized on the hoof, enrichment and fortification with synthetic nutrients, and the combination of soy products with wheat flour and with pulverized meats as protein supplements and binders and soybean meat analogs.

Geneticists are working on problems such as how to reduce fat and cholesterol content of eggs and milk.

Consumer demand for individual foods by the end of the twentieth century will also be influenced by technological changes in home food preparation and storage.

The family activity pattern will dictate the choice between a meal including home-baked bread, slowly browned roast, and potatoes and one prepared in seconds by microwave or other techniques for reheating of prepared dishes. Preparation of both meals might be controlled by instructions stored in the family computer.

Shorter work weeks and the likelihood of greater flexibility in school schedules will also contribute to increased leisure time activity and to eating on the move.

Use of prepared foods will be encouraged by portable units which can heat the casserole and keep the ice cream hard at the same time. These units, already in use, will be very popular with families on the go in cars and boats.

A common alternative fare may be the complete on-the-run meal—portion controlled, prepackaged, precooked—sold through carryout stores and factory vending machines.

Food storage facilities in homes of the year 2000 may be very different from those of today.

When the shopper brings her computer selected and ordered food home from the neighborhood delivery point, each food will go into a particular place in the storage system and each will be registered in a computer memory. Then the homemaker can schedule preparation of meals for a day or a week ahead on computer tape.

Consumers will increasingly shy away from foods requiring special handling or preparation procedures. For example, melons might prove to be so inefficient to handle and store that consumer preference for them may dwindle. Or, the melon may be modified to retain its market.

Just as technology will transform foods as we think of them today, it will transform our lives tomorrow. There will likely be shorter work weeks, staggered work hours, and even flexible times for going to school, as TV-teaching and computerized study take a bigger role in education.

At the same time we will undergo other important changes: trends toward smaller families, rising income, and better knowledge of nutrition. These changes will make us much more demanding about nutritive quality, flavor, texture, and variety in foods.

Nutritional problems may well occur as a result of changes in the kinds of food we eat. For example, the rapid increases in consumption of meat and poultry now underway and in prospect for coming decades could cause a rise in metabolic problems unless the intake of other nutrients—such as vitamins and minerals—are kept in proper balance with the proteins.

The same imbalance threatens our intake of trace minerals. It will be impossible to supply them safely and adequately in synthetic foods until much more is known about quantitative requirements and the role these minerals play in human

Left, orange juice futures exchange. Right, bids come in by phone from several States to feeder pig sale in North Carolina.

health. Already there is substantial evidence that some minerals are toxic if consumed in large amounts.

Many nutritionists urge that only varied diets with few of the synthetic foods be recommended for the general public until there is far more knowledge on exactly how food components work together in the human body.

Largely unforeseen and extensive uses of the National Research Coun-

cil's recommended dietary allowances have prodded nutrition researchers to further study both minimum and recommended levels of nutrient intake. Many people want scientists to identify minimum levels of intake by the day or week, and to identify maximum amounts where known in order to prevent overdoses of certain food nutrients.

A better nutritional knowledge will

Cotton harvesting in Mississippi.

help protect the public from choosing poor diets, misusing dietary recommendations, and falling prey to food quackery.

Accordingly, we may expect much more government activity along the lines of public health regulation and food standards. Also, an information network may be developed to integrate food and nutrition knowledge for use by the public, the food industries, and local, State, and Federal agencies.

All these developments—substitutes for traditional ingredients; new processing, marketing, and storage techniques; and nutritional discoveries—may on balance tend to dampen, rather than to speed up, growth in the overall demand for food. They should contribute not only to greater efficiency, but also to less waste and spoilage and perhaps a smaller per capita intake of food.

By the year 2000, possibly two-thirds of the population may be in families having incomes in excess of $15,000, even without any inflation in prices.

Projections based largely on diets like those of today's high-income families suggest that housewives will purchase more meat and poultry than they do today, although their buying of these items may not rise as fast as it did during the last 30 years. And, from what we can project from patterns of the past, per capita demand for some fruits, many salad vegetables, and processed convenience foods will increase further.

These gains, however, may be largely offset by declines for grain products and some high-calorie vegetables.

Per capita use of veal and lamb likely will continue to drop off in coming decades. The drop will reflect a declining availability of these meats as well as the growing preference for beef and poultry.

Eggs are growing less popular, too, partly because we are trimming the size and leisure of our breakfasts. High-fat products—like lard, butter, cream, and whole milk—also are being used less, reflecting calorie-conscious consumers and concern over possible health effects of high animal-fat intake. These down-trends will continue, but the decline may moderate.

Nonfood uses per person of farm products will likely trend gradually downward, but perhaps more slowly. Synthetics have already made big inroads into regular fiber markets and in industrial uses of fats and oils in soap, paints, and varnishes. Per capita use of tobacco will likely continue to reflect anxieties about smoking and health.

Many American farmers are very concerned about export market prospects for coming decades. Exports of farm products totaled over $6 1/2 billion during the 1969–70 marketing year and prospects point to a sizable increase in 1970–71.

Exports now account for around half of all our wheat, rice and soybean (including oil and meal) production; around a third of cotton, tallow, and tobacco production; and substantial quantities of feed grains, fruits, and vegetables.

Crop exports are equivalent to about a fifth of total crop output.

Export market prospects for farm products remain one of the biggest uncertainties in overall demand expansion for farm products. But in coming decades they will likely continue to be the most rapidly expanding sector of the total demand for U.S. farm products despite great advances in food production in the less developed areas of the world.

This conclusion is based largely on the expectation that U.S. agriculture will continue to have an excess production capacity. Despite widespread publicity and concern, the population problem may remain a critical barrier to righting the world population-food balance. And so long as the United States has excess production capacity, markets will likely be found to export large quantities of grains, vegetable oils and meals, fruits, vegetables, and possibly cotton and tobacco.

To sum up the prospect for total food and fiber demand over the next three decades, a population increase of around 35 percent would create a similar increase in the domestic market for food and fiber. Farm output would increase a bit faster, as in the past, to supply an expanding foreign demand for farm products.

U.S. agriculture has provided in the past for the growing domestic market and rapidly expanding exports. This was accomplished without undue strain and with little change in overall resource use. Our output potential for years to come likely will remain large enough to continue to exert pressure on farm prices and income.

Production has been generally responsive to demand change. Accordingly, we have had production gains for beef, poultry, and feed grains that have outpaced population growth. But production increases have been smaller for hogs, milk, and eggs.

The increase in farm output, a shift from relatively expensive land and labor to more capital, and changes in the size structure of farms have sharply increased productivity per man and per acre. Farm consolidation which combined the smaller, less efficient units into fewer, larger productive units has accounted for much of the increase in productivity in agriculture. This may be a dwindling source of gain if commercial agriculture keeps moving toward larger optimum units.

U.S. agriculture is in an excellent position to wage a war on hunger at home and abroad. In addition to more than 50 million acres being held out of production, another 250 million acres are in capability classes considered suitable for regular cultivation. Higher prices and incomes needed to attract this land into production would also encourage increased use of capital, fertilizer, and other production resources.

There are many other possibilities for expanding food production—synthetics, new products, fuller use of photosynthetic action, and others— if the demand pressures were greatly intensified.

The above prospects sum to a comparatively rosy picture regarding the output potential, which is as it should be. Yet as always, uncertainties loom on the horizon including:

• The much-publicized world food-population race,

• Questions about the longer-run advances in productivity and yields in agriculture, and

• The consequences of possible ecological imbalances and related threats to our food supply from erosion, waste, and pollution.

U.S. agriculture can look forward to rapid technological advances in the years ahead which will lead to fewer, larger, and better-managed commercial farms.

Such advances don't just happen, however. They will require continued research and further advances in the technology of providing food and fiber.

Problems of Land Use Change

FRED H. ABEL and
RICHARD C. MCARDLE

EMPTY storefronts along the main street of a small town in the Midwest. New houses on land in California that once was covered by orchards, citrus groves, and crops. Brush and small trees on pasture land in the Northeast. Houses being torn down to build a freeway in the inner city.

These are examples of changes in land use and economic activity taking place in the United States which can be seen today from a car window. Not so visible to the casual observer are the changes in number and type of jobs, income, and quality of life in general which are associated with these changes.

The next 100 million Americans will be faced with countless decisions concerning land use. Some will be individual—the decision to buy a house in a new suburban development. Some will be collective—a vote on bonds to be used to purchase land for a county park. Some will be commercial—location of a new factory near an interchange on a major highway. Other decisions will be esthetic—the preservation of a wild stretch of river in its natural state, rather than building dams.

All of these decisions affect people, some directly, many indirectly. Joe and John and Bob and Mary are a few who are affected directly.

• His great-grandfather built the solid red brick house over a hundred years ago when he moved his family from Pennsylvania to the quarter-section on the prairies west of Chicago. What changes those 160 acres had seen! Horse-drawn plows and wagons, tractors and pickup trucks, hybrid corn, electric power. The windmill tower still stood near the barnyard, but the metallic creak and clank of the old pump had been replaced by the quiet purr of an electric motor.

Joe stood quietly in the dusk. From the porch he could see the reddish glow in the East—the lights of Chicago and the cities and towns spread out around it. More changes were on the way. The nearby interchange on

*

FRED H. ABEL is an Agricultural Economist in the Economic Development Division, Economic Research Service.

RICHARD C. MCARDLE, formerly with the Natural Resource Economics Division, Economic Research Service, is now with the Foreign Regional Analysis Division.

the new interstate highway guaranteed that.

Ten years ago a real estate man had tried to get an option on the place. In the last 2 years there had been a steady stream of developers and real estate men, all with visions of shopping centers, factories, houses, schools, winding streets, and parks. "Open space," they called it. Joe wondered what could be more open than his 160 acres in corn and wheat.

But changes were bound to come. No one was left to run the farm. Joe's sons had gone to college and were now out on the West Coast. Help was hard to get, and most of the time you couldn't get it. Taxes? Higher every year. New schools, paved roads, and now they were talking about water lines and sewer lines.

The first people who had moved out from the city had bought lots along the roads. They had wells and septic tanks. That didn't take much land. A corner off a farm here and there. But after a few years the farms began to go.

Windy Towne Estates—the old Adams place—about a mile away had over 500 homes now and another 500 on the way. There was talk of incorporation, of sewer and water districts. The tax assessor had stopped by that morning. The feed bill came in the noon mail.

Martha's talk about Florida—the Adams's had moved there—seemed to make more and more sense. Yes, changes are on the way, thought Joe, as he fumbled for the developer's business card on his way to the telephone.

• John is a successful dairy farmer in upstate New York. For years his cows had grazed on an 80-acre pasture and woodlot. In recent years John modernized his operation and now keeps his cattle in a 5-acre dairy feedlot where they are given concentrates, hay, and other roughage. Milk production has increased with these efficient procedures.

The abandoned pasture, too steep and stony for plowing, is overgrown

267

today with weeds, brush, and small trees. An understory of small trees is also beginning to appear in the woodlot which is no longer grazed.

• Bob and Mary live in a Maryland suburb of Washington, D.C. Three years ago they bought an idle 18-acre farm near York, Pa. In the 1920's and earlier, the 18 acres—which included a woodlot—were intensively farmed and supported a farm family. By the end of World War II, active farming had ceased.

Only a large family garden and some apple trees remained as a reminder of the crops, livestock, and poultry which earlier had provided a livelihood as well as food. The "farm" had become a rural residence. The owner earned his living in nearby York.

When Bob and Mary acquired the property, the once-cleared land was overgrown with weeds and brush. Small trees were beginning to appear, seeding in from the adjacent woodlot.

With the help of their three children—and the advice of the local forester and soil conservation representative—the idle cropland is being reforested with pine, a pond is being

New residential areas and superhighways are examples of intensive special uses that take land from agricultural purposes.

dug, and a dream of a weekend retreat is becoming reality. . .

The decisions of Joe and John and Bob and Mary were essentially individual ones and changed their lives greatly. However, their decision touched a large number of other people, too. Joe's decision affects the lives of all his neighbors and the 600 families that will buy a home on his old farm.

Today we are becoming more aware of how these decisions influence the location of economic activity and the use of land, and in turn our national and local economic and social well-being. Of particular concern is the effect of land use on the quality of our environment, and how the location of new industry affects the economic future and choices of individuals and communities.

Land use alone does not determine the location of most economic activity. On the other hand, the location of economic activity does have major impacts on land use in that area. The concentration of economic activity can be very great as in our major cities. And these areas have some of the most serious problems of land use change. Meanwhile in many rural areas economic activity is sparse, the population declining, and land use is changing, too.

Why do industries continue to concentrate in the larger cities? Because that's where the people are.

Over 60 percent of our jobs are in the service industries—retail stores, the government services, education, transportation, communication, and entertainment are examples. Such industries deal directly with people, and must be located near people.

Nearly 30 percent of all jobs are in the manufacturing industry. These industries do not have to be located near large cities. But they do need a large labor supply, with ready access to markets and major transportation routes. Large cities provide these advantages.

Six urban counties (New York City counted as one county) produce

20 percent of value added by manufacturing. These six counties are the core of six of our 10 largest cities (New York, Chicago, Los Angeles, Philadelphia, Detroit, and Cleveland). To stimulate more economic activity outside large urban areas, it will be necessary to get new industries and industrial expansion outside such areas. Only 20 percent of value added by manufacturing is in the 2,788 least industrial rural counties.

Neither the service nor the manufacturing industries use much land directly. Most land use problems for new industries center on where they locate. Should they be grouped together near a shopping center or industrial park; in the center city or scattered in the suburbs; near major urban areas or in smaller more remote cities?

The indirect impact of location of manufacturing industries on land use is much greater. This is the need for land for houses, parks, and roads by families employed in the industries. Nevertheless, the total amount of land required directly and indirectly by such industries is small.

Most of the land is used by two extractive industries, agriculture and forestry. They use 80 percent. These industries as well as the other extractive industries of fishing and mining are geographically dispersed.

Because such industries are tied to natural resources, including land, they are not concentrated in a few dense areas like the urban service and manufacturing industries. However, since less than 10 percent of all jobs are in extractive industries, their location does not have a major impact on where most people live.

Ours is an urban society. This is true in terms of where people live and where most economic activity is.

Let's count as urban all counties identified by the Bureau of the Census as Standard Metropolitan Statistical Areas (SMSA's). These areas contain a city or urban center of over 50,000 population, or a part of a city or urban center with over 50,000

population. There are 243 of these SMSA's, involving 465 counties. These "urban" counties contain about 70 percent of the population.

Economic activity is even more concentrated in urban areas than population. Seventy-six percent of total personal income goes to urban counties. They have 82 percent of total retail sales.

On the other hand, if we count as urban all persons living in towns and cities of over 2,500, then about three-quarters of our population is urban.

During most of our history we were predominantly a rural society. Most of the land use problems concerned changing land from its natural state to agriculture or forestry. But now we are an urban society. Now we are converting land from agriculture and forestry to meet other (mostly urban and recreational) needs.

Besides the difference in economic activity between urban and non-urban areas, there are differences among regions. Some areas such as the Atlantic Coast, the manufacturing belt from New York City to Chicago, and the California Coast have a great deal of economic activity. Other areas like Appalachia, the Great Lakes region, northern New England, the Great Plains, and the mountain regions have relatively little economic activity outside the cities. Some of the last group are poverty areas and several are losing population.

The declining and poverty areas result from shifts in economic activity. Most of the people were employed in extractive industries or were dependent upon serving them. New technology released labor from these industries. Since no alternative jobs were available, the people became unemployed, underemployed (poverty areas) or moved (declining population areas).

Trends in the location of economic activity are continuing and will probably continue through the next 30 years. Rural areas dependent upon the extractive industries will continue to decline. Economic activity will continue to decline. Economic activity will continue to concentrate in major urban belts, such as Boston to Washington, Chicago to Pittsburgh, and San Diego to San Francisco.

There is concern for land use changes in what might be called the three great functional land use categories: urban, rural, and rural-urban fringe. The distinctions are admittedly blurred. Geographers, economists, and sociologists, among others, are still trying to find satisfactory definitions. There are few places today where one can point to a sharp dividing line between urban and rural.

Despite the difficulty of determining what is rural, urban, or rural-urban fringe, the land-use changes are generally quite different. In urban areas the change is from one intensive use to another intensive use. The changes often affect many people directly and are costly. In rural areas the change is from one extensive use to another. In the rural-urban fringe the change is from extensive use to intensive use.

Changes are taking place in all three categories of land use. Some changes are dramatic—new factories are built on farmland on the outskirts of a city. Others are more subtle, or barely noticeable, such as the reversion of pasture to forest.

There is lots of land in the United States, 2.3 billion acres to be specific. Of this, only 29 million acres or 1.3 percent is urban. Although urban land is a small part of the total, decisions on how to use it make up the most important land-use problems. Most important, that is, both in terms of the number of people affected and in terms of cost.

In urban areas, the pattern of land use greatly influences the quality of the environment and the quality of life. Pollution, overcrowded transportation, overcrowded recreation and cultural facilities, tension, crime, noise, poor health conditions—even poor esthetics—can result from lack of harmony in land use.

Pressures on urban land use of the possible 100 million more people anticipated by the turn of the century will be great. Difficult decisions have to be made now: Should slum houses be torn down for urban renewal, roads, or parks? Should expressways be built to help those in the suburbs get into the city? How many parks, recreation areas, high rise apartments, or roads should there be? These decisions will become even more difficult as the urban areas grow.

For the most part, urban land use problems will have to be settled through the political process. However, if industries and people could be kept from moving into urban centers, the pressure on land use would be less. Also, new innovative ways to use urban land to benefit the city dweller, the suburbanite, and all of society at the same time need to be developed.

Over 90 percent of our land is rural or nonurban. It is in crops, trees, or range. In terms of acres, this is where the largest land use changes have occurred and will occur.

About half the land in the United States was covered by forest and woodlands when the first explorers and colonists arrived. Approximately a third of the original natural cover of vegetation was grass. The rest was tundra and desert.

Today only about two-thirds of the original forest land remains. In the East much of the original wooded area was cleared and is now cropland, pasture, urban areas, or put to other uses.

The prairies, once covered by tall grass, are now one of our most fertile agricultural areas. Irrigation and dry-farming methods have permitted large areas of the short-grass plains and desert to be farmed and grazed.

The following trends in rural land use are among the most significant today. First is the shift of cropland, pasture, and forest land to such uses as cities and towns, highways and airports, vacation home developments, and reservoirs. At the same time more land is being restricted to uses as parks, recreation areas, wildlife refuges, and other single use areas.

Second, land formerly in cropland and pasture is now idle, often awaiting urbanization. Some former cropland is in the process of reverting to natural forests, sometimes being planted with trees to speed up the process.

Third, new cropland is "created" by irrigation, draining, and clearing.

Total cropland acreage (excluding cropland pastured) in the United States has shown a gradual adjustment downward since the post World War II high of about 410 million acres. In the middle 1960's cropland acreage was about 375 million. Besides this decrease, about 40 million acres of cropland shifted to land left idle, in fallow, or used for conservation crops.

Cropland did not decline to the same extent everywhere. Recent research detailing cropland shifts on a county basis shows that from 1949 to 1964, a total of 2,204 counties showed an overall decrease of 53.5 million acres, while 868 counties showed an increase of 26.7 million acres during the same period. The net decrease during the period amounted to 26.8 million acres.

Additional cropland is transferred through institutional measures to restricted single-purpose use. Examples are lands acquired for national parks, national recreation areas, State parks, and wildlife refuges. Concern for open space reservation, in the face of an expanding population, points to a continued steady increase in the acreage put to these uses.

In general, most of the acreage in these extensive uses is concentrated in Alaska, the Western States, and the less populous and less productive areas of the East. There is every indication, however, that future land patterns in urban regions will include large blocks of acreage dedicated to recreation and open space.

Total forest acreage, in aggregate, has changed little since the end of World War II. Forest acreage appears to increase where cropland acreage decreases, and to decrease where cropland increases.

National and State statistics sometimes show little of the shifts in acreage in some regions which occur at the county level. A decrease in forest acreage in the part of a State or county is often offset by increases in another.

Land clearing for crops in the lower Mississippi Valley is an example. In some instances bottomland clearing has been offset by reversion to forest in the uplands.

Some of our land is caught between the city and the rural areas. This transition zone on the outskirts of our towns and cities has experienced the largest number of land use changes. It is quite different from the changes in either rural areas or cities.

The rural-urban fringe, often called suburbia, grows by outward expansion adjacent to existing urban or suburban areas, along main transportation routes, and by "leapfrogging" into open land.

Strip development along highways leading out from the cities, and isolated patches of homes and shopping centers in the open countryside, create another characteristic of the fringe: intermingled forest and farmland, actively cropped and idle.

The outward appearance in the transition zone is one of diffusion with low-density housing, widely spaced commercial centers and service areas, and an almost complete dependence upon the private automobile for transportation.

All citizens—urban, rural, or suburban—are affected by developments which result in loss of open space, loss of areas of natural beauty, or take fertile soil out of agricultural production.

Society has a large stake in this land-use change.

The "look of the land" in the future will depend on many things: technological advances, changing attitudes toward land use, domestic economic health, and international peace and prosperity, among others.

Land use changes because our means of producing things from the

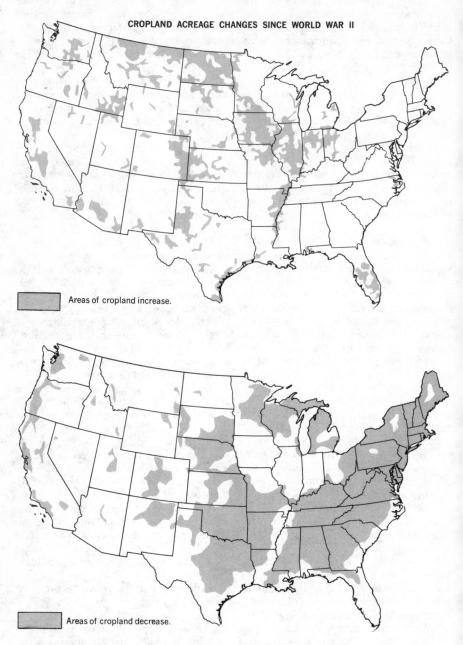

CROPLAND ACREAGE CHANGES SINCE WORLD WAR II

Areas of cropland increase.

Areas of cropland decrease.

land (technology) improves. Land use that shifted for this reason makes our society more efficient, but it may create problems for some individuals. An example is the farmer who has stopped operating his small inefficient farm but has not so far obtained a nonfarm job.

Land use also changes because the number of people is increasing and

272

more space is required for houses, roads, factories, parks, and other special purposes. Finally, the way that people use land also changes.

These things are now happening rapidly. The changes can help society if they improve the quality of life and broaden the range of economic choice available to all.

One important point to remember is that the location of economic activity and the land use patterns of the future will in large measure depend on decisions made in the present and near future. Most changes in land use result from the decisions of one or two people. The change is almost always in their interest; that is, they are better off as a result.

However, in some cases others are worse off. The decision to convert 40 acres of woods into houses may be in the best interest of the buyer and seller, and in the interest of those who might purchase the new houses. However, if the tract is the last open space in a crowded city or suburb, it will have a negative effect on many.

The decision to destroy houses to build a new road will help future travelers but it may hurt home-owners and those who live near the road.

What can be done to utilize land, our most basic resource, in the most rational manner? How can we ensure that this limited resource at the same time provides the widest range of economic choices for all Americans? The problem is one which affects the individual, and the local, State, and national governments. Responsibility for action lies with each.

Barring an unforeseen catastrophe, it is reasonable to assume that enough land will be available to produce the food and fiber needed by an additional 100 million Americans. However, uncontrolled shift of land to non-agricultural uses, such as urban and transportation purposes, might create serious environmental problems.

Competition for land will be keen, and priorities for rational use must be outlined. It is estimated that an addi-

tional 100 million Americans could mean an increase of 15 to 20 million acres in land allocated to intensive nonagricultural uses, such as towns and cities, highways, and airports. At the same time 25 to 30 million acres may well go to other nonagricultural purposes, such as rural parks, recreation areas, wildlife refuges, reservoirs and surface mines. Clearly, some thought needs to be given to these requirements.

It has been known for a long time that individual decisions will not necessarily lead to the best land-use patterns for society as a whole. We are more dependent upon each other now than ever before. Decisions about land use in any one part of the country have the potential to affect many other people, often in different parts of the country. This increased interdependence requires some mechanism by which all our interests are considered when land use changes are planned.

Economic Growth Problems: Ways to Deal With Them

CLARK EDWARDS and
ROBERT C. OTTE

POPULATION of the United States has increased steadily since the Nation's founding. Apart from temporary setbacks, so has income —both total and per person. Growth of the total national economy depends on population growth, growth in employment, and changes in productivity per man.

But not all industries, occupations, or regions grow at the same rate. Some decline while others expand and new ones appear. Demands for products change, as do the technology of production and the resource inputs.

Employment in manufacturing almost doubled between 1940 and 1970. Employment in services, communications, and government more than doubled. Transportation, utilities, trade, finance, insurance, and real estate all showed substantial increases. Two sectors showed declines in employment. Agriculture declined over one-half and mining about a third.

The fortunes of some regions have ebbed and flowed, while others have progressed steadily. Some of the changes in the relative prosperity of a region can be explained by the importance of expanding or contracting sectors there. Areas where agriculture or mining predominate have experienced declines in employment or at least have not kept up with expansion elsewhere.

Location of industry depends in part upon accessibility to inputs and markets. Rapid economic growth in recent years has occurred in areas where resources are readily available and where people want to live because of climate and scenery—the people that provide both labor for industry and a market for products.

Industries are sometimes classified as material-oriented, market-oriented, labor-oriented, or foot-loose. Material-oriented industries are exemplified by mining, lumbering, and agriculture. They are tied to the resource they are exploiting. Market-oriented industries are those producing bulky or perishable goods, or services that have to be performed in place.

Labor-oriented industries are those where the quality and the quantity of labor are important components. These industries tend to seek areas

*

with large numbers of potential employees. The textile industry is an example of an industry seeking a large supply of low-skilled labor. Other industries depend on easy access to a wide variety of high skills. Such industries tend to locate in major metropolitan labor markets where the probability of finding the needed skills is higher.

Foot-loose industries are those in which neither basic resources nor nearby markets nor a large pool of resident labor is an important factor. For example, research and development industries often locate in areas with desirable climates or unusual recreational opportunities and then use these to attract the specialized employees they need.

In recent years, agriculture and mining have been employing fewer people and they make up a smaller percentage of the total output of the country. Market-oriented industries, particularly those providing services (communications, trade, recreation, finance, the professions) have grown both absolutely and in relative importance. Transportation costs count for less in location decisions than they used to. Business, industries, and people are becoming more free to locate where they please.

These factors have reinforced one another in the migration of people to Florida, California, and the Southwestern desert. People have moved to these areas for the amenities; and market-oriented, labor-oriented, and foot-loose industries have followed them.

Accessibility is a matter of transportation costs rather than distance. For example, water transportation is usually cheaper than truck and railroad. Rates vary for different commodities, sometimes favoring the raw materials and sometimes the finished product. Also, the interstate highway system has lowered transportation costs for many areas, providing a wider range of locations for industry.

A major industrial area of the country is a belt that runs from the

CLARK EDWARDS is Chief, Area Analysis Branch, Economic Development Division, Economic Research Service.

ROBERT C. OTTE is an agricultural economist with the Natural Resource Economics Division, Economic Research Service.

Middle Atlantic States on westward through Illinois and Wisconsin. This area accounted for almost three-fourths of all manufacturing employment at the turn of the century. It has continued to grow rapidly in economic activity although some other areas grew even faster; by 1970, it still accounted for around 60 percent of manufacturing employment.

Further gains in job opportunities and continued decentralization of industry have resulted in substantial gains in nonfarm job opportunities in the remaining rural and semirural counties scattered through this belt. Agriculture, particularly in the eastern part, has lost some of its percentage share of total agricultural production.

The metropolitan west coast is the other major area with a high level of general economic activity. Growth in this area is largely metropolitan, but agriculture there is growing rapidly and increasing its share of national agricultural production.

Smaller areas with high levels of income and output appear as scattered islands here and there elsewhere in the Nation. Otherwise, much of the rest of the country is relatively less developed.

The industrializing upper south, particularly the Southern Piedmont area, historically has had a general level of economic activity substantially below the average for the country. However, the trend had changed somewhat by 1970. The area had a large share of its labor force in manufacturing, and economic growth was leading to rapid gains in nonfarm job opportunities for residents of rural and semirural counties as an alternative to outmigration. In addition, agriculture in the area gained a larger share of national agricultural production.

Much of the rest of the country has a lower than average level of income, is growing more slowly in terms of nonfarm job opportunities, and is losing ground in its share of total agricultural production. People have been moving out. This area extends from the central Appalachian counties westward through the Ozarks and fans out to include large portions of the Plains and Mountain States as well as parts of the lower south and the cut-over country west of the Great Lakes.

In general, the more rural areas of the country are less well off economically. Studies show that urban areas have higher incomes, more education, higher levels of economic activity and spend more money for government services. Even farm income tends to be somewhat higher near cities.

Although most rural areas improved economically during the 1960's they did not grow fast enough to close the gap in economic well-being between themselves and the urban areas. To close this gap, means must be found whereby education, local governmental services, income, quality housing, quality of occupation mix, and the level of general business activity can be increased over the rate experienced in the early 1960's.

However, projection of the trends of the 1960's toward the year 2000 suggest that the income gap is narrowing sufficiently to abate the economic pull of the major urban centers on migrants from rural areas. In addition, local improvement in quality and quantity of the labor force and of job opportunities in rural areas suggest a lessening of the push of migrants from depressed areas during the next two or three decades.

Several large areas have special economic problems. For example, let's look at Appalachia, the Great Plains, and the Ozarks.

Appalachia, the most populous of the three areas, comprises the eastern mountainous section from southern New York to northern Alabama. Here employment in mining and agriculture has declined dramatically and employment in manufacturing has not kept pace with the Nation as a whole. By 1970, agricultural employment was only about a quarter of the 1940 level and mining employment was around a third. While employment rose approximately three-fourths on a national basis, during the same period employment in Appalachia increased only about a half.

The Great Plains, largest of the three areas in terms of geographic extent, has a generally thriving agriculture but contains many counties where nonagricultural industries have not expanded rapidly enough to employ the large number of people released from agriculture as farms have become larger and more mechanized. Agricultural employment was halved between 1940 and 1970.

Employment in manufacturing in the Plains area tripled, compared to a doubling nationwide. However, this did not offset the loss in agricultural employment. The Great Plains had a slower growth in total employment than did the country as a whole, and experienced heavy outmigration during the 1960's.

One of the most important problems throughout the Plains is that many people are scattered over large areas and isolated from easy access to metropolitan central services. Education, medical services, fire protection, and roads are difficult and expensive to provide.

The Ozarks area has a history similar to Appalachia. Employment in agriculture in 1970 was only a little more than a quarter of what it was in 1940. Population barely maintained its 1940 level. Total employment did not keep pace with the Nation as a whole.

The U.S. Department of Agriculture assists in economic development in rural areas in various ways. Throughout the country there are rural development committees. They consist of or work through representatives of county Extension, the Soil Conservation Service, the Farmers Home Administration, the Rural Electrification Administration, the Farmer Cooperative Service, and the Forest Service. In addition, they include representatives from the agricultural experiment stations and the land-grant colleges.

These committees work with local people in planning for economic development, and provide liaison services for those Federal programs that have a role to play in the local development plan.

Resource Conservation and Development (RC&D) projects of the U.S. Department of Agriculture in cooperation with local groups speed up resource programs in multicounty areas. RC&D projects generally consist in part of water management structures, often for water supply or flood control. Impoundments may be used for recreation or fish production. Land may be developed for recreation or wildlife. People may be trained in new skills. Additional industry may be attracted to the area.

The Great Plains Conservation Program, in effect since 1956, consists of long-term cost-sharing agreements between Great Plains farm or ranch operators and the Federal Government to establish needed conservation measures and land-use changes. A major aim has been establishment of permanent grass on land highly susceptible to wind and water erosion. While the program has had little direct effect on development of nonagricultural sectors of the economy, it has encouraged conservation measures and land use adjustments needed to maintain a stable agriculture, the most important industry in the region.

Besides those in USDA, programs affecting rural economic development operate in almost every Federal agency. Principal among them are: Programs in the Economic Development Administration of the Department of Commerce to provide technical and financial assistance to areas with high unemployment or low income; programs in the Department of Housing and Urban Development to plan expansion in nonmetropolitan areas; and programs in the Department of Labor to upgrade skills of the labor force and deal with unemployed and underemployed persons.

The above, and other Federal, State, and local public and private programs, tend to be single-purpose programs each dealing with a part of the problem. Yet local economic development problems often are many sided; programs need to move in a coordinated way on a number of fronts at once to deal with the problems effectively.

One approach to a comprehensive attack on rural development problems is through multicounty area planning and program implementation. On this basis, the Nation can be delineated into some 500 multicounty economic program areas. Another approach is through regional commissions dealing with interstate development problems.

The Public Works and Economic Development Act of 1965 provided for identifying multistate regions with common problems of economic stagnation. Upon being designated a problem region, the States involved are invited to participate in regional commissions.

Commissions have joint Federal-State membership—a member from each State and a Federal member appointed by the President with the approval of the Senate. Each commission analyzes economic problems of the region and develops a strategy for economic growth. Projects are geared to take advantage of existing Federal programs. In addition, a commission can give financial aid to supplement local cost shares for Federal projects.

As of 1970, five regional commissions had been established under the Act—for the Ozarks, New England, Four Corners (parts of Utah, Colorado, Arizona, and New Mexico), Coastal Plains (parts of North Carolina, South Carolina, and Georgia), and Upper Great Lakes. The Appalachian Regional Commission was established independently by the Appalachian Regional Development Act of 1965.

Where employment has been decreasing, particularly areas in which agriculture or mining has been the most important activity, people find themselves without work unless they move. The ones who move are mostly young adults; they leave behind those younger and older. The communities where this has happened need schools, hospitals, and welfare services while productive people who could support them have left or are jobless.

And expanding areas have their problems. Not all the new migrants are qualified for the available jobs. Even where they find jobs, housing must be built, sometimes faster than the over-burdened municipal and county officials can provide control. Schools must be established and other public services supplied.

Population expansion does not necessarily create such problems. But there are many situations where the local government faces increased demands for services and does not have a commensurate geographic area from which to raise the necessary funds.

Solutions to problems of slower growing regions frequently require actions that are beyond the means available to individual residents. An individual can do only so much regarding a good education for his children if the best schools are in another school district; and only so much about a better job if the expanding demand for workers is occurring in another State.

On the other hand, neither does the solution lie entirely in direct action by the Federal Government through nationally uniform monetary and fiscal policies. National policies with respect to balanced regional growth and rural economic development are necessary to set up a favorable, general environment. But such policies are not sufficient if local leaders and individuals do not take responsibility for dealing with local policies, both public and private.

That is, these problems involve regional questions which need to be dealt with by all of those affected through group action on roads, schools, zoning, taxes, credit, residential construction, industry location, community facilities, and environmental quality. And those affected include not only the directly and obviously disadvantaged, but other local residents as well, whether they live next door, in a nearby town, or in another county; whether they are poor or well-to-do; whether they live in a rural or an urban place.

In this sense, rural residents have more in common with their city cousins, an hour's drive from the farm, than they do with other rural people living a day's journey or more away.

A rational basis is needed for developing plans, perhaps at a multicounty or multistate level, with public and private interests represented, to find solutions to problems that are beyond the control of individual firms or households yet are not of uniformly national scope. Enlightened groups, acting constructively with variations in problems at a regional level, can find new ways to promote area growth, help bring about new development, and provide an environment in which those who live in disadvantaged areas can also find economic opportunity.

Farm Production Capacity Can Meet Our Needs

ORVILLE E. KRAUSE

OUR NATION'S farmers are expanding output faster than the rise in our population. Moreover, the average person's diet is on the increase even while we are exporting more than we used to. And, on top of all that, we are doing this with less and less land and fewer farmworkers. The reason—greatly increased efficiency, sometimes called the agricultural revolution or just plain "technology."

To look at the trend since 1950, we are now using 11 percent less land for crops, but have expanded the output of all farm products by 40 percent. Because our population has increased only 33 percent, that makes a farm production boost of about 6 percent per person.

To look at the consumption side— the average person not only consumes about 6 percent more food than 20 years ago, but a bigger part of it is in animal products. Although we each consume fewer eggs and less dairy products now, meat consumption per person is up 20 percent. There hasn't been much change in the proportion of fruits and vegetables in our diet. Cereal products are down and sugar is up by about a tenth.

Not only has our Nation's agriculture supplied an increase in the food per person, but it has done so on an economical basis. Prices received by farmers have increased only 6 percent since 1950, while prices in general have risen 50 percent. Consumers now spend only 16 percent of their disposable income for food, compared with 22 percent in 1950.

What's more, we produce enough food to provide a satisfactory diet for everyone. And among consumers there is a growing awareness of the types of food needed for a balanced diet.

Besides boosting output sufficiently over the last 20 years to increase food consumption 6 percent, we also doubled our exports to other countries, partly by government programs but mostly in the commercial market. Because of our great upsurge in production, however, the proportion of our supply exported has risen only a little.

Our greatly expanded output in recent years resulted from what farmers did on each acre, rather than from increasing crop acreage. Our larger output is the result of the improved efficiency relative to land and labor

*

ORVILLE E. KRAUSE is an agricultural economist in the Economic Research Service.

achieved from adopting new or improved technologies. They include more efficient farm organization, greater use of agricultural chemicals like fertilizers and pesticides, improved crop and livestock species and managements, more irrigation, and the shift to better land.

In addition, increased credit was available to finance the adopting of those technologies which replace land and labor resources.

So a consideration of our farm production capacity requires an appraisal of the potential of each of these productivity factors, as well as an estimate of additional land which could be used for agricultural production if needed. It now appears that there is still great technological potential, and that farm productivity will increase in the foreseeable future as fast as our population. Thus we will not need additional land for agriculture.

Many changes have occurred on our Nation's farms over the last two decades in order to supply the expanding population with an increase in food per person. Total acreage in farms doesn't change much; it's about half our land area. But since 1950 the number of farms dropped from 5.4 million to only 2.9 million now. Hence, the average farm size rose from 234 to 376 acres.

During the same time the number of workers on farms dropped from about 10 million to around 4 million. The acreage of cropland used for crops dipped from 377 million acres to 337 million.

Along with these trends came great changes in efficiency. Output per man-hour is three times what it was in 1950. Production per acre of land used for crops has risen more than 50 percent.

This has all been accomplished by efficiencies resulting from farm consolidation, improving land and buildings and increased expenditures for machinery and various other inputs such as fertilizer, improved seeds, pesticides, and better stock.

As a reflection of the trend towards more purchased inputs, production expenses have doubled. The value of land, buildings, and machinery has almost tripled. But the cash receipts of farmers since 1950 have increased only 78 percent.

In order to finance these changes, farm debt rose more than four times above the 1950 level. In 1950, farm debt was only $12.4 billion, or well under half of the $28.7 billion in cash receipts. In 1969, farm debt was $54.6 billion, or 7 percent more than total cash receipts.

Because of the great drop in number of farms from consolidations to increase farm size, the changes per farm are even more dramatic. The average farm now has physical assets with a value of nearly $100,000, almost five times the 1950 amount.

Cash receipts per farm in 1950 were a bit more than $5,000 a year, but production expenses were only two-thirds that amount. Cash income is now almost $18,000 per farm, with production expenses three-quarters of that.

To take advantage of the new technologies in order to increase output and efficiency, farmers have also had to call on the credit system for additional financing. Production expenses two decades ago were only two-thirds of cash income but now have risen to three-fourths. Farm debt now is 20 percent of the value of all physical assets, compared with less than 10 percent in 1950.

If our farmers are to feed the 100 million or so more people anticipated between now and the turn of the century, the credit system will need to —and is expected to—supply the greatly increased capital requirements for more large-scale, efficient farming.

It appears there is additional land which could be used for crop production if needed, and also that we won't lose much agricultural land to urbanization in the foreseeable future.

Land in farms occupies about half the Nation's total land area of 2.3 billion acres. In addition, our farmers use another 300 million acres, mostly

Federal land, for livestock grazing. That makes a total of some 1.3 billion acres, which means that 58 percent of our land area is used for agricultural purposes (excluding forestry). Another fourth is in forests and an eighth is wasteland.

Land for urban purposes, although accounting for the bulk of our economic activity, still takes only 2½ percent of our land area. This includes land in airports, railroads, and highways, as well as all places with above 1,000 population.

Even by the year 2000, with the possibility of up to 100 million additional people, urban areas will probably need only about 4 percent of our land area. Some of the additional land will come from agriculture, but the amount would probably be no more than 4 percent of present cropland. In any case, much of this cropland would be abandoned due to technological obsolescence, even if the cities stopped growing now.

Of the land in farms (a billion acres), about half is in pasture and range. In addition, farmers use about 300 million acres of public land for grazing livestock. Grazing land is an important resource, as it supplies about a third of our livestock feed.

To look ahead, this acreage is about the limit as there is little additional land available for grazing. But prospects are bright for the future supply of more grazing (for the increased livestock needed to feed 100 million or so more people) by means of pasture improvement to raise productivity. Some has already been cleared, reseeded, and fertilized to greatly increase grass supplies. Huge additional acreages are well adapted for this treatment.

The bulk of our farm output, however, comes from cropland used for crops, which supplies two-thirds of our livestock feed and all of our food and fiber crops. We have more land for this purpose, should it be needed. And much land now used for other purposes is capable of crop production if improved.

Land classed as cropland on farms (430 million acres, or 20 percent of our land area) is only partly used for crop production. About three-fourths is actually used for crops. The other fourth includes cropland pasture and more than 35 million acres of cropland now idled under farm programs but available if needed. Brought back into production, this acreage would increase our cropland used for crops by 10 percent.

In addition, the Nation has a quarter of a billion acres of land in other uses but considered suitable for regular cultivation should it be needed.

This land, if converted to crop production, would increase our cropland used for crops by 70 percent. However, the land would all require improvement, including drainage or irrigation, some at such great cost that it would be done only of extreme necessity. Furthermore, part of this land is in areas where the growing season is too short to grow the higher valued crops. And some—such as lowland needing drainage or dryland subject to wind erosion—needs to be preserved to maintain ecologic balance.

Some of the land judged suitable for cultivation already is reclaimed every year. New cropland since World War II appeared in a number of well-defined areas at the rate of about 1.3 million acres a year.

Reclamation in Florida was associated with both drainage and irrigation projects, in the Delta with clearing and drainage and in the Texas High Plains, California, and Washington with expanded irrigation facilities.

Expansion was associated with improved dryland farming techniques in northern Montana and with various farm-oriented techniques (drainage, clearing, contouring, and leveling) throughout the Corn Belt.

In other regions, however, cropland was abandoned at the rate of about 2.7 million acres a year. Abandonment was found largely in the States south and east from the Corn Belt

Geneticist examines cotton plants treated for resistance to wilt.

except the Delta and southern Florida. Abandonment east of the Mississippi resulted from low soil fertility, and where features of the terrain are not adapted to efficient use of modern machinery—many fields are small, rough, and isolated.

In large areas of eastern Oklahoma and Texas, cropland reverted to grass as the apparent best use of the land in this area.

The net effect has been some geographic shift of cropland to areas with more productive soils and/or land better adapted to improved technologies. Hence, on balance, this geographic shift in cropland has itself helped to increase the Nation's cropland productivity, a trend expected to continue.

Crop yields have risen greatly in recent years. Up through the 1930's, crop production per acre didn't change much, but since that time yields have about doubled due to the technological revolution. In the last two decades, yields soared more than 50 percent.

The best-known explanation is the wide use of better seeds, particularly hybrid seed and the big increase in the use of agricultural chemicals. Hybrid corn and sorghum grain had been adopted by almost all farmers by 1960. And chemical fertilizer nutrients, applied at a rate of only 7 pounds per acre in 1940, rose to 14 pounds by 1950. Since then use of nutrients has more than quadrupled to now exceed 70 pounds per acre.

Chemical pesticides for weed and insect control are widely used to reduce labor requirements and enhance crop yields. But widespread adoption has been quite recent. Back in 1964, only an eighth of our crop acres were treated for insects and a fourth for weeds. Up to that time the big increases in crop yields were largely explained by other technologies.

To avoid excessive environmental pollution, the trend is already underway toward less noxious chemical substitutes and toward more selective application (that is, application only where and when needed and hence in much smaller amounts).

While these developments have been important, many other crop technologies have been developed and then adopted by farmers to achieve this great jump in production per acre.

Some of the promising research going on now includes breeding not only for higher yields but also for improved quality, for handling hardihood (to reduce harvesting and marketing losses), for disease resistance, for drought resistance, and to utilize increased fertilizer rates much more effectively.

The whole breeding program is expected to become much more efficient and effective by the use of electronic equipment which facilitates storage of the great amount of data on the characteristics of trial crosses, and enables the analysis of experimental results.

Equipment is being developed for improved seedbed preparation, for minimum tillage, and for more efficient harvesting. Harvesting machines not only damage the crops to some extent, but also miss an appreciable part of the crops and leave it in the field as a loss.

Weeds, insects, plant diseases, and fungi which cause plant losses are being studied for means of control. Much effort is going into the search for nonharmful chemicals and other techniques such as insect sterility, to use as substitutes for noxious pesticides.

Livestock and livestock products from our Nation's farms have increased by a third since 1950, or about the same as the rise in our population. That's an average gain of close to 2 percent a year, a trend expected to continue.

When looked at by product, we find considerable differences in the increase since 1950—poultry and egg output is up by three-fourths, meat animals by more than a third, but dairy products rose only 5 percent.

Breeding research in the past has been hindered by the monumental job of keeping up records of all the characteristics and performances of livestock and then analyzing the huge mass of data in order to choose promising experimental pairs or crosses. This work is being shifted to the computer to make records analyses never before possible. In addition, added emphasis is given to the collection of superior genetic material.

Efforts are underway to develop improved feeding efficiency and also improved quality of meat, such as less fat. And because we get less than one calf per cow each year and in addition there is an appreciable death loss, breeding for reproductive efficiency is carried out to develop strains with decreased sterility, increased live births and even twinning in cattle, and more pigs per litter in hogs.

Also promising is the potential for sex control to achieve more female births in dairy herds, and more male births in beef herds. In broiler production the aim is for a higher ratio of male chicks, because males are faster growing and are more efficient feed converters. Other aspects of livestock production being researched are ration mix and control, insect control, and nutrient needs including the minor ingredients and growth additives.

Increased productivity in crop and livestock production has resulted from the development and adoption of many different improved breeds, materials, methods and techniques, and has not been dependent on major breakthroughs. The broad-based research program continues with many promising developments. So for the future we can feel confident that new technologies will continue to be available for adoption to continue our rising efficiency relative to labor and land.

Agriculture is the Nation's major consumer of water. Of all the water used in the Nation from ground and surface supplies, 86 percent is consumed by agriculture, mostly for irrigation. The nonagricultural sector withdraws more water than agriculture does, but returns most of it to its source for further use downstream.

Irrigation of cropland has almost doubled in the last two decades, and is now increasing about 900,000 acres each year. Most of our irrigation is found in rain-deficient western regions. Only about 4 percent of our cropland was irrigated 20 years ago; now it's more than 10 percent.

Because water can be applied when needed, the yields of major crops (cotton, sorghum, and wheat) on irrigated acreage run a half to two-thirds above the national average. Besides, much irrigated acreage is in high-value crops like fruits and vegetables, so the 10 percent of our crop acreage which is irrigated now yields 20 percent of the value of all farm crops. Irrigation also helps explain the rise in output per acre in the national average.

We can't continue this increase in the future, however, because of water limitations in some of the western regions.

Water supplies are adequate and acreage will continue to rise in the

Far West, and in a broad belt extending from the Missouri Valley southeasterly to the South Atlantic regions. In addition, irrigation for supplemental purposes will continue to gain in the Corn Belt. But in the area from Texas to Nevada, including the Colorado River Basin, water supplies are already used close to the limit. While a third of our irrigated acreage is found in these areas, not much increase is expected in the future.

Various existing—or emerging—methods would enhance or increase the value of water supplies. These include the development of underground reservoirs, large interbasin transfer projects, the reduction of conveyance losses and the losses to weeds and brush along canals, the shifting of water allocation to higher valued crops, and land management methods to reduce evaporation.

Unless some of these projects are adopted on a big scale, however, irrigation over the next three decades will probably gain an average of only about 400,000 acres a year.

For the next three decades it appears that water supplies will be adequate to further increase the irrigated acreage. In addition, rising productivity will be augmented by more efficient water management.

To sum up, during the last two decades farm output rose a little faster than population. We are producing more per person with less land and farmworkers because of improved technology. And a look at these various technologies shows us there is still a great potential for the foreseeable future.

Much additional land is available for crop production if needed. But to bring this land into production would probably slow down the uptrend in productivity or efficiency. Cropland now idle is somewhat less productive than the cropland currently used for crops.

Other land suitable to be reclaimed for regular cultivation would require considerable expenditures for improvement. Some of this land probably should remain in its present use because reclamation would seriously impair the ecologic balance of the area. On the whole, however, there is probably enough land available so we could boost crop production acreage by about a third on a practical basis.

On the other side of the coin, however, are some developing problems which may dampen our productivity prospects.

There is evidence that agricultural chemicals contribute to environmental pollution. While selective application and the shift to substitutes ease the problems, future limitations on use could slow slightly our uptrend in productivity.

As farms are consolidated and grow larger, and as the farm business requires greatly increasing capital to take advantage of technology, the capital markets will need to be geared up to supply the necessary funds.

In many areas, soil erosion is still a problem. Conservation programs at some cost must be continued or even expanded in order to preserve and improve our soil base.

There are, however, good prospects for further increase in productivity from more widespread adoptions of improved technology, as well as from

Windstrips of rye protect young corn in New Jersey from being shredded by sand.

new research. Many output-increasing techniques do not affect the environment adversely and will not be faced with limitations or restrictions. And besides the land now used for crops, we have a large acreage that could be taken out of retirement and much more land that could be reasonably reclaimed if it were needed for crop production.

Requirements for Timber

ROBERT S. MANTHY

THREE and two-thirds acres of forest land for every man, woman, and child. That's how much forest there is in the United States. One third of our Nation's entire land area is covered with trees. In 1968, this forest land totaled 762 million acres, a rise of 50 million acres since 1910.

Some 510 million or approximately 2 in every 3 acres of our forest land is classified as commercial, being capable of growing timber for harvest and not officially withdrawn from timber use.

Vast as our forest reserves are there is still some doubt about our ability to provide for future lumber, plywood, paper, and other timber product requirements. The concern is not simply one of harvesting sufficient volumes to meet consumption needs. Rather, it is the problem of providing and marketing adequate volumes of timber products at prices that consumers are willing and able to pay.

Forests of the United States annually grow far more wood than is harvested or consumed. This has been true for several decades.

In 1970 we consumed 12.8 billion cubic feet of roundwood timber. According to the Forest Service, production from domestic forests supplied 11.8 billion cubic feet of the total (92 percent). Net imports of 1.0 billion cubic feet provided the remainder, mainly in the form of lumber, wood pulp, and paper products. In 1967, the latest year for which data are available, the net increase in the volume of growing stock on commercial forest land was estimated at 17.3 billion cubic feet.

These figures show we are growing about 46 percent more timber than we are cutting. If our net imports of timber products had originated on domestic forests we would still be growing at least 35 percent more timber than we are harvesting.

The average acre of commercial forest land in the United States contains 1,264 cubic feet of growing stock wood. In terms of this average, our consumption of timber in 1970 represented approximately 2 percent of the Nation's 510 million acres of commercial forest land.

In other words, enough timber is standing on our commercial forest land to supply timber product needs at 1970 consumption levels for nearly 50 years. Actually, there is much more than a 50-year supply. Since the natural growth of our forests exceeds the annual harvest, the total physical volume of timber is increasing.

However, it should be noted that the major portion of our forest growth occurs on young trees. More than half of the timber harvest is from older, larger size trees needed for producing lumber and plywood. By log use, our 1970 roundwood harvest was: sawlogs, 45 percent; veneer logs, 8 percent; pulpwood, 33 percent; and other minor products, 14 percent.

The favorable current growth-cut

*

ROBERT S. MANTHY is an Associate Professor of Forest Economics and Policy at Michigan State University, East Lansing.

284

Ownership of Commercial Forest Land, 1968	
Ownership	Million acres
Public	
Federal_____	112.7
State and Local_____	29.2
Private	
Forest industry_____	65.6
Farm_____	140.9
Miscellaneous_____	161.8
All Ownerships_____	510.2

Source: U.S. Forest Service

relationship must also be viewed in recognition of the fact that the 1970 timber harvest is considerably smaller than future harvest will have to be to provide for the requirements of our growing population. According to one recent estimate, by the year 2000 our annual timber consumption will have grown to 23.8 billion cubic feet. Net imports are expected to supply 2.8 billion cubic feet. Domestic forests will have to supply the remaining 21 billion.

If this consumption projection materializes, one of three things must happen. Either the basic forestry conservation principle of sustained yield will have to be abandoned, our forests will have to become more productive, or we will have to rely more heavily on imports for our consumption needs.

In its simplest form the concept of sustained yield management of forest lands holds that the volume of the periodic harvest from forest reserves should be equal to the net periodic growth of the forest. That is, the volume of timber harvested should be equal to or less than the volume that has grown since the last cutting.

The forest that is left after a harvest (inventory) is preserved as if it were a sum of banked money from which interest payments (growth) can be periodically withdrawn (cut) forever.

As measured by annual growth on inventory, the present productivity of our forests will not indefinitely support the projected harvest levels. In less than a decade, anticipated growth levels will have fallen below the level of expected harvest. If productivity or imports are not increased, a portion of the inventory will have to be harvested to meet needs.

If our forests are not made more productive, and we are unable to increase imports, the extent to which the future harvest would have to be taken from inventory is larger than just the difference between growth and the anticipated domestic cut. An unknown but presumably significant portion of our commercial forest land is used for home sites, recreation, watershed protection, and other uses that prohibit or severely restrict harvesting.

Because of these unofficial withdrawals, available data overestimate the extent of our commercial forest land and therefore the growth that is available for harvest under sustained yield.

Foresters have traditionally rejected the abandonment of sustained yield management, and because of a desire to be as nearly self-sufficient as possible they have also been reluctant to rely upon imports. Instead, they have committed their efforts and professional talents to the job of increasing the productivity and usefulness of our forests as a source of multiple goods and services.

Failure of earlier predictions of "timber famine" to materialize indicate that foresters have been more than moderately successful. But what of the future? Can we assume that foresters can continue to improve the productivity of our forests sufficiently to meet our growing needs?

The answer is a conditional "Yes". The hedged reply is necessary mainly because of the nonuniform nature of our forests, their ownership and geographic dispersion, and the need for an acceleration of the trend toward more intensive management on all our forest lands.

More than two thirds of our commercial forest land is located in the North and South. Thirty-nine percent is in the South, 34 percent in the Northcentral and Northeastern States, and 27 percent in the Rocky Mountain and Pacific Coast States.

Nearly 72 percent of this forest land is privately owned. In the South, 91 percent is in private ownership, and in the North, 90 percent. The 28 percent that is in public ownership is highly concentrated in the West. Nearly 70 percent of Western commercial forests is in Federal (65 percent) and other public (4 percent) ownership.

In terms of forest types, about two-thirds of the net volume of the growing stock on commercial forest land is softwoods (needle-bearing or coniferous trees) and one-third hardwoods (broadleaf or deciduous trees). Softwoods account for about four-fifths of the lumber, nearly all of the plywood, and aproximately two-thirds of the pulpwood produced in this country.

The West (which, again, accounts for only 27 percent of our commercial forest land) contains three-quarters of our softwood growing stock, mostly on the Pacific Coast. In contrast, 90 percent of our hardwoods, used primarily for manufacturing and pulpwood, are in the North (54 percent) and South (36 percent.)

Based upon the nature of its forest reserves, each forest region in the country can be expected to play a somewhat different role in supplying timber products to the Nation. The problems that must be solved and the opportunities that can be exploited if we are going to meet projected timber products requirements also differ by region.

The South contains 23 percent of the Nation's growing stock inventory and 19 percent of the inventory of sawtimber. Sawtimber means trees of sufficient size and quality to contain at least one log suitable for lumber or veneer.

Although 60 percent of the South's 199 million acres of commercial forest land is occupied by hardwood, the major part of the harvest comes from softwood. In 1967, removals of softwood growing stock totaling 3.5 billion cubic feet were 1.5 billion less than softwood growth. Growth of softwood sawtimber exceeded the 1967 removal of 12.9 billion board feet by 6 billion board feet. Hardwood removals were about equal to growth.

Thus there appears to be room for a significant expansion of southern forest industry, particularly that part which uses softwoods. Opportunities seem particularly favorable for industries such as pulp and paper where large size, high quality timber is not required for efficient production.

In the North, hardwoods predominate. On some 83 percent of this region's 176 million acres of commercial forest land, the principal timber species are hardwoods. The North contains 49 percent of the Nation's hardwood sawtimber volume and about 54 percent of the hardwood growing stock.

As in the South, there is an excess of growth over removals for both sawtimber and growing stock volume, only in this case the major excess occurs in hardwoods. But once again the current excess of growth over cut is in tree sizes and classes and species that are principally valuable for pulp and paper products.

Northern forests currently do not have enough hardwood timber of sufficient size and quality to support a significant increase in the harvest of high-quality hardwood sawlogs and veneer logs.

A quite different forestry environment occurs in the West. The West contains 54 percent of the growing stock and 69 percent of the sawtimber on the Nation's commercial forest lands. Of the 135 million acres of commercial forest lands in the West slightly more than half, 69 million acres, is in the Pacific Coast states of Washington, Oregon, and California. These three States contain 53 percent of the Nation's softwood growing stock and 63 percent of the softwood sawtimber inventory.

The 1967 increase on the western growing stock inventory from natural growth was 17 percent less than removals. Growth on sawtimber was about half the volume of removals, largely because the old softwood forests in the West are being liquidated at a faster rate than existing growth can replace.

The need to replace old growth forests with young faster-growing forests is reflected by the large volume of timber annually lost to natural mortality. In 1967 mortality of western softwood trees totaled 2.8 billion cubic feet, about 58 percent of the 1967 volume of growing stock removed by man.

As a result of the necessary and desirable liquidation of old, overmature forests, the net volume of the softwood inventory has been slowly declining. Between 1953 and 1968 the inventory of softwood sawtimber on the Pacific Coast dropped 12 percent. There has also been a slight drop in the Rocky Mountain States.

The preceding inventory of regional forestry environments can now be summarized in terms of its implications for meeting future national timber requirements. In brief, during 1967 growth exceeded removals for both hardwoods and softwoods in all regions of the country except the Pacific Coast.

Removals of growing stock totaled 13.3 billion cubic feet; growth totaled 17.3 billion cubic feet. In other words, the harvest of growing stock on commercial forest land can be increased substantially without jeopardizing our sustained yield capacity.

Growth-removal relationships for sawtimber are less favorable. Total removals of 57.5 billion board feet in 1967 exceeded growth by 3.8 billion board feet. The South and North had a surplus of sawtimber growth over removals, but the surplus was not large enough to offset heavy Western removals. However, softwood forests in regions outside the West can support an increase in sawtimber harvest equal to 1.5 times the 1967 harvest.

For hardwood sawlogs there is a national surplus of growth over removals totaling 4.1 billion board feet. The major portion of this surplus is in the North, where the hardwood sawlog harvest can be just about doubled.

These comparative data indicate we will be able to safely increase our timber harvest in the near future as long as we are able to use small-sized, low-quality growing stock material and hardwood sawtimber in place of softwood sawtimber.

One recent projection of timber

Regional Distribution of Commercial Forest Land, Sawtimber and Growing Stock Volume, 1967

(Percent)

| Region | Commercial forest land | Volume on commercial forest land | | | | | |
| | | Sawtimber | | | Growing stock | | |
		Total	Softwood	Hardwood	Total	Softwood	Hardwood
North	34	12	4	49	23	8	54
South	39	19	13	40	23	17	36
Rocky Mountain	13	16	20	2	16	22	3
Pacific Coast	14	53	63	9	38	53	7
United States	100	100	100	100	100	100	100

Source: U.S. Forest Service

product levels required to meet future needs indicates that the major increases in timber production will occur in pulpwood, where size and quality of material is not critical. In the year 2000, pulpwood production requirements are projected to account for 55 percent of the timber harvest, compared to 33 percent of the harvest in 1970.

Production of sawlogs is expected to decline slightly while veneer log consumption will double. The projected increase in production of softwood sawtimber for lumber and plywood is 14 percent.

However, timber removals are increasing more rapidly than growth. The expected harvest will exceed current growth by the early 1980's.

Recent but unpublished Forest Service projections suggest that demand for timber will exceed supply much sooner, perhaps by the mid-1970's. Shortages are likely to be particularly large for softwood sawtimber used to produce lumber and plywood.

If expected deficits are allowed to occur, we can expect substantial price increases for forest products. Corresponding reductions in the amounts of these products consumed would then occur to bring demand for timber back into balance with supply.

Major price rises and reduced consumption caused by timber shortages can be avoided. Recent Forest Service studies show that with adequate financial investments our forest resources can be expanded considerably through management intensification and better utilization.

Opportunities for increasing the current productivity of our forest reserves over the next 30 years are good. Forest Service data show that the average cubic foot per acre growth on commercial forest land in the United States is far below productive potentials.

By comparing productivity by ownership within each region it does not appear unreasonable that growth can be increased sufficiently to meet expected demands under sustained yield management. For example, the projected roundwood production requirement for the year 2000 is only 3.7 billion cubic feet more than current growth. An increase of less than 5 percent in average growth per acre will meet this projected requirement.

Even assuming that a significant portion of our commercial forest land will be withdrawn from timber production, say as much as 10 percent, it is likely that the remaining forest land has the productive potential to compensate for the losses in inventory.

Major routes to increasing forest productivity include reduction of mortality from fire, insects, and diseases, planting with genetically superior trees, conversion of understocked hardwood stands to pine, timber stand improvement through thinnings and other cultural practices, fertilization, constructing access roads needed for management intensification, and improved logging procedures.

Increased efficiency in harvesting and using timber offers another opportunity for meeting projected timber requirements. L. E. Lassen and Dwight Hair of the Forest Service have estimated that our effective wood supply can be increased by 4.7 billion cubic feet by 1980 through more efficient utilization of our timber resources. Only those improvements in utilization that were judged technically and economically feasible are included in this estimate.

Reuse of paper, fiberboard, and wood debris could result in an effective increase in wood supplies of 1.3 billion cubic feet, according to Lassen and Hair. Other potential gains include 1.4 billion cubic feet in reduction of logging residues, and 2 billion cubic feet through increased efficiency and use of residues in primary and secondary wood products manufacturing.

My review of this country's forest production capacity has shown that we are currently growing at least 35 percent more timber than we are harvesting. By the late 1970's expected removals of timber will exceed growth. Softwood sawtimber supplies available under sustained yield forest management will fall short of demand sooner, possibly by the mid-1970's.

Should these shortages occur, major price increases for forest products can be expected. However, with continued improvements in the efficiency of timber utilization and more intensified management of public and private forests, the supply of timber can be greatly increased.

Potential productivity of our forests is great enough to supply the timber requirements of our growing population. What is needed is a willingness on the part of public and private owners of forest land to make the needed investments in research and management programs.

Conservation
In Modern
Farming

R. C. BARNES, JR., and

B. D. BLAKELY

POPULATION explosion; more mouths to feed. Rising labor costs; a narrower margin between cost and returns of production. These are some of the reasons why many farmers intensify their operations and crop their land more intensively.

Labor requirements are being reduced through the use of larger and specialized equipment. Correct fertilization, proper use of chemicals for insect and weed control, and improved crop varieties are helping to boost yields.

Increased pressure on the land can bring more runoff and erosion and requires that conservation measures, based on trials and research, be changed to meet these new demands. This trend will continue for the foreseeable future and conservationists must be diligent in staying ahead with modification of old conservation methods and development of new ones.

Not many years ago, two-row planters were common in many parts of the country. They are still around, but they have become almost a novelty. Six- and eight-row planters have taken their place.

The principles of soil management and conservation farming are the same today as they have always been, but the methods of achieving them have changed to meet the needs of present day farming equipment. Conservation practices used a decade or two ago to reduce soil losses—terracing, stripcropping, contouring, and grasses and legumes—are still good in this era of mechanized farming.

They can and are being adapted to wide tillage equipment, powerful tractors, and big harvesting machines. In addition, research and knowledge lead the way to new practices that will be compatible with modern farming.

The large, often in tandem, machines are difficult to use on the irregular terraces and sharp-curved contour lines of earlier times. Farmers try not to use field layouts or practices that add point rows which cause extra turning. They want conservation practices that do not slow their speed of operation or require extra time. And conservation practices are designed to meet these demands.

Many farmers have increased the acreage of row crops and decreased the acreage of sod crops, so they are

*

R. C. BARNES, JR., is an Agricultural Engineer in the Soil Conservation Service.

B. D. BLAKELY, an Agronomist in the Soil Conservation Service, retired in April 1971.

looking for ways to control wind and water erosion and, at the same time, to increase the efficiency of their operations.

Inexpensive nitrogen has replaced the need for legumes in crop rotation. Herbicides have replaced the need for cultivation for weed control and, in some cases, for seedbed preparation.

These changes and many others have affected the kinds of conservation practices needed to reduce erosion and runoff caused by rainfall. They have also affected the practices used to reduce soil blowing.

Based on long-time erosion research studies, made on the behavior of different kinds of soil under the forces of rainfall and strong winds, it is now possible to design cropping systems that will keep soil losses to a minimum, both for water and wind erosion, and still be in harmony with the farmers' needs and equipment.

Likewise, based on research studies of the behavior of soils relative to water intake, it is possible to improve irrigation systems and water management practices on irrigated land.

Water and wind erosion are major problems on the Nation's croplands. It is estimated that in 1967, some 50 million acres of cropland were losing more than 10 tons per acre annually. Soil, as sediment, by volume is the greatest source of pollution in streams, harbors, and lakes. Soil can also be an air pollutant when it starts to blow.

Erosion begins when raindrops fall on bare soil and continues when detached soil particles are carried by rain down the slope. Wind erosion or soil blowing starts when the wind is strong enough to move soil particles.

Conservation farming is in harmony with the national concern for improving our environment. To the same degree that our nation's croplands are adequately managed to reduce soil loss, the environment of our streams, rivers, harbors, and lakes will be improved. This soil loss reduction will also improve the air we breathe.

In the last few years, increasing numbers of farmers are using one or more of the numerous minimum tillage methods to plant row crops without plowing. Minimum tillage refers to tillage methods that require fewer trips across the field to grow a crop than are required by the conventional plow-disk-harrow-plant and cultivate methods.

Today, machines can prepare a seedbed, apply fertilizer, and put on herbicides, all in one operation, and at the same time keep the soil covered with residues. Not only is the farmer benefited by the labor-saving conservation practice, but water and air pollution are greatly reduced.

There are many minimum tillage methods, and they are known by various names, usually by the kind of planting equipment used.

"No tillage" or "zero tillage" prepares a seedbed only in the area where the seed is to be planted—on about a tenth of the soil surface. The rest of the soil is not tilled, and residues are left on the surface.

"Strip tillage" prepares a seedbed about 6 to 10 inches wide on about a third of the soil surface, leaving residues on the remaining two-thirds. Strip tillage works well on soils that do not warm up early in the spring. It works best, however, when done on the contour so that water does not run down the tilled strip.

Minimum tillage.

290

"Till planting" is done by tilling the soil over the old crop row and pushing the residues and some soil to the center of the row.

"Chisel planting" is done with narrow spikes or shovels; it disturbs most of the soil surface without burying the residues.

Other methods can be used to get the same benefits as minimum tillage. One is leaving a good cover of crop residues on the soil surface. Another is planting small-grain stubble or cover crops in corn, sorghum, or soybean residues or in grass sod. This allows many farmers to double crop their land, especially where soybeans or corn can follow winter grain harvest. They can plant their soybeans or corn after grain harvest without plowing or disking. Research and experience show that yields are maintained and in many cases improved, with less cost and time per acre.

There is no one method or planting equipment that fits all soils, crops, and climatic conditions, but all will reduce costs, labor, and soil losses. Compared with conventional tillage, the amount of soil loss reduction through minimum tillage depends on how much residue is left on the surface after planting.

Five to 6 thousand pounds of cornstalks or half that amount of grain stubble will reduce soil loss as much as 90 percent compared with using the plow-disk-harrow-plant-cultivate type of tillage.

It is well known that if it had been possible to keep grain stubble on the soil surface in the Great Plains during the third decade of this century, there would have been no "dirty thirties." A vegetative cover, dead or alive, has the same beneficial effect in reducing erosion from intensive rains.

Recent innovations in farm equipment and agricultural methods make it possible for the farmer to treat his soil in accordance with its need.

Terraces are one of the major conservation practices for controlling erosion and slowing water runoff from cropland. They have been in use since the early 1900's.

Terraces control erosion by breaking up the slope into short segments, thus reducing the distance which runoff water must travel down the slope. Once the water reaches the terrace it moves slowly down the terrace to an outlet or, in less humid areas, is held by the terrace until absorbed by the soil. In other words runoff water is made to "walk" rather than "run" off the field.

Early terraces were narrow and crooked. The farming interval between terraces was sometimes wide at one point and narrow at another.

This meant point rows requiring frequent turning in the field when plowing, planting, and cultivating.

The small single- or double-row equipment then in use did not present much of a problem.

Not so any longer. Terracing methods have been revamped to fit the large multirow farm equipment now in use. This equipment requires larger fields, smoother fields, and less turns for most efficient and least costly operation.

Terraces are now made parallel, an equal distance apart throughout their length. The spacing fits the type of farming equipment to be used, allowing for an even number of rows between terraces. Point rows that cause extra turning of equipment have been reduced or eliminated.

Installation of parallel systems has been simplified by the use of the computer and heavy earthmoving equipment that can do necessary smoothing, cutting, and filling. The land smoothing eliminates rills and high and low spots, which means smoother surfaces on which to plant, cultivate, and harvest.

In areas of excess rainfall, terraces are graded to an outlet. This allows water to move slowly down the terrace channel to the outlet.

Outlets are generally of two types —grassed waterways and underground pipe or tile. The grassed waterway is changing shape, also. It is being constructed wider and with flatter side slopes to provide greater ease of crossing with large farming equipment. This eliminates any extra turning.

There is a growing trend toward replacing grassed waterways with buried pipe to carry runoff water from parallel terrace systems. The size of pipe depends on the expected flow. For each terrace, there is an individual inlet, placed in relation to the ridge to cause least interference with operation of large equipment.

In less humid areas, on soils that can absorb extra water, terraces are constructed with no grade. They are level from end to end. The ends are blocked so that excess water is held in the terrace interval until the soil absorbs it. This type of terrace not only reduces erosion but also holds the maximum amount of water for crop use.

Shape and size of terrace ridges have changed, too. The size of equipment to be used rather than the water-carrying capacity of the terrace becomes the determining factor. On moderately sloping fields, the terrace ridge is made broad enough for the side slopes to accommodate the full width of equipment to be used. This way the entire terrace is farmed. This is known as a broad-base ridge terrace.

On steeper fields, the frontslope of the terrace is made broad enough to accommodate the equipment to be used, while the downhill or back-slope is made steep and is seeded to grass. Only the frontslope is cultivated. This is known as a grass backslope terrace.

These terraces are usually constructed from the lower side, thereby removing a part of the cross slope in the terrace interval. This provides flatter land for farming.

In areas of low rainfall, a conservation bench or flat-channel terrace is frequently used. These are parallel terraces that are constructed with no grade. The ends are blocked so water does not leave the terrace interval.

The channel and part of the interval upslope from the terrace ridge are leveled with heavy earthmoving equipment. All side fall is eliminated in the leveled part. This is done by taking material to construct the terrace ridge from the channel area during the construction process. It may result in a flat channel from 12 to 24 rows wide which has no slope from end to end or side to side.

The leveled area receives extra water from the rest of the terrace interval above. And the water is spread over a greater area than normal for the regular level terrace. This makes better use of excess water.

Trends in irrigation are toward more ways of reducing labor and more general acceptance of sophisticated equipment, particularly in new irrigation systems on large fields.

Increasing numbers of new systems are mechanized, at least partly automated, and may involve relatively high capital investment.

Solid set sprinklers, consisting of permanent lines to each sprinkler head, are being used more for producing high-value crops such as citrus, vegetables, and berries. This eliminates the labor once required to move portable systems.

Large self-propelled sprinklers are the biggest, most spectacular change, however.

These and other developments, such as surface irrigation using automatically-timed gates, have potential for improving the timing and amount of water application, still the biggest need in conservation irrigation.

Daily climatic data, together with knowledge of soil-moisture-holding capacity, are beginning to be used with good success for scheduling irrigations. For example, this kind of scheduling procedure has been developed in the Northeast and in the Salt River Valley of Arizona.

A new, more practical method of controlling stream size for initial and final flow in furrow irrigation is gaining acceptance, particularly in the Corn Belt States. This is a furrow

Self-propelled irrigation sprinkler in Nebraska.

stream cutback system which uses a variable furrow stream to obtain a more uniform soil penetration with little waste of water.

New materials are available for irrigation pipelines and flexible canal lining membranes. Some changes also have been made in pipe or appurtenances for concrete, steel, and asbestos-cement pipelines.

Work is in progress on an inter-agency publication by two U.S. Department of Agriculture agencies and the Interior Department's Bureau of Reclamation that describes a new technique for estimating irrigation water requirements. This method is based on the use of solar radiation data and other climate factors.

Research in irrigation includes a study of the effect of continuous small flows of water fed into the soil (trickle or drip irrigation); a method for determining the proper time to irrigate a crop based on plant physiology rather than soil moisture content; and a study of automatic or timed gates for surface irrigation methods.

To handle new farming technology and meet needs brought about by added pressure on the land, conservation systems have gone modern. The results will be less erosion,

better use of water, more economical operations, and a better and more beautiful rural America.

The job doesn't stop here. New research must be done and improved practices must continue to be developed to meet the foreseeable changing needs of the future.

Pollution Poses Threat to Man, Farms, Nature

W. C. SHAW,

H. E. HEGGESTAD, and

W. W. HECK

POLLUTION is a threat to the production of adequate supplies of high-quality food, feed, and fiber and to human health and welfare. Pollution has caused changes in the populations of some plants and animals while the quality of some

293

species has been impaired. Air pollution is believed to be a primary cause for the increased death rate from diseases of the respiratory system.

In reaching our goals for material things, the quality of our environment has deteriorated. Ecological effects of technology were not always accurately assessed.

Too often man has acted as the master and has exploited nature as his subject. In this often strange relationship, life appears to have become a struggle of man against his environment, and not a joint venture for mutual benefits. Future progress, including improvements in the quality of our environment, will require greater emphasis on the ecological consequences of technological development.

We who enjoy the fruits of this productive land and country must make a new commitment to the principles of ecology—a word read and heard frequently, but not well understood. In lay language, ecology is simply the science to explain the intricate web of relationships between living organisms and their living and nonliving surroundings. Man himself is the dominant organism that makes up these interdependent living and nonliving parts which we call an ecosystem.

Since man has the highest intellectual capability of all the organisms in an ecosystem, he is capable of manipulating and managing the relationships between the living organisms and their living and nonliving surroundings. Cornfields, forests, lakes, and estuaries are examples of ecosystems.

*

W. C. SHAW is an Agricultural Administrator, Plant Science Research Division, Agricultural Research Service.

H. E. HEGGESTAD is Leader, Plant Air Pollution Laboratory, Plant Science Research Division.

W. W. HECK, Plant Science Research Division, is Leader of cooperative air pollution research with the Environmental Protection Agency, North Carolina State University, Raleigh.

Biomes are larger ecosystems or combinations of ecosystems which occur in similar climates and share a similar character and arrangement of vegetation. The Arctic Tundra, prairie grasslands of the Midwest, and the deserts of the Southwest are examples.

The earth, its surrounding envelope of life-giving plants, soil, water, and air, and all its living things, comprise the biosphere. Finally, man's total environmental system includes not only the biosphere, but also his interactions with his natural and manmade surroundings.

Changes in ecosystems occur continuously. Many interactions take place every moment of every day as plants and animals respond to changes in their surroundings and to each other.

Evolution has produced for each species, including man, a genetic composition that limits how far that species can go in adjusting to sudden changes in its surroundings. But within these limits the several thousand species in an ecosystem or the millions in the biosphere continuously adjust to outside stimuli.

Since interactions are so numerous, they form long chains of reaction. Thus, small changes in one part of an ecosystem are likely to be felt and compensated for eventually throughout the system.

A simple ecosystem such as a cornfield is more easily manipulated by man but is subject to very great reactions from outside stimuli. By contrast, a forest is a more complex ecosystem. It is more difficult to manipulate and often the changes are subtle with long-term impacts.

Processes of concentration that exceed acceptable tolerance limits impair the quality of our ecosystems, our total environmental system, and thus the quality of our lives. Familiar examples of concentration are: too many automobiles and too many people in our cities; too many cattle per feedlot; too many plant nutrients in irrigation water; too much ozone per cubic meter of air; and faulty chemical waste disposal methods.

Pollutants can be said to be "resources out of place." Actually the substances that we consider undesirable pollutants under some circumstances, may become very valuable materials under others.

Two types of pollutants are of concern—those created recently by man, and ones that have long existed in the environment. Some of the recently created ones are radioactive substances and industrial chemicals.

Examples of natural materials that have long been in the environment but now may be out of place are dust, plant nutrients, mercury, lead, and human and farm wastes.

It is important to remember that the natural ecosystems encountered by man when he discovered this country were not sufficiently productive to sustain our country's current populations of humans, domestic animals, and wildlife. Survival and the maintenance of natural ecosystems were incompatible.

Man's survival and his standard of living depend upon his manipulating the environment. He must produce an ecological balance favorable for the growth of food crops and livestock, the protection of his natural resources, and all other values in his environment.

Five types of constructive manipulation of ecological processes are primarily responsible for the affluence of the modern world: (1) simplification and increased productivity of ecosystems, (2) management of natural biological and biochemical cycles, (3) concentration of powerful sources of energy, (4) introduction and adaptation of species into new environments, and (5) induced genetic and behavioral changes in organisms.

A simplified ecosystem can be illustrated by the cornfields that replaced the more complex midwestern tall grass prairie. In order to feed our current population, it was essential to replace the tall grass prairie with productive fields of corn. The oak-hickory forests of the Southeast are esthetically pleasing for recreation. However, from a utility standpoint, a conifer forest is more productive in providing lumber for use in constructing housing. Thus man manipulates a shift from oak to pine trees.

The whole history of agriculture and forestry is basically man's efforts to create simple systems in which preferred crops are kept free of insects, diseases, nematodes, weeds, and other competing species that reduce yields through competition for light, moisture, and other growth factors or interfere with harvest. In general, the more productive the system is, the simpler it must be.

Pest control is one of the major environmental manipulations necessary in a simplified ecosystem that is designed for the efficient, safe, and economical production of food crops.

It is essential for us to understand the ecological situation in which food crops are produced. They compete in a simplified ecosystem with a complex and hostile environment shared by about 50,000 species of fungi that cause more than 1,500 diseases. About 30,000 species of weeds are distributed throughout the world. More than 1,800 of these compete with crops and cause serious economic losses each year.

About 15,000 species of nematodes attack crop plants, and more than 1,500 of these cause damage. More than 10,000 species of pest insects add to the serious losses that occur each year.

Poisonous weed seeds that contaminate our seed and food crops are pollutants. Insect weevils in our grain are pollutants. The fungi that attack seeds and rot our tomatoes are pollutants. Aquatic weeds pollute our lakes and streams. Food and water are important components of our environment, and pests pollute them.

Pests are among the most damaging pollutants in our environment. They compete directly for human and animal resources.

In our efforts to meet human needs, we must use pesticides and biological control methods effectively and safely so there are no side effects in our environment. When such practices are followed, pesticides are antipollutants. However, if these valuable resources get out of place, in excessive concentrations, they also become pollutants.

A major result of the industrial and agricultural revolution of the past two centuries is a significant increase in man's capability to alter natural biological and biochemical cycles. The use of plant nutrients, especially nitrogen, is a good example.

Plant nutrients used judiciously and effectively have revolutionized production of crops. However, when used excessively, they move from land to water systems where they stimulate the growth of aquatic weeds which clog irrigation channels, cause flooding, and reduce irrigation efficiency. Excessive levels of plant nutrients may also cause undesirable changes in the chemical composition of food crops.

Technological advance from the machete through the sickle, hand hoe, wooden plow, metal plow, and tractors equipped for cultivation and the application of agricultural chemicals, illustrates an enormous concentration of dispersed energy. The change from human energy to the energy of domestic animals, to that of tractors, trucks, automobiles, and other equipment with internal combustion engines had far-reaching impacts upon the environment.

These and other advances greatly reduced the need for farmworkers. The population shifted from rural areas to urban centers. A stream that half a century ago could assimilate and biologically degrade the waste of 10,000 people cannot today absorb the effluent from a half million people without causing serious pollution.

We greatly concentrated sources of energy and contaminated our atmosphere with new pollutants when we changed from human and animal energy to the internal combustion engine.

Introduction of new crop species, and advanced production techniques, were needed to meet demands for higher production of food and fiber to sustain our expanding population. Associated with these developments have been shifts in crop resistance and susceptibility to insects, diseases, and nematodes. These significant behavioral changes necessitated the increased use of fertilizers, pesticides, other agricultural chemicals, and other production inputs in order to produce adequate supplies of high-quality food, feed, and fiber.

The five types of constructive manipulations of ecological processes we have discussed have been used by man since he began civilized development. All that has really changed is the intensity of the manipulations.

In the future as we continue to constructively manage ecological processes, agriculture is concerned with (a) pollutants that originate from nonagricultural sources which have an impact on agriculture, and (b) pollutants that result from agricultural practices which have an impact on agriculture or other aspects of our society.

Basic components of our environment that are critically important to agricultural production are air, water, and soil.

Primary pollutant emissions from nonagricultural sources that contaminate the air over the United States total more than 200 million tons each year. These pollutants include carbon monoxide, sulfur oxide, hydrocarbons, nitrogen oxides, and particulates. They result from transportation, fuel combustion at stationary sources, industrial processes, and solid waste disposal.

Secondary pollutants such as ozone and the peroxyacyl nitrates are formed from certain primary pollutants as a result of photochemical reactions in the atmosphere.

Relatively uniform distribution of secondary pollutants over extensive

296

areas of State or region may cause serious injury to large acreages of forests and agricultural crops. These pollutants are believed to cause far more serious losses to agriculture than do the pollutants that originate from agricultural practices.

Air pollutants from agricultural practices include chemicals and particulates that result from burning forest and crop residues, infectious agents and allergens, pesticides and other agricultural chemicals.

Agricultural burning produces some nitrogen oxides and hydrocarbons from which a small amount of photochemical air pollutants are produced. In 1970, it is estimated that crop residues on 1,117,990 acres, equivalent to 3,625,075 tons, were burned as a way of reducing the losses caused by plant diseases and other soilborne pests, and also as a means of disposing of crop residues.

Natural dust, from industrial and agricultural operations, is emitted into the atmosphere of the United States at the rate of 30 million tons each year. Airborne infectious agents and allergens, such as fungal spores and weed pollens are known to cause plant, animal, and human diseases.

Weeds produce pollens and toxins that cause serious human allergies in most of our heavily populated areas. Allergies from weed pollens each year result in an estimated 12½ million cases of asthma, hay fever, or both. Odors from agricultural practices also contribute to this growing problem.

Agricultural chemicals including pesticides, when used properly, have resulted in great benefits to man and his environment. Conversely, when they are misused or used carelessly they cause harm. The adverse effects have been relatively minor in relation to the great benefits that have resulted from safe and effective pest control and improved crop and livestock management.

Water pollution comes from many sources but the major ones are industrial, municipal, and agricultural.

The more than 300,000 water-using factories in the United States discharge three to four times as much oxygen-demanding waste as all the human wastes discharged into sewers. Moreover, many of the wastes discharged by industry are toxic. Output of industrial waste is growing several times faster than the volume of sanitary sewage.

Waste from livestock feedlots also pollute water resources. Beef cattle, poultry, and swine feeding operations, along with dairy farms, represent the major sources of actual or potential water pollution from animal wastes. In the United States today there are approximately 564 million domestic animals. Wastes produced by these animal populations are estimated to be the equivalent of the wastes produced by 2 billion people.

Pollutants entering water sources have been broadly classified as: (a) domestic sewage and other oxygen-demanding waste, (b) infectious agents, (c) plant nutrients, (d) organic chemicals such as pesticides and detergents, (e) other minerals and chemicals, (f) sediments from land erosion, (g) radioactive substances, and (h) heat from power and industrial plants.

Soil pollution is a special threat to agricultural production. For practical purposes, the land can be considered as a major sink for residues coupled to the atmosphere and fresh-water streams and estuaries. Two principal categories of the land pollution problem are: use of soils for disposal of solid wastes, and maintaining agricultural soils in proper condition for efficient crop production.

Two types of soil pollutants are of particular interest—long-lasting radioactive elements from nuclear blasts, and excessively persistent pesticides and other agricultural chemicals.

Currently, neither of these sources of pollutants seems to present a serious hazard to plant life or to the animals that consume the plants. Nevertheless, continuous monitoring of the soil must be maintained to assure that harmful chemicals or radioactive substances do not accumulate and persist in quantities that would be harmful to plants, animals, or man.

Total damage caused by pollution in the United States cannot be precisely calculated, but it amounts to many billions of dollars each year. Annual air pollution damage alone to agricultural crops is estimated at more than a half billion dollars and it is increasing at a rapid rate.

The cost of controlling pollution will also be high. For example, the cost of controlling air pollution from the major industrial and municipal sources in 100 metropolitan areas of the United States has been estimated at $2.6 billion. However, the benefits of pollution control are expected to far exceed the costs of control.

Damage to agricultural production from pollution can be reduced or prevented by (a) control of pollution at the source, (b) removal of pollutants from the air, soil, and water, and (c) reduction of the damage caused by pollutants.

It will probably never be feasible to eliminate all the sources of pollution, or to be completely effective in removing pollutants. Therefore, the primary mission of agriculture will undoubtedly continue to be the implementation of research, regulatory, educational, and information programs that are designed to assure the production of an abundant supply of high-quality food, feed, fiber, and timber to sustain the human, domestic livestock, and wildlife populations of our country.

Agriculture is playing a major role in using technological know-how to achieve this objective. At the same time, we are providing greater technology to assess the nature of the problem and reduce pollution from agricultural sources and thereby protect our resources and improve our environment.

Agriculture is continuously assessing those agricultural practices that cause pollution. When risks outweigh their benefits, such practices are modified, corrected, or discontinued and replaced by safer alternates. When alternates are not available, agricultural research is emphasized to develop them.

Agricultural scientists are currently conducting a wide array of investigations to prevent pollution and to reduce losses caused by pollution. Their efforts include research to develop: plants and animals that are more resistant to pollutants; plants that stabilize soils in a wide variety of environments to reduce airborne dust and sedimentation; and methods of controlling infectious agents and reducing airborne allergens.

Scientists are also seeking improved fertilizer practices and effective, selective, safe, and nonpersistent pesticides and other agricultural chemicals that do not pollute the soil, plants, air, or water.

Research is being emphasized to develop safe methods for disposing of pesticide containers, and pesticide wastes; improved systems for disposing of animal wastes; and methods for disposing of crop residues without burning. New technology developed from these studies will have a significant impact on improving the quality of our environment.

A hundred million more! Yes, agriculture can provide for the 300 million Americans expected by the year 2000. We must develop and manage high-yielding agroecosystems that are compatible with a quality environment.

The 25 million new families can have timber and other material for better housing. Improved technology can provide the 50 percent more food of higher quality that will be required. We can also have cleaner air, soils of greater productivity, and adequate water of higher quality. Far more fiber and space for living and economic growth can also be provided.

We believe achieving these goals and the improvement of environmental quality are compatible. A commitment must be made now to provide the research and educational resources to develop the technology that will be needed to achieve these objectives.

It is probably a fallacy to assume that pollution problems can be readily solved by legislation, treaty, or high resolve. For often the spoilers of environmental quality are not always profit-hungry industrialists who can be fined into submission, or lax public officials who can be replaced.

More often it is the consumer who demands—or at least allows himself to be cajoled into demanding—newer, faster, bigger, and cheaper things, without counting the cost in terms of a dirtier, smellier, and sicklier world.

Our most important goal is to achieve and maintain a fine ecological balance. On the one hand, health and comfort, with the production of ample food and fiber. On the other hand, a better grasp of the ecological significance of agricultural practices and their relation to pollution and control.

Utilizing Agricultural Wastes

WALTER R. HEALD and

RAYMOND C. LOEHR

AGRICULTURAL wastes are all byproducts we have not yet learned to use. They may be manure and crop residues on farms; residues from food processing; waste products from forestry and lumbering; or water used in cleaning and processing agricultural products, plus the runoff from irrigation.

Opportunities to recycle and use these "wastes" are enormous and are limited only by man's imagination. The challenge is to develop opportunities which are technically and economically sound, socially acceptable, and legal according to local, State, and Federal regulations.

Since 1945, total farm output in the United States increased over 40 percent, while man-hours and acres decreased. In 1969, one farmworker produced enough food for 42 people— about a 400 percent jump since 1940. This great rise in crop production on fewer acres and the increase in animal density per acre are the major causes of today's waste management problems.

Our rapidly growing population and the rising per capita consumption of certain meats and poultry will require a continued boost in total animal production in the United States, and an ever increasing amount of wastes. The most rapid expansion will be beef cattle, poultry, and hog production.

Distribution of wastes, particularly from animals and food processing, complicates the problem. These operations tend to be concentrated close to suburban boundaries as the trend toward automation and centralization continues.

The movement to larger installations has proceeded faster than the development of methods to collect, treat, use, or ultimately dispose of wastes without polluting the environment. There are signs that present research and development is rapidly permitting us to catch up. How soon we can catch up will depend more upon limits that the economy and society place on technology, rather than on technology itself.

One of the leading problems of

*

WALTER R. HEALD is a Soil Scientist in the Northeast Watershed Research Center, Agricultural Research Service, stationed at University Park, Penn.
RAYMOND C. LOEHR is Professor of Agricultural and Civil Engineering at Cornell University, Ithaca, N. Y.

animal production today and in the future is the handling and disposing of waste. In 1969, about 107 million cattle, 57 million hogs, 21 million sheep, 141 million egg-laying chickens, and about 2 billion broilers were on U.S. farms. These animals produced at least 10 times the amount of biological waste produced by the people of this country, or over a million tons per year of animal waste that must be handled.

The animal population will certainly increase at least 50 percent by the year 2000 and produce wastes approaching 3 million tons a year. Obviously, this tremendous quantity demands a strong effort to avoid polluting the environment.

Using and reprocessing wastes offer interesting possibilities. Keys to successful processes are development of a beneficial use, a market for it, and an economical—although not necessarily profit-making—method. Many processes would be satisfactory if the overall cost is less than alternatives.

The land has been and will continue to be the ultimate disposal point for animal wastes. Manure as a fertilizer or soil conditioner is no longer as economical as it once was, because of the low cost of commercial fertilizers. Value of manure rarely offsets the investment and labor required to handle it. At present, land spreading must be considered as a least expensive, rather than an economical or profit-making, method.

The challenge is to incorporate animal wastes in a controlled land management program so they do not contribute to environmental problems such as the contamination of ground water, stream pollution caused by runoff, odors, or insect breeding.

Benefits of manures to soil are greater than their nutrient value alone. A better overall physical condition normally results. The soil becomes a better medium for plant growth, plant growth cover protects the soil from erosion and increases the infiltration of water, and the manure can serve as a mulch to reduce the loss, by evaporation, of the moisture from bare soil.

Until recently, land application had not been practiced widely. The increase in animal production and the need for a complete and nuisance-free disposal has led to a number of subsoil animal waste injection systems.

The plow-furrow-cover method in New Jersey, soil injection of liquid poultry wastes in New York, and deep-plowing experiments in Texas are approaches that appear feasible under certain circumstances. Maximum quantity that can be handled depends upon the type of soil and cover crop, rainfall conditions, and potential ground water pollution. Again, these operations are not economical, but social pressures may well force their employment.

A number of methods have been investigated for using animal wastes; for example, composting, feed supplements, and energy (methane) production. Horse manure as a medium for growing mushrooms is a very specific but practical method.

Composting offers an opportunity to recover and reuse a portion of the nutrients and the organic matter. These wastes can be composted alone but frequently are combined with wastes that may have a high carbon content such as sawdust, corncobs, paper, and municipal refuse.

Major objectives in composting are to stabilize putrescible organic matter; conserve as much crop nutrient and organic matter as possible; and produce a uniform, relatively dry product, suitable as a soil conditioner and garden fertilizer.

Research and full-scale operations have demonstrated that composting can be technically successful with poultry, beef, and dairy wastes. Composting can be feasible for specific animal production operations under unique regional conditions, but a market for the compost must be available. Without a market, virtually all the original dry matter remains for further disposal.

Drying and dehydrating wastes are

not utilization processes, but create a product suitable as a soil conditioner or feed supplement. Animal wastes are likely to have more value if they are dried, packaged, and sold to the home gardener, florist, or nurseryman. Without a suitable market, drying of wastes can be costly, with the cost generally exceeding the return.

Animal wastes contain considerable energy and nutritive value. Energy is produced when the gases resulting from the anaerobic decay of animal wastes are collected and burned as fuel. The practice of incorporating animal and food processing wastes in feed rations for animals is not a new concept, although it has received publicity only recently as a potential technique.

In general, the nutritive value incorporated in feed rations is greater if the wastes of single-stomached animals are added to the feed ration of ruminants and if the ruminant wastes are treated chemically before being added to feed rations. Experimental use of animal wastes in feed ration is not confined to the United States. This approach has been reported in South Africa, Canada, Australia, and England.

Available information indicates that when nutritional principles are followed, animal wastes can be used as a feed supplement. Certain unknowns related to transmittal of drugs, feed additives, and pesticides to the second animal and to the agricultural product, such as eggs and milk, remain to be clarified.

For this reason and several others, the Food and Drug Administration specifies that animal wastes may not be used as animal feed. However, research suggests that refeeding is a significant possibility for at least a portion of animal wastes.

A biological technique was suggested many years ago, with housefly larvae and insects consuming the wastes and then being harvested as a protein source for feed. U.S. Department of Agriculture research demonstrated that this can be done with poultry manure to produce a protein source which could replace soybean meal in the diet of the growing chick. By additional processing, the remaining biodegraded, dried animal waste could be employed as a soil conditioner or fertilizer. Large-scale feasibility of this method remains to be investigated, although the method shows considerable promise.

During the anaerobic digestion of animal wastes, gases containing 60–80 percent methane can be produced when consistently high rates of digestion are maintained. These gases can be considered as an energy source if they are used close to the site where they are generated. Approximately 8–9 cubic feet of gas can be produced per pound of volatile solids added to the digester if wastes high in organic content such as from poultry, beef cattle, and hogs are digested.

The controlled conditions, equipment, and associated costs make this method more expensive than alternatives. Consequently, it is finding little use at present, although remaining a potential source of future energy.

The amount of residue such as straw, stubble, leaves, and tree limbs from crops and orchards is in the order of hundreds of millions of tons. In some areas drastic measures, such as burning, are used to dispose of troublesome residues and to control plant disease and seeds. Burning is gradually being eliminated and more and more of the material returned to the soil as a mulch which is later plowed under. A small fraction of the residue, such as straw and peanut hulls, is used as bedding for farm animals. This eventually is returned to the soil, too.

In 1969 over 35 billion pounds of meat were processed in the United States and about the same amount of edible fats and oils was produced. The meat industry is an example of what can be done to put wastes to work profitably. Practically nothing requires disposal excepting in the water used.

Meat packing wastes, counting in

those collected during water disposal procedures, are now raw materials for several industries including those manufacturing soap, leather, glue, gelatin, and animal feed. Other by-products and their uses are: edible fats—lard, oil, edible tallow; inedible fats—tallow, greases; meat scraps and blood—animal feed; bone—bone meal for fertilizers; intestines—sausage casings, surgical thread; glands—pharmaceutical products such as hormones and enzymes; and feathers—feather meal for feed.

It is predicted that the United States will consume 30 percent more beef in the next 10 years and certainly more than 100 percent by the year 2000. Even so, byproducts of the meat industry will still provide economic returns.

Wastes from vegetable and fiber-processing plants have been intensively studied many years for possible use as feeds, raw materials for manufactured products, and a source of chemical compounds. However, at this time the nature of processing operations rarely makes it economical to collect and process the wastes.

Value of these wastes depends largely upon how well one can separate and collect the usable fraction from the millions of gallons of water discharged by a processing plant. The reusable material is present in this water in very dilute suspensions of highly variable composition consisting of peels, skins, pulps, seeds, and fibers. The liquid fraction may be saline, alkaline, or acidic and contains a large variety of soluble organic compounds.

In some processing, separation difficulties are minor and an economical byproduct results. A good example is production of molasses and pulp, widely used as animal feed supplements, from processing of sugarcane and beets.

Approaches that have been studied for technical feasibility are paper making from rice, cereal straw, and bagasse (the fibrous residue from processing of sugar cane). Others include chemicals such as furfural extracted from cereal straw, tartarate from wine grape residue, and monosodium glutamate from sugar beet pulp.

Fruit and vegetable wastes are being fed to animals. Tomato skins and seeds have been dehydrated for animal feed, as have corn husks, cobs, and trimmings.

Solid wastes from canning peas, corn, grapefruit, or oranges, and some solids screened from the liquid wastes of other processes, are being converted into a dried cattle feed.

These many wastes, however, may not be economically worthwhile at this time because of the availability of other materials.

About 117 billion pounds of milk were produced in this country in 1970. This was converted into 57 billion pounds of fluid milk, some 18 billion pounds of cheese, 25 billion pounds of butter, and 18 billion pounds of other milk products, such as condensed and dried milk and ice cream.

Manufacture of milk products results in millions of gallons of waste water containing suspended and soluble milk solids which must be removed before discharge to rivers and lakes. Much of this waste water is put to work irrigating crops after the milk solids are removed.

There is a considerable expansion in the disposition of milk solids as animal feed, feed supplements, a starting material for some chemical products such as alcohol, and as a growth medium for micro-organisms which can produce pharmaceutical chemicals.

In the past much of the water used by food processors was to dilute the soluble and solid wastes to a level that could be handled safely by the environment when discharged into surface waters or sprinkled on soil. The great increase of soluble and solid wastes has caused many changes to take place in the industry regarding the possible reuse of water, and more changes are being incorporated every year. In some areas these waste waters irrigate crops.

Processing plants are being renovated so that the highly contaminated waters are not mixed with wash and cooling waters. These latter waters can be safely discharged into rivers and lakes after minimum treatment, and may irrigate any type crop. The resultant small volume of highly contaminated water can then be more easily handled by waste treatment methods and/or applied to the soil.

Among the larger producers of agricultural wastes are wood and wood product industries. Although they use some of their wastes, the problem of disposing of the quantity of logging residue, sawdust, bark, and shavings without causing pollution is major. Twenty-five million tons of logging debris are left on the land during an average year. Controlled burning is one of the best available disposal methods at present but contributes to air pollution.

Alternatives for handling wood product debris cost many times more than controlled burning. A method that may have increasing potential is production of bark and wood chip mulch for pulp in paper manufacturing and commercial and home gardens.

In the pulp and paper industry, about half of a tree ends up as waste. Methods are being instituted in the pulp industry to produce such items as road binders, linoleum paste, and growth media which may then be used as food supplements, plus a large variety of chemicals such as artificial vanilla flavoring and raw materials plastic production.

A paper factory has many ways to recover waste paper and chemicals, but a large fraction of the wastes remains for disposal. Methods that may show promise include producing chemicals through fermenting the water and making new building items such as board, paper, and blocks.

Agriculture is a major user of water, primarily in food processing and irrigation. These waters become wastes in the same sense as solid wastes. Because of the importance of water, much research is taking place on how to reuse it, thus decreasing environmental contamination.

Irrigation is changing, in that irrigation water is now better controlled not only in the sense of how much to irrigate, but how to irrigate for maximum efficiency. Reuse of irrigation water is rapidly growing. It is usually done by a pump-back system where normal runoff is caught in shallow ponds, and then reapplied to other fields by pumping. Primary goal is to increase the efficiency of irrigation water use. A secondary effect is that soluble and solid materials usually lost in runoff are kept on the farm.

A possible major reuse of agricultural waters is the recharge of groundwater. Here the water is directly discharged into groundwater following treatment to avoid contaminating this natural resource.

Use of agricultural wastes is just beginning. Detailed information on the costs of most methods is not available and must be developed before the broad value of methods can be determined. A variety of costs must be known: cost of utilizing the method, net cost as it affects the producer's profit, and ultimate cost to the public.

Interdisciplinary approaches for seeking solutions to agricultural waste management problems are needed. Individuals from a variety of occupations should be involved.

The greatest opportunities for satisfactory use of agricultural wastes for the near future are in feed supplements, fertilizers, and soil conditioners. If feed supplements of wastes are to be widely applied, more information is needed about the effects and transmission of drugs, feed additives, pesticides, and other residuals that may be in the wastes.

Land application always will be an important method of agricultural waste and water utilization. Techniques need to be developed to assure that pollution and nuisance problems will not result from applying wastes to the land.

The future will demand that the Nation adequately use agricultural wastes since they are a valuable part of our national resources.

Water Quality and Farming

RONALD G. MENZEL and

PAUL F. SAND

NEEDED increase in agricultural production by the year 2000 will require greater use of fertilizers and pesticides. But these materials and others of agricultural origin can pollute our water supplies. Much research is now being done to determine the extent of pollution from intensive agriculture and to devise ways of controlling it.

Natural waters contain many substances that affect water quality. These include nutrients essential for plant and animal life in lakes and streams. Other substances can enter water from municipal, industrial, agricultural, or natural sources.

For most purposes, absolutely pure water is not desired. Low concentrations of many salts can be tolerated in drinking water, but poisonous metals and pathogenic bacteria obviously cannot. Water used for recreational fishing must maintain the proper temperature range and supply enough oxygen and nutrients to support the growth of desirable fish. But too much nutrient can cause excessive growth of algae.

Farmers are directly affected by the quality of water available for crop and livestock production. In 1970, more than 130 million acre-

304

feet of water was used for irrigation in the United States. (One acre-foot of water is enough to cover an acre of land a foot deep.) Another 2 million acre-feet was used for watering livestock. By 2000, these requirements will increase to nearly 170 million acre-feet for irrigation and around 4 million acre-feet for watering livestock, according to the U.S. Water Resources Council.

Agricultural use in 1965 amounted to nearly 10 percent of the total runoff carried in rivers of the 48 contiguous States.

One would expect farming to have considerable effect on water quality because most of the land area is devoted to agriculture. Around a fourth of the U.S. land area is cropland and a third is pasture. These fractions are not expected to change much by the year 2000, but production will be more intensive on the land that is used.

Deserving special attention among the many materials that would enter water from agricultural lands are: sediment, plant nutrients, pesticides, animal wastes, and salts.

Sediment constitutes by far the greatest mass of material moved by water. Some 4 billion tons of sediment are washed into streams in the United States each year. Around a fourth of this reaches the oceans. Most plant nutrients and pesticides in water are carried on sediment.

Dr. C. H. Wadleigh, director of USDA's Soil and Water Conservation Research Division, has estimated that at least half the sediment arises from agricultural lands and another 30 percent may be considered geologic erosion. Construction sites may be important local sources of sediment. Construction activity will probably increase greatly by 2000.

*

RONALD G. MENZEL is Director of the U. S. Agricultural Water Quality Management Laboratory in Durant, Okla.

PAUL F. SAND is an Assistant Chief Staff Officer, Nematodes and Plant Diseases, Plant Protection Division, Agricultural Research Service.

Sediment should be reduced for many reasons. It is fertile topsoil lost. It is unsightly in streams. It fills reservoirs and stream channels, sometimes resulting in disastrous floods. It necessitates filtration of water for drinking and many other purposes.

Studies have shown that soil losses from meadow or small grain fields are much lower than from cultivated row crop fields. This is because crop or crop residue cover absorbs most of the energy of raindrops before they strike the soil and also slows the velocity of water flow. Even with continuous corn cropping, soil losses have been reduced by using winter cover crops, leaving the crop residues, or plowing under manure.

Soil conservation practices have been developed for both agricultural lands and construction sites. On agricultural lands, strip cropping, contour cultivation, and terracing can be used to interrupt the flow of water across the soil surface, and thus to reduce the velocity and erosive power of water.

Construction sites should be fitted to the topography, saving trees and vegetation where possible. Graded land should be exposed in small areas and for short periods of time whenever practical. The structures should be completed and vegetation planted as soon as possible. Sediment basins can be used to catch sediment from the runoff water during development.

Sediment yields from agricultural watersheds where good conservation practices have been used have ranged from 10 to 50 percent of those without such practices. Dramatic reductions in sediment yields from construction sites have been observed, although controlled experimental studies have not been possible.

Crop or crop residue covers and soil conservation practices usually increase infiltration of rainfall and reduce the amount of runoff. While this prevents some sediment from reaching streams, it increases the movement of water-soluble, mobile substances through soils. Thus, measures taken to control sediment production may increase the likelihood of salt, nitrate, or certain pesticides entering ground water.

Plant nutrients of most significance in water quality are nitrogen and phosphorus. In the forms of nitrate and phosphate, respectively, they are readily absorbed by plants. Concentrations of nitrate and phosphate in lake water are thought to often control the growth of algae.

However, sediments usually contain much more nitrogen and phosphorus in organic forms than is found as nitrate and phosphate in the surrounding water. Phosphate is readily adsorbed (bonded onto particle surfaces) on most sediments. Organic nitrogen and phosphorus and absorbed phosphate are potential sources of nitrate and phosphate in water. All of these forms must be considered in maintaining water quality.

Eroded topsoil carries much of the nitrogen and almost all of the phosphorus that enters streams and lakes. The concentration varies greatly, but each ton of eroded topsoil probably contains from 5 to 10 pounds of phosphorus and a slightly greater amount of nitrogen. Soil conservation measures that reduce soil losses will help control this movement of nitrogen and phosphorus.

Very little phosphorus moves through the soil in solution. This is shown by accumulations of phosphorus in the surface of fertilized soils where erosion does not occur, and extremely low concentrations of phosphorus in ground water, usually less than .01 part per million.

In contrast, nitrogen moves easily through the soil as nitrate. Concentrations ranging from 1 to 10 parts per million are common in ground water.

Nitrate is produced in soils by microbial action, which is greatest in warm, moist soils. Most of this nitrate can be taken up by plants growing on the soils. However, certain late-planted crops may not develop quickly enough to use the nitrate before some of it has leached from the soil.

Increasing use of fertilizers in agriculture has been blamed as a source of water pollution. Fertilizer use has been rising rapidly and this trend is likely to continue.

About twice as much fertilizer as is currently used would be required if all crops received the applications recommended by the State agricultural experiment stations. However, the current annual addition of about 7 million tons of nitrogen in fertilizers is less than the amount of nitrogen removed in crops, estimated at 9 million tons. The amount of phosphorus added in fertilizer is now about equal to that removed in crops. Additions of both nutrients are small compared with the amounts naturally present in soils.

In view of the mobility of nitrates, efficient use of nitrogen fertilizer is important for maintaining water quality. George Stanford, a U.S. Department of Agriculture soil scientist, estimated that an acre of corn recovered 50 pounds of nitrogen from the average application of 66 pounds in Iowa in 1964. Experiments in Nebraska showed that corn recovered 25 pounds of nitrogen from a summer sidedress application of 40 pounds per acre. The percentage of recovery was lower from spring or fall applications or with higher rates of application.

Many Federal, State, and industrial experiment stations are conducting research on increasing the recovery of nitrogen fertilizers by crops.

The fate of unrecovered nitrogen is not well known. Many experiments have shown little accumulation of nitrogen in fertilized soils. A portion leaches to ground water. An unknown portion is microbially reduced to nitrogen gas by the process called "denitrification." It is then indistinguishable from nitrogen of the air.

Although field estimation of the amount of denitrification is difficult, it is apparently very effective in some situations. The concentration of nitrate nitrogen in the soil solution leaching through an irrigated soil in southern California decreased from an average of 2.4 parts per million in the top 3 feet to .7 parts per million at the 6- or 8-foot depth of the tile drains.

Pesticides are used in agriculture to control insects, plant diseases, weeds, and rodents. Improved pest control will be essential for obtaining the increased agricultural production that will be required in the year 2000. There will be a need for improved pesticides as well as alternative methods of pest control.

Many pesticides are acutely toxic to fish and wildlife, directly killing them when sufficient amounts of pesticide are absorbed. However, this does not normally happen unless there is an accidental spill of pesticide or something unusual happens to cause a concentration of pesticide in the water to reach toxic levels. Persistent pesticides may have slow, cumulative effects on the reproduction or food value of fish and wildlife even though they enter water in minute amounts.

Monitoring studies by the U.S. Department of Agriculture indicate no progressive buildup of pesticide residues in soils in farming areas where pesticides are commonly used for crop production. However, in some orchards, the soil residues of certain pesticides are relatively high.

If orchards are taken out of production, the soil should be tested for pesticide residues and caution used in selecting crops to be planted on these soils. It is important to control movement of soil particles from such areas.

Most pesticides are strongly adsorbed on soils. In addition, many of the more persistent pesticides are not very soluble in water. Movement of these pesticides in water usually results from movement of soil or sediment that has adsorbed the pesticide. Good soil conservation practices will minimize this movement.

The disposal of pesticides should be

avoided in areas where they could enter ponds, streams, or ground water.

Much current research is aimed at developing very specific, short-lived pesticides and methods of controlling pests without chemicals. Many problems of water contamination would be avoided by using short-lived pesticides which degrade before entering bodies of water. However, applications might have to be repeated many times for control of persistent pests. In addition, short-lived pesticides such as parathion are highly toxic to man and animals.

Certain herbicides are used to control aquatic weeds in ponds and irrigation ditches. Many herbicides, such as diquat, simazine, sodium arsenite, silvex, and 2,4-D, do not injure fish at the concentrations required for aquatic weed control. At higher rates they may be toxic to fish, humans, livestock, and crops.

Alternative methods of pest control under active investigation include biological controls of insects and weeds, trapping of insects, release of sterile insects, breeding of disease-resistant crop varieties, and improved cultural practices. Many of these methods avoid the use of chemicals that could contaminate water.

Chemicals have been used to sterilize insects or to attract them to traps. In these uses there is little possibility of water contamination. Mixtures of baits and pesticides have been used successfully to control the fire ant and the Mediterranean fruit fly with greatly reduced amounts of pesticide.

Animal manure may create serious water quality problems. Runoff from feedlots contains much decomposable organic matter, many bacteria (possibly including pathogens), and sometimes high concentrations of salts. Instances of poisoning of fish or cattle have occurred downstream from large feedlots.

Concentration of thousands of cattle, swine, or poultry into single production units intensified the problem of manure disposal. The expense of hauling manure from such units is appreciable, and sometimes the manure accumulates to become a potential water pollution hazard. The growing catfish feeding industry poses a similar waste disposal problem with direct effects on water quality.

Disposal of manure on land has been practiced for centuries. Its value as a soil conditioner and source of plant nutrients is generally accepted. One ton of cattle manure contains about 20 pounds of nitrogen, 5 pounds of phosphorus, and 20 pounds of potassium, as well as other plant nutrients.

But it has become much easier and cheaper to spread the same quantities of plant nutrients from a bag of commercial fertilizer.

Water pollution could occur from manure spread on the land or directly from feedlots. Spring runoff from manure spread on frozen soils is thought to contribute a major part of the agricultural nitrogen and phosphorus reaching the lakes at Madison, Wis. On the other hand, allowing organic wastes from a cannery at Paris, Tex., to trickle over sloping grassed areas removed about 95 percent of the decomposable organic matter, 90 percent of the nitrogen, and 55 percent of the phosphorus.

If manure is spread on vegetated areas with good soil conservation practices, runoff should not be a problem.

One way to minimize manure distribution costs is by spreading the maximum amount in an area. However, excessive amounts may interfere with crop production. Studies at Bushland, Tex., show that good corn and sorghum yields are maintained when as much as 60 tons of feedlot manure is applied per acre. When 120 tons are applied per acre, the yields are limited by concentrations of salt or ammonium.

Other ways of handling manure that are being studied include drying to reduce weight, and developing liquid manure distribution systems.

One of the primary considerations in the use of irrigation water is its salt content. The salinity is considered low if water contains less than 150 parts per million and high if it contains more than 1,500 parts per million of dissolved salts.

Low salinity water can be used with most crops and soils. High salinity water can be used with very few crops and soils. With higher salinity water, soils must be better drained; more water must be used to leach salt accumulations from the soil; and crops that tolerate higher salt levels—such as barley, sugarbeets, or cotton—must be grown.

Irrigation agriculture necessarily increases the concentration of salts in water. Of the 130 million acre-feet of water used annually for irrigation, only 55 million acre-feet is returned to streams as drainage, the remainder evaporating in crop production. Yet the 55 million acre-feet must carry all the salt added in the original 130 million acre-feet. Otherwise the irrigated soils would soon be too salty for crop production.

Soil conservation practices can affect the movement of salt by increasing the amount of infiltration. When the soils or underlying materials contain soluble salts, more salt will be moved by the increased flow of water through the ground. The salt may appear in streams or in surface seepage areas. In parts of North Dakota, stubble mulching for moisture conservation has increased the number of salt seeps.

Streams and ponds in most agricultural areas are still relatively clean and pure. It may never be possible to control all potential polluting materials from agriculture. However, the major sources of sediment—plant nutrients, pesticides, animal wastes, and salt—can be limited through good soil conservation practices.

In addition, alternatives to some pesticide uses are being developed, as are new methods of handling animal wastes.

Widespread research will continue to help protect water quality and agricultural production.

308

New Approaches to Pest Control

H C COX

THE NEED to control insect pests and reduce or eliminate their depredations will be more critical in the year 2000 than it is in 1971—and certainly the need is an important one today.

An estimated 25 million or so additional new families by the turn of the century will be just as anxious to rear their children in the absence of insect-borne diseases as we are. They, too, will want to live in homes and enjoy recreation areas free from damaging or bothersome insects. And certainly our Nation must continue to provide an abundance of wholesome food, with a minimum of loss due to insects, if we are to maintain or exceed our present high standard of living.

How can research make this goal possible if our Nation does not continue to rely heavily upon conventional chemical insecticides for insect control? U.S. Department of Agriculture scientists are working today to develop selective methods to use against insects that cause the greatest amount of damage or account for the greatest use of insecticides in the United States.

We have already devised a variety of selective methods of control for some pest insects and have used them successfully. But we are only in the process of developing other—perhaps even more imaginative—methods for use against the many additional pest insects. As a result, conventional insecticides must be used to control most present-day insect problems.

Noninsecticidal methods of insect control are not new. For generations, man has used every conceivable method—from slapping mosquitoes to crop rotation—to combat insect enemies. "Cultural practices" such as delayed planting, strip cropping, destruction of volunteer plants and crop residues, and improved harvesting are still used to control a number of pests.

And parasites, predators, and pathogens are not new. They are natural forces that help control many destructive insects and keep myriads of other potential pests from reaching damaging numbers. In fact, without these beneficial organisms, man would be overwhelmed by insect pests despite effective insecticides.

There is a law of nature, however, that limits the activity of natural enemies of pest insects: populations of parasites and predators cannot increase until the populations of the pests they live on have already increased. During this time serious damage can occur. But even worse, the balance that is finally established between pests and their potential enemies can allow a level of damage which is unacceptable to the farmer or consumer.

What is more, man also interferes constantly with beneficial insects. His needs for food, living space, and industry, and his ability to accidentally transport pest insects into new areas, often alter the balance in favor of the destructive species so that they become even more damaging than they were originally in their natural environment.

On the other side of the scale, both scientists and the public now have a greater awareness of the limitations and potential benefits of the natural forces working to control pest insects. Therefore, future methods of insect control, whether they are new or merely adaptations of old techniques, will be designed to permit or encourage beneficial species to work for us.

One of the older "classic" methods of biological control of pest insects

*

H C COX is Assistant Directior of the Entomology Research Division, Agricultural Research Service.

makes use of the knowledge that many of our most destructive pest insects were accidentally imported into North America from other countries so that they arrived without the parasites and predators that hold them in check in their original homes.

Our native parasites and predators, though often of great value, are incapable of keeping such new pests from reaching epidemic numbers. That is why efforts to improve biological control often involve exploration. Entomologists go to the country where a pest insect originated to find the parasites and predators that play major roles there in natural suppression. Then after appropriate screening and study, these beneficial insects are brought back to the United States and released to become established, spread, and play a significant role in reducing populations of their host.

In the late 1880's, a USDA entomologist made the first effort to take advantage of the ability of one insect to control another. He introduced the vedalia beetle which is native to Australia into California where it became established, increased in number, and controlled the cottonycushion scale which then threatened California's growing citrus industry. This introduction cost about $5,000 and saved an industry eventually worth millions from extinction.

Unfortunately, importing good insects to control bad insects frequently does not work because the new insect does not survive in its new environment. Over the past 80 years, about 520 species of friendly insects have been introduced in attempts to control about 80 pest insects in the United States. Some 115 have become established, but only about 20 are really important control agents of some of our worst pests.

However, considering the investment made, the effort has been highly productive, and plans call for a continuation and expansion of this control method.

USDA scientists are now working on newer approaches to the use of

309

good insects to control bad insects. One that is particularly promising has to do with ways of avoiding the limitations imposed by the relationship between parasites and predators and their hosts.

If populations of a beneficial insect that attack a pest insect can be manipulated so that large numbers of the parasites or predators are present in the field at a critical time in the development of the pest population, the time lag can be eliminated and sufficient numbers will be on hand to provide immediate control. Such inundative releases will then achieve what chemicals can do except that live beneficial insects are substituted for an insecticide.

For example, insect parasites have already been mass reared and released to control the pea aphid, a spreader of pea enation mosaic and pea streak virus, both damaging diseases of peas. Since this aphid overwinters in alfalfa, millions of small parasitic wasps were reared to the adult stage very early in the season, long before they normally occur, in Washington State. Release of these parasites suppressed the build-up of winged aphids in about 18,000 acres of alfalfa so they did not migrate to where some 130,000 acres of freezing and canning peas were growing. As a result, the peas were protected from both diseases.

Scientists still have many problems to be solved before such manipulations can be used widely. The rearing of vast numbers of any given parasite or predator requires much research and the development of many new techniques. Moreover, the habits and relationship of each parasite and host must be studied if practical programs are to be devised. However, parasites and predators of insects appear to be generally highly selective. Their use would therefore be no hazard to man and the environment.

Insect pathogens represent another natural force that can be harnessed to help us control pest insects. Insects, like man, are subject to a number of diseases, and fortunately these insect diseases do not infect or harm higher animals. Also, they are highly specific, that is, they infect and kill only one species. And many are self-perpetuating in nature.

Probably the best-known example of a disease used for insect control is milky disease, which is caused by a bacterium and has been used on a commercial basis for many years to control Japanese beetle larvae. Another bacterium, *Bacillus thuringiensis*, has been effective against the larvae of some moths that are pests on tobacco and on cabbage and similar leafy vegetable crops. USDA scientists have now found new strains that are several times more effective.

Virus diseases hold new potential for insect control. Laboratory and field studies with a nuclear polyhedrosis virus against the cabbage looper have been encouraging.

When this virus is applied as a spray, much the same as insecticides, the control obtained has been comparable to that from insecticides. However, before viruses can be used commercially, they must be approved and registered by the Environmental Protection Agency.

Economical methods of production must be developed. Currently, insect viruses can only be produced by growing them in living insects, a costly procedure. Also, many viruses are damaged by the ultraviolet radiation in sunlight so they must be formulated in such a way that they will survive once in the field. We believe these problems can be solved by research.

USDA has pioneered in research to develop crop varieties that are resistant to insects. Its entomologists and plant scientists cooperate in evaluating germ plasm of plant species collected all over the world in an effort to find varieties that either resist feeding by insects or that grow and produce despite their attack. When such resistance or tolerance is found, it is incorporated into commercially acceptable varieties that are adaptable to different growing conditions and seasons.

Such development takes many years. However, once a resistant or tolerant variety is developed, farmers need pay no more to grow it than to grow a susceptible one. Equally significant, control by the use of resistant plants leaves no undesirable hazardous residues and does not adversely affect beneficial insects.

Wheat resistant to the Hessian fly is an outstanding example of success with resistant crop varieties. Thanks to long and difficult research, millions of acres of wheat are now nearly immune to the fly. As a result, the fly population is so reduced that relatively little damage occurs, even though susceptible wheat varieties are still planted in many areas.

We have also developed high levels of crop resistance to the spotted alfalfa aphid; the sugarcane borer; the wheat stem sawfly; the sweet clover weevil; the cereal leaf beetle in small grains; the greenbug in barley; and the European corn borer, corn earworm, corn rootworm, and rice weevil in corn.

Good progress has therefore been made in using resistant varieties to reduce damage caused by serious insect pests, and we are confident that scientists will continue to add new crops to the list. But despite those successes, most important pest problems cannot be solved in this way.

A new method of insect control that will certainly be used more frequently as time goes on involves the use of sterile or genetically altered insects.

Sterile male insects were first used to eradicate the screw-worm, a serious pest of cattle and wildlife, from the Southeastern United States. Then the same procedure was used to eradicate species of tropical fruit flies from the islands of Guam and Rota. Today the method is being used to provide continuous suppression of the screwworm in the Southwestern United States and northern Mexico, and to prevent establishment of the Mexican fruit fly in southern California.

Basically, control with sterile or genetically altered insects requires mass production and release of large numbers of altered insects that can compete with insects in nature for mates. The reared insects must therefore be sterilized before release (usually by ionizing irradiation, though chemicals can be used), or must carry harmful traits which can be passed to their offspring. Such traits may result in death due to sterility, inability to overwinter (live through the cold season), males unable to separate from females after mating, or all male offspring.

Sterile insects cannot be used to control all pest insects. Since the procedure requires overflooding the natural population with reared insects, it cannot be used if the natural population is too high. We must also be able to rear insects economically in sufficient number to achieve the required rate of overflooding, and to sterilize the reared insects without seriously reducing their ability to compete in nature.

Such methods of suppression are therefore most likely to be useful after the natural populations have been greatly reduced by other means. Thus, they may play a major role in integrated population suppression systems. They will be considered for and directed against insect species that cause the highest losses and are most costly to control by other methods, like the boll weevil, corn earworm, codling moth, pink bollworm, certain kinds of mosquitoes, tsetse flies, cabbage looper, tropical fruit flies, and the tobacco hornworm.

Much additional research and development by insect nutritionists, entomologists, geneticists, and engineers will be necessary before we can realize the full potential of this highly selective method of insect suppression or eradication.

When we think of insecticides, literally insect killers, we generally think of the conventional chemical compounds that have been commercially available for about 25 years.

Practically all these compounds are nonselective, that is, they are toxic to a wide range of organisms. Now, thanks to years of basic research by insect physiologists at a number of institutions, a possibility exists that we will be able to develop "insecticides" that will control a target species without endangering man or other forms of life.

These physiologists have made real progress in isolating and determining the nature of the compounds (hormones) in insects that regulate growth and development. As a result, some of the naturally occurring regulators have been synthesized, and other similar new chemicals that are even more active are being discovered.

These new selective hormones disrupt the development or behavior of insects. Some sterilize. Others stop the growth of immature forms. Still others cause physical abnormalities that prevent mating.

Much research will have to be done before practical use can be made of these substances, but some field tests are now in progress. Also, the toxicological studies are still to be undertaken. However, the hormonelike compounds look so promising that private industry has undertaken concentrated research programs.

Attractants are another group of chemicals that have very recently become potential agents for pest control. In nature, insects are stimulated to activity by natural chemical substances—light, sound, and, possibly, as yet unidentified radiation. Obviously, the strongest stimuli are associated with food, mating, and egg laying. Investigation of these attractants, particularly those that are chemical, is now progressing rapidly.

Sex attractants, chemicals that are often called pheromones, attract one sex to another for mating. They have been observed to occur in more than 200 insect species. Among them are such major pests as the boll weevil, corn earworm, gypsy moth, Japanese beetle, and European corn borer.

Produced in extremely minute quantities, these compounds are cap-

able of causing a response in the opposite sex. The fact that the quantities are so minute has made it difficult for chemists to isolate and determine their nature. They have identified and synthesized the sex attractants of such important insect pests as the boll weevil, gypsy moth, cabbage looper, red-banded leaf roller, and European corn borer.

Sex attractants have considerable potential in the control of insects, especially over a large area, because they may permit us to trap all of one sex of a species.

Without mates, most insects are unable to reproduce and, therefore, cannot survive.

The sex attractant might also be distributed in such quantities in an area that the pest insects would be confused and unable to locate mates. Or the attractants could perhaps be combined with sterilants or pathogens.

Such approaches to control are largely untested at this time, but one fact does seem certain. Practical and effective control with attractants will have to be areawide. They are not capable of protecting the plants in one field or the animals on one farm.

Since attractants occur naturally in insects, there is little likelihood they would pollute the environment.

Attractants are already aiding in the battle against several damaging insect pests. Traps baited with disparlure, the gypsy moth sex attractant, are being used to detect the presence of gypsy moth infestations in areas not known to be infested. Similarly, a substance known as hexalure is used to detect new infestations of the pink bollworm. Baited traps are also used to detect Japanese beetles, European chafers, and several species of tropical fruit flies.

Early detection of new infestations by this means permits treatment of the areas before populations buildup to damaging numbers. Thus, in the fall of both 1969 and 1970, small numbers of the oriental fruit fly, a serious pest of citrus that does not occur on the mainland of the United States, were found in traps baited with methyl eugenol in California. Quick application of small amounts of a lure-insecticide mixture to the trunks of citrus trees in the area eliminated the pest before it became established.

Medlure, another fruit fly lure, was used to detect early infestations of the Mediterranean fruit fly, also a major pest of citrus and one that does not occur on the mainland. When the fruit fly invaded Florida in 1956–57, a spray containing the bait and insecticide was so effective that only about a fourth of the usual amount of insecticide was needed to eradicate the pest.

Long before chemical insecticides became available, farmers used cultural, mechanical, and environmental methods—although they probably did not call them that—to manage most pest populations. Today, there is renewed interest in such time-honored methods as crop rotation, early host plant destruction after harvest, delayed planting, strip-cropping, deep plowing, and clean fallowing.

These approaches to insect control are directed more toward preventing insect damage than destroying infestations, so they are seldom spectacular. However, such control methods are often economical and significantly reduce insect damage. They will undoubtedly play a greater role in insect control by the year 2000.

Work by USDA scientists in Washington State demonstrates how these cultural and physical methods can be effectively combined with insecticides.

The green peach aphid, a vector of yellows virus of sugarbeets, normally overwinters in the egg stage on peach trees; the summer (winged) form of the aphid overwinters on weeds (often infected with yellows virus) along the edges of drainage ditches fed by warm springs. Control of the aphid was obtained by spraying the peach trees to eliminate overwintering aphid eggs, by destroying overwintering beets and sprouting beet culls that serve as sources of the virus, and by using flame burners on weeds that harbor aphids along drainage ditches.

This program cost about $1.60 per acre of sugarbeets and reduced the number of infected plants about 85 percent. Previously, only partial control was obtained by spraying with conventional insecticides at a cost of more than $18 per acre.

What is involved in perfecting the new approaches to insect control if our Nation, including the 100 million more people anticipated by the year 2000, is to maintain its present high standard of living? First, we must continue both fundamental and applied research because we need to know more about the biology of our more important pests—their rate of reproduction, flight range, interrelationship with natural enemies, and general ecology.

Second, but equally important, new methods must be tested in the laboratory and the field. Those that look especially promising must be evaluated on a pilot scale. Entire populations of major pests must be attacked in an organized coordinated manner. This effort will call for adequate financial resources and will often require that the pilot test be conducted in a large, isolated area, perhaps an island. Success at this stage would mean that the method is ready for actual use.

Protecting Our Food Resources

F. A. JOHNSTON,

E. E. SAULMON, and

DONALD R. SHEPHERD

AMERICAN agriculture is one of the outstanding success stories of the 20th century. For the American farmer is considered to be the most productive in the world.

This superior productivity is attributed to such factors as soil improvement, advanced technology, and organized research. One factor often overlooked is our relative freedom from the many destructive pests and diseases that ravage livestock, crops, and forests in other countries of the world.

Hour after hour, year in and year out, a never-ending battle is waged between man and the plant and animal pests that constantly jeopardize his food resources. The result of the battle to protect our food resources is evident in our own country where food quality is high, the abundance is great, and a smaller part of our total income is required for food as compared with other countries. Many Americans are inclined to take all this for granted.

The U.S. Department of Agriculture has for many years followed a three-phase program of: 1. preventing dangerous pests and diseases from entering the country by a rigorous inspection and quarantine system at ports of entry; 2. maintaining a strong surveillance system to detect any disease or pest gaining entry; and 3. eradicating or controlling plant and animal diseases and pests.

Scientists estimate that there are from 625,000 to 1,500,000 different kinds of insects on earth. We have to fight 10,000 kinds of insects, 1,500 plant diseases, and 250 animal diseases that are already established in the United States. In addition, hundreds of foreign plant and animal pests are bombarding our borders daily.

In recent years, USDA inspectors have intercepted a dangerous alien plant pest every 12 minutes around the clock.

*

F. A. JOHNSTON is director of the Agricultural Quarantine Inspection Division, Agricultural Research Service (ARS).

E. E. SAULMON is deputy administrator for Veterinary Services, Office of the Administrator, ARS.

DONALD R. SHEPHERD is director of the Plant Protection Division, ARS.

Our relative freedom from foreign plant and animal diseases and pests is not an accident. This status results from carefully drawn plans to keep them out of the country, and, if they gain entry, to quickly eradicate them. Protecting food resources is a giant job which will become even more vital for both America and the world as our population increases an estimated 100 million or so by the year 2000.

Action programs of USDA include quarantine and inspection at ports, borders, and airports; a nationwide public news media program; public education-and-information programs aimed at overseas-bound residents and at alien visitors; early warning detection programs; and immediate steps to eradicate pests before they can obtain a foothold and spread throughout the country.

First line of defense is the quarantine program maintained at air, sea, and border ports of entry to prevent destructive pests and diseases of crops and livestock from getting into the country. "Keep them out if you can" —this is fundamental.

A few dollars for early defense actions can save later expenditure of millions for control and the need for repeated applications of pesticides We know from experience that it can cost tens of millions of dollars to either eradicate or live with pests once they get in.

Inspectors must check live animals and animal products, plants and plant products, ships and planes, commercial cargoes, mail shipments, and the baggage of travelers in the never-ending fight to keep out of the United States foreign animal products and plants that carry pests and diseases.

This may perhaps be annoying for the traveler, but it is essential for the Nation. Foot-and-mouth disease, the most feared animal disease in the world, can reach our shores in the sausage innocently packed away in a suitcase. For if that sausage had been produced from an animal in a country infected with foot-and-mouth disease, and a portion of the sausage found its way into garbage which was subsequently fed to swine (still a widespread practice in the United States), we might well find ourselves faced with our first outbreak of foot-and-mouth disease since 1929.

Fruit flies destructive to citrus and many other fruits can arrive in coffee berries carried in a pocketbook or fresh fruit picked up overseas and stowed away in a hand-carried bag. The straw packing or the wrapping material protecting glassware or pottery picked up in a foreign land could be the means of bringing in the dreaded rinderpest animal disease, or the khapra beetle, a very destructive pest of stored grains.

The vast quantities of plant and animal products imported commercially into the United States each year are also subject to regulations designed to keep foreign pests and diseases out of the country. These requirements may vary from allowing the almost unrestricted importation of some plant and animal products to the outright prohibition of others. The regulations and the efforts of the men who enforce them have but one purpose—to keep American agriculture healthy.

Our livestock have stayed free of a number of the most destructive diseases, such as rinderpest, African swine fever, African horse sickness, Rift Valley fever, and lumpy skin disease. Serious forest and crop pests that have not been known to occur in the United States include the senn pest, yellow peach moth, green oak tortrix, Queensland fruit fly, South American bollworm, and the red legged earth mite.

It was relatively simple to maintain defenses against pests in the early days. Today the situation is different—the danger is greater. Tomorrow the threat will be even higher. People will travel more, farther, and faster. In 1970, over 231 million people entered or reentered the United States. By the year 2000, it is estimated that 448 million people will be arriving at U.S. entry ports.

Contaminated products can be brought from any part of the world in a few hours. This increases the chances that some returning traveler will inadvertently introduce a dangerous foreign insect or disease.

New international airports are opening in the interior of our country, and with increasing use of the St. Lawrence Seaway, the danger of pest introduction directly into many major U.S. agricultural areas becomes greater. USDA must have the public's help to keep these pests from slipping past the Nation's guard.

Inspection service is maintained at all major air, ocean, Great Lakes, and border ports of entry in the continental United States. Stations also are in Hawaii, Guam, Puerto Rico, the U.S. Virgin Islands, Bermuda, and Nassau.

Baggage of incoming passengers is examined in cooperation with Customs for plant and animal material. Importations of nonagricultural materials also must be inspected. Khapra beetles, destructive snails, golden nematodes, and other pests have arrived with such products as imported automobiles, sheet steel, gums, barbed wire, burlap sacks, and other nonagricultural items.

In this endless battle, we get help from many sources—including the Bureau of Customs, Immigration and Naturalization Service, State regulatory officials, and the Public Health Service.

Most important of all is the American citizen's understanding of the need for plant and animal quarantines and his cooperation in observing them. He may not understand how big his stake is in the success of the battle, how much a new crop pest could cut the yields of our crops, or how many milk cows a new disease could kill.

That is why we supplement inspection and other procedures with leaflets, reminders in the passport book, TV and radio announcements, and many other public information outlets to inform travelers about quarantines and ask their cooperation in observing them.

Despite all quarantine precautions, foreign plant pest and animal diseases do occasionally gain entry into the United States.

Introduced plant pests are a special threat to our crop and forest resources since they invariably leave behind their natural enemies. Unencumbered by natural control, they can quickly become established and spread over their ecological range.

If a new pest is promptly detected and control or eradication measures taken to restrict its spread, extensive losses can be avoided. Farmers and householders are relieved of expensive treatments, and the overall amount of pesticides needed to achieve effective control is kept to a minimum. The consumer ultimately benefits from the lower cost of an abundant food supply.

Since 1951, the Cooperative Economic Insect Survey has played an integral part in detecting new foreign pests in the United States. This cooperative undertaking uses information from State and Federal agricultural agencies throughout the Nation.

Information on local insect conditions is submitted from each State for inclusion in USDA's "Cooperative Economic Insect Report." This weekly publication is distributed to over 3,500 readers in the United States and foreign countries. At the same time, county agents and State regulatory and control agencies are immediately apprised of a new foreign pest introduction or a population buildup of an established pest.

In addition, information concerning the distribution, abundance, and extent of damage caused by economic pests that attack or threaten crops, forests, livestock, and public health is extracted from the State reports and microfilmed for incorporation into the national Scientific Records System.

This information is available for instant retrieval to all interested parties.

Another means of detecting new foreign insect pests is through various types of lights or lures. USDA operates an extensive network of insect traps using blacklight (ultraviolet) and bait attractants to draw insects at strategic points throughout the United States.

The blacklight traps are located at the major ports of entry and recently they were installed at several military airbases receiving cargo from overseas which may carry hitchhiking pests. Insects collected from the traps are submitted weekly for identification, providing a rapid means of spotting new pests that may be introduced.

In addition, approximately 40,000 lure traps containing attractants to destructive fruit flies are maintained in the chief citrus-producing areas.

The trapping program has succeeded in reducing the time interval between initial detection and eradication at a substantial savings to the taxpayer. For example, when the Mediterranean fruit fly was discovered in the United States in 1956, it took 600 days to eradicate it, at a cost of $12 million. Ten years later, another infestation was promptly detected and eradicated in just 44 days, at a cost of $290,000.

To aid in evaluating new plant pest introductions, the New Pest Work Group was established in 1968. It reviews each new pest that has been introduced and recommends a course of action. The group has succeeded in reducing the time interval between initial detection of a pest and Federal-State action which may be needed.

As with plant pests, early detection of invading animal diseases is of paramount importance for a successful eradication effort. To this end, livestock in marketing channels are under constant surveillance of State and Federal livestock inspectors and veterinarians. Animals are continually observed so that disease conditions (domestic and foreign) can be brought to the attention of proper officials.

One of the most vital cogs in the early detection system is the foreign animal disease diagnostician. These USDA veterinarians, specially trained to diagnose foreign animal diseases, are strategically located throughout the United States and are prepared to travel to any place in the country on a moment's notice. Each year they investigate many disease conditions suspected to be of foreign origin.

Eradication of a newly introduced foreign animal disease would be accomplished through the State-Federal Emergency Animal Disease Eradication organizations which are set up in each of the States. Through regular training and test exercises, these organizations have developed the capability of quickly mobilizing equipment and manpower to contain and eradicate a foreign animal disease. Cooperating agencies, such as the military, National Guard, State Police, and conservation departments aid in eradication.

In cooperation with the States, USDA carries out active control and eradication programs against plant pests and animal diseases that are established in the United States.

Foot-and-mouth disease has been eradicated nine times, the last time in 1929. The United States is one of the few countries now free of this dreaded disease. Contagious bovine pleuropneumonia, which still plagues much of the world, has been eradicated as has dourine and glanders in horses, fowl plague, cattle tick fever, and other livestock diseases.

Screw-worm flies have been eradicated from the continental United States by the sterile fly technique. The native male population was overwhelmed by releasing large numbers of male flies which had been rendered sterile through subjecting them to cobalt radiation. As the female fly commonly mates only once, and most are mated with the sterilized males, the population rapidly declined.

Each month, millions of sterilized screw-worm flies are dropped by airplanes along our Mexican border and deep into Mexico to prevent any buildup of flies there which would eventually reach and become established in the United States.

When we embarked on the nation-wide brucellosis eradication program in the mid-1950's, it was the largest livestock disease eradication program ever attempted here or elsewhere in the world. We intended to eradicate a disease that was well established across a great continent and several large islands which contained over 100 million head of susceptible cattle located in approximately 3 million herds.

All herds in the country were tested, and those disclosing infected animals were quarantined until the disease could be eradicated. Milk from dairy herds is now tested on a repetitive basis, and blood samples are tested from adult cattle consigned to slaughter. Any evidence of infection is rapidly investigated.

This has relieved the livestock owner from the burdensome task of periodically assembling his cattle for testing as only those herds are tested that have disclosed evidence of disease by the milk test, slaughterhouse screening tests, and tracing from infected herds.

By these systems and vaccinating calves in areas where the incidence of disease is high, brucellosis in our cattle population has been reduced from approximately 11 percent to less than one-half of 1 percent. It now appears that this costly disease of cattle can be eradicated during the present decade.

A number of other large-scale animal disease eradication programs are currently in progress, and most should reach a successful conclusion during the 1970's. Sheep scabies, once the major disease problem of U.S. sheep, is almost eradicated. The past year has seen rapid progress in hog cholera eradication so that eradication should be accomplished within the next few years. Bovine tuberculosis is at an all-time low, and it is hoped that an increased effort will result in its eradication during this decade.

Humans are also susceptible to several of the diseases of livestock which are being eradicated or controlled. As brucellosis and tuberculosis were reduced in our livestock population, a corresponding dramatic reduction of these diseases in humans occurred.

New techniques are being field tested to determine whether mastitis and anaplasmosis abatement are feasible. If field projects are successful, perhaps national programs will be developed to combat these costly cattle diseases.

USDA at present is carrying out control or eradication programs against more than 20 major plant pests which are established in the United States. The programs are designed to reduce or prevent further pest spread to noninfested areas and to reduce pest outbreaks in generally infested areas.

Several major plant pests have already been eradicated from the United States, including the citrus blackfly, citrus canker, khapra beetle, Hall scale, Hoja Blanca disease, and Mediterranean fruit fly. Other plant pests, such as the golden nematode, Mexican fruit fly, witchweed, and peach mosaic have been held to very low levels.

These control or eradication programs are jointly planned, financed, and executed with the involved States and local groups.

The most effective and safest methods of control or eradication of plant pests are employed by integrating chemicals, biological agents, and cultural control techniques when feasible. Rapid population buildups of pests often reach the level where they could potentially cause considerable loss in crop yields, thus requiring immediate control with chemicals to prevent economic losses. The use of chemicals for plant protection programs is closely supervised to assure that application is made only to areas designated for treatment and to minimize the hazard to humans, domestic animals, wildlife, and other environmental elements.

A number of biological control methods are being used successfully against plant pests.

Sterilization techniques similar to those against the screw-worm have replaced pesticides in control of the Mexican fruit fly along the U.S.— Mexican border. Similar sterile release techniques are being employed against the pink bollworm.

Parasites are used effectively against the citrus blackfly in Mexico, gypsy moth in New England, and cereal leaf beetle in the Midwest.

A bacterial spore dust is reducing high populations of Japanese beetle larvae in soil.

Cultural control techniques include crop rotation, delayed planting and early plowup, withholding host crops from infested fields, land fallowing to reduce pest populations, and resistant varieties of crops.

These are but a few of the ways in which our food resources are presently protected. By the year 2000, some 25 million more families will place even greater demands on rural communities. To help meet these demands, USDA is continually developing and testing new methods of pest and disease control. The methods must be integrated successfully to provide a maximum protection against losses. In this manner America will continue to provide an abundant food supply for its increasing population.

Animal Product Needs and How to Meet Them

R. E. HODGSON and

E. J. WARWICK

OUR PEOPLE who live in the year 2000 will want to eat at least as well as we have in 1971. Hopefully, a greater percentage of the population will be eating a better balanced diet and enjoying it more.

Importantly in this diet will be liberal supplies of a variety of foods of animal origin. Some of them are considered protective foods for they effectively supplement those of plant origin. All of them add to the variety, and therefore the pleasure, of good eating.

Major strides may be taken in the chemistry of foods. Some foods will be made more nutritionally adequate. New products as well as imitation food products will be developed.

Even with changes such as these, it is our opinion that the great body of consumers will continue to want liberal amounts of animal foods in their daily fare in the year 2000.

As we add up to 100 million more people to the table, the major task will be to produce a sufficient volume of food, but there must also be considerations of quality, palatability, and variety. One wonders how it will all be produced. There are fixed limits to our land area, but the productivity of the land has great potential for increased yields as new technology is applied to production methods.

Large land areas are used to grow the feed needed to nourish animals producing meat, milk, and eggs.

Animals are relatively inefficient in converting feed nutrients to food compared to direct human consumption of crop products.

It should be pointed out, however, that a relatively small percentage of the major nutrients contained in food and feed grain crops ever reach the table in edible form. For example, only about half the calories produced in a wheat crop is in the grain and much of this is milled out before it is offered as human food.

In 1970 about half of our land in farms was used for pasture and forage production. Also, many grain byproducts and crop residues provide animal

*

R. E. HODGSON is Director of the Animal Science Research Division, Agricultural Research Service.

E. J. WARWICK is Assistant Director of the Division.

food, and a very large percentage of the feed grains find a market through livestock and poultry.

This pattern of production and use may be expected to continue, with increases in production per acre through the application of new technology, both in food and feed crops and in pasture and forages.

Improvements in genetic ability and in the rations of livestock and poultry will improve efficiency of animal production and will aid in reaching the needed production goals.

However, as increased pressure for grains comes by virtue of an increasing population, a larger percentage of feed grains may have to be diverted away from livestock and poultry into the direct food chain. If and when this occurs, the livestock industries will become more dependent on grass and other forages and byproducts. Ruminants will be least affected since they are adept at utilizing these kinds of feed resources.

As we look to the year 2000, how much production of the various animal foods will be needed? This will depend on the size of the population and the anticipated and desirable per capita consumption, among other factors. The next big question after these targets are set is how do we go about attaining the production to meet them?

A number of forecasts on the size of the population and the total volume and per capita consumption of food products for the year 2000 have been made. From these we have developed a forecast which indicates the magnitude of the problem facing us. (See table on next page.)

Needs have been estimated in terms of the number of production units (number of milk cows and laying hens and number of animals slaughtered as meat animals) that likely will be required. The estimates are based on forecasts of what yields per animal will be in the year 2000.

For milk and eggs it is based essentially on a straight line projection of the yearly increase per animal during the period 1938–1968. In the case of

319

Projected Animal Requirements in the Year 2000 for a Population of 300 Million People

Product	Probable per capita consumption	Numbers required	Percent increase or decrease over 1968
Beef	105 lb.	53.5 million to slaughter	+ 51
Veal	9 lb.	19 " " "	+244
Lamb and mutton	6 lb.	36.5 " " "	+301
Pork	75 lb.	131.5 " " "	+ 52
Broiler meat	40 lb.	4.6 billion " "	+ 78
Turkey meat	9 lb.	180 million " "	+ 69
Eggs	360	394 million laying hens	+ 25
Milk	610 lb.	11 million milking cows	− 22

meat-producing animals, we have used the 1968 yield per animal slaughtered.

Although changes from present market weights for cattle, calves, hogs, sheep, and broilers may occur, major rises in production will be through increases in numbers slaughtered.

Assuming that the targets are desirable and our projections realistic, the big question is how do the livestock and poultry and related input groups tool up to achieve these objectives?

In looking back over the past 30 years, we see that significant increases have occurred in the production of animal products, both in total and per animal unit. This is especially true with milk production per cow and eggs produced per hen.

Increases in the meat-producing animals, however, have come about principally through increases in the numbers of animals slaughtered. Increases in animal numbers and improvements in production per animal have come about because of assured markets, reasonably adequate prices, and by the application of new technology in production practices over a broad spectrum.

Based on historical information, we have confidence that increases and improvements will continue over the next 30 years. Their extent will continue to depend on demand, fair market prices, and the development and application of new technology. The competitive situation will become sharper as time progresses, as will demands on resources for alternative uses.

The status of efficiency of produc-

tion, while it varies with the different classes of livestock and poultry, is such that—with some significant breakthroughs—major improvements can be made to increase output and at the same time promote efficiency. What are some of the areas where we believe major improvements will be made that will help to assure an adequate amount of high quality and safe animal food supplies for the future?

An animal cannot produce beyond the inherited potentials which it receives from its sire and dam, no matter how good its environment.

Producing ability can be influenced by bringing together in an individual's genetic makeup the inherited factors for high performance.

In order to do this, the sire and dam must possess and have the ability to transmit to the offspring factors for high performance. Improvement in producing ability, then, requires programs to locate and identify animals with these qualities to produce the next generation. To accomplish this requires performance recording, that is, measurement of the production of parents and their offspring.

When superior transmitting sires (the sire has the same influence on an offspring as the dam, but it is used on many dams) are so identified they need to be used over the widest possible female population to produce the next generation.

We have well developed records of performance programs for dairy cattle and poultry populations. Effective programs are beginning with beef cat-

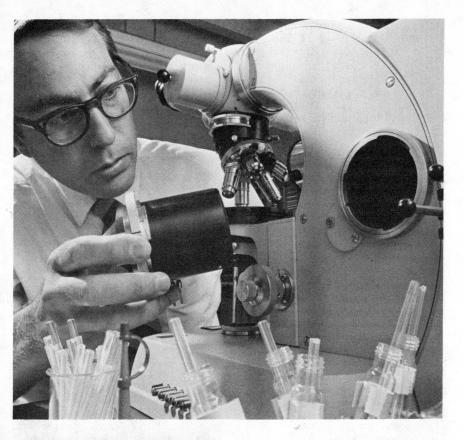

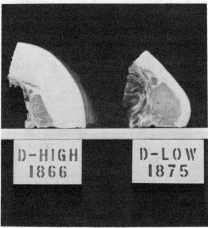

D-HIGH
1866

D-LOW
1875

Top, film cassette is loaded into microscope to photograph swine semen, to improve use of frozen semen in artificial insemination. Above, loins from lines of swine selected for 15 generations, for high or low backfat levels. Potentials for genetic change are immense.

tle, hogs, and sheep. When these are well developed and used widely we have the soundest basis to make faster progress in improving the producing ability of the farm animal populations.

Artificial insemination is used widely in the dairy cow and turkey populations and is beginning in the other classes. Once we are able to freeze, store, and manipulate male germ plasm of all species as we can presently with cattle, and then use artificial insemination widely so that the services of superior sires can be widespread, faster progress will be made in the genetics of producing ability. This will do much to assist in achieving production goals for the year 2000.

Scientists have found that by crossbreeding, mating sires of one breed with dams of another breed, the offspring exhibit hybrid vigor. This is expressed by greater vigor, a greater

321

ability to survive, more rapid growth, and more efficient use of feed. This can result in a 15 to 20 percent advantage over straightbred offspring of parents of the same breeds.

Poultry and hog producers use crossbreeding extensively. It is receiving widespread attention by beef producers. Apparently the wider the genetic difference in the breeds used in a cross, the greater the hybrid effect. This gives credence to the great interest among beef producers in importing exotic breeds to use in crossing to produce cattle for slaughter.

The practice no doubt will find wide use in the future, particularly in the meat producing classes of animals. But if this program is to achieve maximum success, crossbreeding must be based on the use of sires from production tested seedstock herds in which breeding animals have proven their transmitting abilities.

Further investigations in basic biochemical and population genetics promise to bring us yet new techniques and procedures which will further enhance the producing ability of our herds and flocks.

Reproduction in the cattle population averages about 75 to 80 percent. About the same percentages of ewes and sows mated actually produce young. This in itself imposes a heavy drain on efficiency and limits the amount of production.

In some classes, reproduction does not begin early enough in life and there is frequently too long a time interval between births due to delayed conception for one reason or another.

Conditions such as brood animals in a nonreproductive state cause a lag in production and add to the costs of production. The hatchability of eggs is of about the same low order as reproduction in cattle, and in turkeys it is even lower. Correction of these conditions, much of which can occur with presently available technology, would improve both efficiency and yield by an estimated 10 to 20 percent.

Cattle normally give birth to only one offspring at a time. By the time the offspring reaches marketable age, a year to 18 months after birth, the cost of maintenance of the mother and that of raising the offspring is considerable and must be met from the sale value of the offspring. Of course, the mother should have produced another calf by that time. This time period is one reason why the efficiency of the beef cow is so low in terms of conversion of feed to beef.

Working out ways to make the cow produce twins at each birth would have a great impact on the beef industry. It would mean we could produce as much beef with essentially half the size of the present beef cow herd. On the other hand, while this practice would increase the efficiency of the beef industry, it would also contribute greatly to achievement of the goal of meeting the requirements for beef by the year 2000.

If three-fourths of the births were twins by the year 2000 and the yield per slaughter animal remained the same as for 1968, the supply required could be provided with about the same size herd as we had in 1968.

The technology to induce twinning is not at hand presently. However, research to date appears encouraging enough to suggest it is possible. Benefits would also accrue to the dairy herd, but probably not to the extent they would in beef production. However, as we look to the surplus stock coming from the dairy industry as producers of meat, twinning takes on added significance.

Induced multiple births coupled with more frequent lambing would also favor lamb and sheep production. While twins and even triplets are frequent, the phenomenon is by no means universal. Multiple births coupled with more frequent lambings (say three in every 2 years) would have a significant favorable impact on sheep production in achieving future production goals for lamb and mutton.

Pigs generally produce 8 to 10 piglets per litter. By using somewhat the same techniques mentioned previously, it would appear possible to increase litters to 12 or 14. This alone could account for perhaps a 20 percent increase in pork production without increasing the size of the breeding herd.

The concept of multiple births, coupled with better management of the reproduction cycle by estrus synchronization and the use of the best germ plasm available through artificial insemination, would not only improve the economic situation of the livestock producer. It would also go a long way toward achieving the volume of production of meat and milk estimated as needed by the year 2000 with essentially the same size breeding herds.

It is known that males grow faster and more efficiently than females. Capitalizing on this, if the sex ratio of offspring could be controlled, it would be possible to produce females from those parents for which herd replacements are desired. The remaining parents could be utilized to produce males for market purposes. This could result in an increase in meat production from cattle, sheep, and hogs of perhaps 10 to 15 percent.

Multiple births and sex ratio control can be achieved if we put our minds and efforts to it.

Feed is the largest cost input in production for all species of farm animals. It accounts for half or more of the total costs. The higher the production per animal unit the more important it is that the ration be adequate in both quantity and quality.

Cattle and sheep are ruminants, multiple-stomach animals. Hogs and poultry are single-stomach animals. This makes a difference in rationing the two types.

Hog and poultry rations generally are made up of grains and grain, oilseed, and animal byproducts that are low in fiber because these animals cannot tolerate much of this material. Because of that, hogs and poultry are in much more direct competition with humans when these kinds of feeds are in short supply.

Cattle and sheep, because of their rumen (forestomach) can utilize coarse fibrous material, in fact they need it for best digestive function. These animals normally receive from 65 to 90 percent of their feed from pasture, hay, and other forages. While in practice these forages are supplemented with feed grains and byproducts, they are much less in competition with humans for grain resources.

Further, ruminants can utilize nonprotein nitrogen from which they can derive much of their protein needs. The use of urea, a form of nonprotein nitrogen, is increasing and will become much more important in feeding cattle and sheep in the future as more is learned about its efficient use.

Because forages of different kinds are so important in feeding cattle and sheep, major attention should be given to make them as adequate as possible. Sadly, the opposite is all too true.

Farmers and ranchers just do not give the same attention to production of their forage crops that they do to cash crops. As a result, forages are generally low in yield and the resulting feed is of poor quality. Yet they are major sources of protein, energy, essential minerals, and certain needed vitamins.

Pasture and range provide the forage in summer. Harvested forage, hay, silage, straw, etc., provide the forage in winter.

Forages undergo great changes in harvesting and storage. During harvesting they are subject to weather conditions. It is not unusual for good forage to lose from one-fourth to one-half the protein and energy during harvesting and storage. That limits production and adds to the cost of meat and milk production.

This great forage resource, grown on about half of the land in farms and on publicly controlled ranges, has a much greater role to play in livestock production than at present. Development and effective use of forage will be important in feeding ruminants to achieve the needed production goals.

Effective rationing of the different classes of animals has become a very precise science. This is shown best in broiler feeding where the rations are power packed with all of the known needed nutrients to provide rapid growth and a feed conversion of about 2-½ to 3 pounds of feed required per pound of growth.

Tailor-made rations for hogs, finishing rations for beef cattle, and concentrate mixtures for dairy cattle are approaching this precise effectiveness. Use of chemical feed additives in these rations aids in growth promotion and efficiency in the use of nutrients.

The commercial feed industry has performed a great service to livestock and poultry producers by mobilizing ingredients and preparing uniform, highly efficient concentrate mixtures prepared in a most acceptable form, such as pellets.

Current limitations in the effectiveness of preparing feeds will be lifted as we learn more completely the precise requirements of the different classes of animals for their several functions. This will aid producers in delivering future amounts of the required animal products.

Animal production has become more intensified over the last decade. There are fewer production units and they are larger. Each herd or flock contains much larger numbers of animals and they are maintained under more confined conditions.

This has several important advantages. The animals are more comfortable, it requires less labor to care for them, they are fed more adequately, they produce more efficiently, and it is easier to check on and control diseases.

That trend will continue, and while it may require greater capital investment for the producer it will aid in increasing unit and total production of animal products.

The more complete control and eradication of troublesome diseases will be important in meeting future needs for animal foods. Our herds and flocks presently are essentially free of tuberculosis. Brucellosis is well on the way to complete eradication, as is hog cholera. Good strides are being made to free poultry flocks of the troublesome leukosis disease complex.

Our animal health officials are diligently guarding the livestock population against the dreaded foot and mouth disease. Other troublesome diseases are steadily yielding as research finds out how to cope with them and eradication programs are developed.

Producers can look forward to situations where they can better avoid and eliminate disease problems and this will be a great aid in achieving production goals.

50 Pct. More Crop Output Seen by 2000

AUGUST E. KEHR,

LOYD A. TATUM, AND

GEORGE A. WHITE

AN INCREASE in U.S. population from today's 200 million to a possible 300 million by the year 2000 will create need for a 50 percent increase in crop products. Unless we can supply that food increase our grandchildren could face food problems unheard of in this country today.

Can our agriculture — with its shrinking numbers of farmers, tightened margins of profits, loss of agricultural land, dwindling supply of farm labor, and continued need to supply food to underdeveloped countries— meet these challenges? The authors, along with others in agricultural research, are confident we can.

This feeling of optimism has its basis in the ever increasing number of scientific advances in production technology. These advances have brought about a level of agricultural achievement unparalleled in the world's history.

As a result of using research findings from many scientific disciplines, U.S. farm output reached a new high last year. Farm output was 21 percent over the 1957–59 average. One farmworker today feeds 45.3 other persons compared to 10.7 only 30 years ago. American farm technology, when exported abroad along with food for underdeveloped countries, has fostered progress of such great magnitude that nations abroad have aptly termed it "The Green Revolution."

Prime components of the Green Revolution are:

• Genetic improvement of crop varieties.

• Improved cultural practices, including fertilization and irrigation.

• Development of chemical plant growth regulators and improvement in disease, insect, and weed control.

• Mechanization of farming operations.

• Discovery of new crops that open doors to added areas of agricultural production opportunities.

The new high-yielding wheat and rice varieties, now planted on millions of acres of land, have had an untold effect in increasing the world's food production capacity. This advance came as the result of introducing important genetic factors into commercial varieties—the stiff straw character that makes the plant resistant to lodging (falling over), a responsiveness to heavy fertilization, earlier maturity, and wider adaptation because of insensitivity to day-length.

Meeting the needs for more crop products could be considered from the

*

AUGUST E. KEHR is Chief of the Vegetables and Ornamentals Research Branch, Crops Research Division, Agricultural Research Service.

LOYD A. TATUM is Chief of the Cereal Crops Research Branch, Crops Research Division.

GEORGE A. WHITE is Leader of Chemurgic Crop Investigations, New Crops Research Branch, Crops Research Division.

point of view of (1) more kinds of crops or crop products or (2) the amount of crop products. With present surpluses of staple crops the first is quite revelant, but by the year 2000 we may be most concerned to have an adequate supply of basic foods and fibers.

We may make a contribution in both respects as breeders develop varieties with special qualities and higher yield potential, and as other scientists contribute to effective pest control and discover ways to manage soils and crops for greater productivity.

Cereals normally are thought of as energy sources but they also supply significant amounts of protein. This protein is not self-sufficient because it is low in certain essential amino acids, especially lysine and tryptophane.

There is now genetic control of amino acid ratios as well as of protein level available in cereals germ plasm. Breeders can develop varieties with biologically balanced proteins and protein contents at least 25 percent above present levels without an important sacrifice in yield level.

This will be especially important when population pressures on the food supply require direct consumption of cereals rather than their use as feed grains. Twelve percent protein corn thus would meet the requirements of a diet for adults, and 20 percent protein oats would be adequate for growing children. Changes of a comparable magnitude may be possible in contents of other constituents such as vitamins and minerals if the need arises.

Plant breeders can be proud of other achievements that are providing more crop products for us. A fourfold increase in corn yields has been obtained since 1930. Likewise the yields of processing tomatoes have quadrupled in the last three decades. Additional genetic potentials for new levels in productivity exist in all crops—ready to be used. They are our guarantee for a brighter tomorrow.

The higher yields we witness result from the genetic manipulation of the

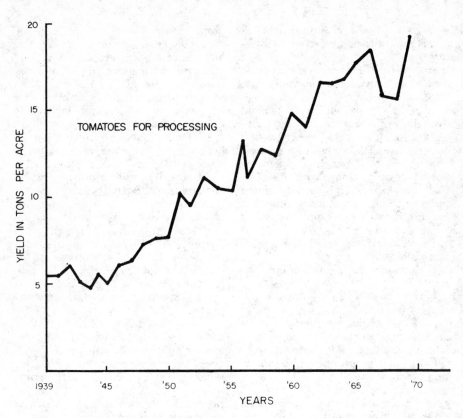

TOMATOES FOR PROCESSING

YIELD IN TONS PER ACRE

YEARS

Yields of tomatoes for processing have gone up 400 percent in last 30 years.

plant's inheritance only in part. Such overall improved biological efficiency is attained by a similar upgrading of cultural, fertilization, pest control, weed control, and irrigation practices.

Being developed in today's research are plants of the future with superior nutritive value by increased protein and vitamin content. Such plants of the future will be earlier maturing, more responsive to fertilizer, have built-in resistance to diseases and insects, and possess maximum ability to absorb the sun's energy and to transform this energy to food.

Exciting developments are underway in which plants resist attacks from a myriad of disease-causing organisms, hungry insects, nefarious nematodes, and omnipresent viruses. These new plants with multi-pest resistances reduce our dependence upon chemical pesticides as a mean of control. Grow-

ers are pleased because they can reduce pesticide use with such plants and hence improve their production efficiency. Consumers are likewise pleased with these disease- and pest-resisting plants because U.S. food safety, already among the highest in the world, is assured at even a higher level.

Characteristic of such multi-pest resistance is a tomato line developed at Beltsville, Md., with the following desirable characteristics: a resistance to fusarium and verticillium wilts (soilborne diseases); resistance to early blight and stemphylium blight (foliage diseases); resistance to spider mites and aphids (insect pests); early maturing, high yielding, noncracking (desirable horticultural attributes); bright red color—interior and exterior, good for processing (quality factors); and is machine harvestable (for efficiency of production).

Such pyramiding of all available genetic resistances and desirable attributes into one variety means more and better food for consumers and greater production efficiency for producers.

With the perfection of biological controls of pests and the increasing instances whereby pests can be controlled by genetic plant resistance, the concept of "unified control" has been emerging. Under this concept the three basic methods of control (biological, genetic, chemical) are all teamed together to provide a "knockout punch" for plant pests.

The unified concept could well mean that the age-old struggle of protecting our crops against the ravages of plant pests will be decidedly swayed in the favor of man well before the year 2000. If so, our food larders will have a healthy growth as a result.

Just as the modern car would perform poorly on the gasoline and roads of yesteryear, so would modern crops perform poorly without accompanying improved cultural practices.

Mechanized operations require more plants per acre of land. In turn this necessitates precision planting, different spacings (frequently not in rows), direct seeding, and improved variety tailored to the special needs of mechanization. Seeds are often coated. The coating serves three purposes: a size and shape to adapt to the new precision planters, protective substances against diseases and insects, and often fertilizers for quick emergence.

At critical stages of growth, water needs are being met by irrigation—often using some of the new developments such as automatic sprinklers or trickle irrigation with plastic tubes. Water requirements are being reduced by such means as asphalt underlayers, plastic and other mulches, and even breeding plants with lower moisture needs, or tolerance to relatively high salt content of the soil in which they are grown.

By the year 2000 at least twice the present 370 million acres could, if necessary, be under actual cultivation.

Our drylands contain much low-use land that could be used to advantage.

Dryland areas have maximum production potentials because of their favorable temperatures, the high light intensities, and conditions that allow improved disease and insect control. Irrigation in such places permits year-round use.

As the 21st century approaches, cropping patterns will be changed to accommodate high yielding varieties. Weed-free fields are possible as a result of using prescription weed control. Climate can be modified, such as cooling the air by fine moisture sprays during hot weather and warming the air by similar means to avoid frost danger when temperatures drop for short periods below freezing.

It is likely that some crops will be grown with no tillage or no cultivation. Controlled release and liquid fertilizers—some applied directly to the foliage for efficiency—may be used to supplement, or even replace, today's dry fertilizer.

The flowering, fruiting, growth in size, and shape of plants—particularly horticultural plants—are being tailored by predetermined doses of growth-regulating substances. Auxins, kinins, gibberelins, growth inhibitors, and growth retardants enable us to change many phases of plant metabolism, growth, and development. Chemicals may be used to thin or increase fruit set, or to concentrate yields of vegetables for mechanical harvest.

Researchers are presently perfecting many other substances that will assist in producing crops of the future.

Gibberelins, produced by a fungus much the same way as penicillin, are used to produce table grapes with larger berry size and a more open cluster.

Use of an ethylene-producing substance on tomatoes not only increases the yield of marketable fruit, but also concentrates the amount of fruit that ripens at one time. Uniform ripening is an essential feature of once-over mechanized harvesting operations.

A major problem in the mechanical

harvesting of citrus fruit is removing fruit from trees. Citrus fruit is firmly attached to the stem and does not readily drop, even with severe agitation of the branches by mechanical shaker devices. Experimental chemicals have now been found that uniformly loosen the fruit from the stem and hence increase efficiency of fruit removal at the time of harvest.

Man has competed with diseases, insects, and other pests since the day he first began cultivating plants and animals. American agriculture is keenly aware of its mission to produce crops unblemished by pests. Despite this our crop losses still amount to nearly $4 billion annually, or more than 20 percent of the value of all crops.

The control of disease, insects, and weeds in most crops is expensive, in others imperfect, and for some impossible. Unless the technological advances in many areas of biological controls are supplemented by chemical controls, we could neither meet today's requirements for crops nor those for the year 2000. But better chemical controls are needed.

Promising in this regard are chemicals that are absorbed into plant tissues to control pests. By this means the plant is supplied with an ability to resist diseases and pests in a manner akin to vaccinations in animals. For example, these systemic controls offer new hopes for protecting emerging seedlings from microbial attacks and hence improve yields because there are no missing plants in the field.

A remarkable breakthrough is insect control by such means as sex attractants, insect juvenile hormones, viruses, and bacteria. For example, coupled with a means of destruction such as a trap or poison bait, sex attractants lure harmful insects to their doom, leaving no need for further controls in the field.

Similarly the juvenile hormone, effective at a level of 1 gram per acre, prevents young insects from developing into adults, thereby effectively destroying them. A bacterial parasite, *Bacillus thuringensis*, attacks and destroys only insects, and is harmless to other animal and plant life.

These techniques leave no residues and pollute no streams.

The age-old drudgery of hand labor on American farms in our grandfather's time has yielded to extensive use of machinery on farms today. Gross capital expenditures for machinery and farm motor vehicles in 1968 were 82 percent above the outlay in 1960! At this rate of growth the 21st century almost certainly will usher in an era in which practically all farm production operations will be mechanized.

Today many growing, cultural, harvesting, processing, and marketing practices still require high inputs of labor per unit. Labor requirements for vegetables and fruits are especially high, in contrast to many agronomic crops such as feed grains. Even with feed grains, labor inputs were not always low.

Those of us who grew up on farms in the 1920's can recall the long hours of cutting grain with a reaper and binder, putting it up into shocks, and then on threshing days bringing in huge crews of friends, neighbors, and hired hands to carry on the needed hand and machine work.

Today mechanized operations have brought the number of man-hours used to produce a given unit of feed grains from an index number of 435 in 1910 to 52 in 1969. Hence today one man with his machinery can accomplish the same amount of work as eight men accomplished six decades ago, and with less physical effort and personal discomfort.

The dramatic shift to mechanization of tomato production in California is a forerunner of similar changes in other crops. In 1962 about 98 percent of the tomato crop in California was handpicked; seven years later only 5 percent was handpicked, almost a complete shift to mechanization. In Maine, an estimated 7 percent of potato acreage was harvested with mechanical harvesters in 1960, compared to 65 percent in 1968. On larger farms the use of mechanical harvesters reduced annual labor requirements as much as 44 percent.

With such momentum, by the year 2000 it appears likely that the tilling, planting, culturing, harvesting, processing, and marketing processes will approach 100 percent for all crops—from the seed to finished product without being touched by human hands. The handpicking champions in the Midwest cornfields will exist only in memories.

Advantages of mechanized operations are striking. Crops can be harvested at just the right maturity and at the peak of field quality. As a result the crops have improved eating quality when they reach the market. Any uncertainties of labor supply are reduced or eliminated.

Costs of mechanized production of crops are far less than costs using hand labor (see table).

Reduced harvesting costs encourage increased consumption in home markets and provide improved competition in markets abroad.

Of more than 250,000 seed-bearing plants, only about 666 provide man's food, feed, fiber, and other useful products. We believe that additional plants can serve as new crops.

New crops offer opportunities for crop diversification, efficient land use, and new or more versatile raw materials. They may also contribute to man's improved health and means of disease treatment. Soybeans and safflower are examples of new crops that have been added to American agriculture since 1930. Their impact has been tremendous.

Because of our abundance of food grains, industrial applications of new crops through utilization and crops

research offer a unique and new dimension to the commercial use of plant constituents. Often there is a valuable byproduct of these findings such as high-protein seed meals.

The plant kingdom offers an intriguing array of seed gums, unusual oils, fibers, medicinals, natural pesticides, and other constituents. For example, fatty acids from seed oils are being discovered that have unusual structure and reactivity. These could either directly or by simple conversion serve as versatile intermediates in the manufacture of many consumer and industrial products.

Kenaf (*Hibiscus cannabinus*) is a possible new source of paper pulp both in the United States and abroad. Increased population and per capita consumption of paper suggest a bright future for kenaf. The grower will realize an annual cash return. But methods of harvesting and storage will be different than for wood.

This tall, fast-growing plant is well adapted to the Southeast. Resistance to root-knot nematodes is a prime objective of varietal improvement.

The leaves of *Tephrosia vogelli*, a tropical legume, contain significant amounts of the insecticide rotenone and related rotenoids. Tephrosia is adapted to the Southeast, Puerto Rico, and many tropical areas.

Crambe (*Crambe abyssinica* and *C. hispanica*) seed oils are rich in erucic acid. Potential uses of the oil include mold lubricants for continuous casting of steel, rubber additives, and industrial nylons.

Agronomic characteristics are favorable for crop development.

The seed oil of *Vernonia anthelmintica* contains a high amount of epoxy acid which can be used in stabilizers, plas-

	Handpicking	Cost per ton machine picking	Location
Green beans	$65	$39	New York (AE Res. 138) 1965
Processing tomatoes	$17.07	$ 9.84	San Joaquin County (U. of Calif. Report) 1966

Name	Comments
Chinese gooseberry or Kiwi—*Actinidia chinensis* Planch.	Egg-sized fruit from vine, produced in California and imported.
Carambola—*Averrhoa carambola* L._____	Subtropical fruit, some produced in South Florida, available in fruit markets.
Lychee—*Litchi chinensis* Sonner_____	Red, rough-skinned fruit, some produced in Florida.
Pistachio—*Pistacia vera* L._____	Tree nut crop in California, common in food stores, mostly imported.
Chinese waterchestnut—*Eleocharis dulcis* (Burm. f.) Trin.	Edible corms retain crispness and flavor after cooking.

ticizers, surface coatings, and other products. Plant improvement, particularly better seed retention, is needed.

Meadowfoam (*Limnanthes* spp.), an attractive winter annual, is native to California and Oregon. Gardeners sometimes use meadowfoam for showy masses of flowers in the spring. Better seed retention—and more erectness—would enhance meadowfoam's crop potential. The seed oil contains long chain fatty acids which can be converted to quality waxes.

Folklore, sometimes more imaginative than factual, frequently alludes to the use of plants in home remedies. Indeed, plants have contributed much to man's health and have much to offer. A recent example is the Mexican yam (*Dioscorea* spp.), an important cortisone, birth control drugs, and other pharmaceuticals. Most of the yam tubers are harvested from wild stands. Commercial acreage most likely will provide the long-range source of these drugs.

Extracts of more than 10,000 species of plants have been screened for anticancer activity. Drugs from a select few are undergoing clinical testing. One of these, *Camptotheca acuminata*, a native tree of China, is very promising. The recently-found active alkaloid, camptothecin, is now being used experimentally with marked success.

Only a few trees were raised to maturity in the United States. However, from these, USDA researchers are establishing large populations of fast-growing seedlings. Thus, this obscure Chinese tree may become a lifesaver.

Additional plants show favorable anticancer activity and still others are being examined.

We have briefly shown part of the role that new crops could play in meeting man's complex needs of the future. Doors of the storehouse of plant resources are slowly opening, but the long-term task ahead will not be easy. Continued support, much cooperation, and dedication are necessary ingredients for successful development of new crops.

Wood Products for City and Country

DWIGHT HAIR and

H. O. FLEISCHER

IN 1970 enough wood was consumed in the United States to build 104,000 miles of highway a foot thick and 24 feet wide—a highway that would reach nearly halfway to the moon. And by the year 2000, enough wood may be consumed annually to build a similar highway all the way.

Now of course, wood use is not measured by the mile but in cubic feet. And the outlook for 2000 is not based on the need for a highway to the moon but on recent trends in wood use and expectations about future growth in population and economic activity.

So in more common terms, the volume of wood in round form—saw logs, veneer logs, pulpwood—and other products such as fuelwood, poles, and piling consumed in 1969 amounted to 13.1 billion cubic feet. This is a high in a trend that has been rising fairly rapidly during recent years.

Since the early 1960's, for example, the volume of roundwood consumed has increased 15 percent. This rise reflected the growing consumption of industrial timber products— saw logs, veneer logs, and pulpwood.

Before the 1960's, increases in consumption of these products were largely offset by decreases in the use of fuelwood and miscellaneous products such as fenceposts, piling, and mine timbers. Now the decline in the use of fuelwood and most miscellaneous products appears to have about run its course. Thus, the use of wood in future years is likely to rise in line with demands for industrial products.

The things we know about population and economic activity indicate that the demands for industrial timber products are likely to grow rapidly. For example, if recent levels of fertility and immigration continue, the country's population in the year 2000 may be somewhere around 280 million people—40 percent more than in 1970.

Residential construction, the largest end use for lumber and plywood, is also expected to grow rapidly. As early as 1980, the number of housing starts could approach 2.2 million a year—about 50 percent above the

*

DWIGHT HAIR is Assistant to the Director, Division of Forest Economics and Marketing Research, Forest Service.

H. O. FLEISCHER is Director of the Forest Products Laboratory, operated by the Forest Service at Madison, Wis.

number in 1970. Mobile home production may show a similar percentage increase.

Between now and 2000 economic activity may triple. To support this economic activity, and the growth in population, the Nation will need to build enough new houses, schools, stores, and factories to establish some 100 cities the size of Indianapolis, Ind.—a city of about 750,000 people. It also will be necessary to rebuild the central cores of most existing cities and replace much of the Nation's commercial and industrial plant.

Actual increases in consumption of wood will, of course, depend in part on other factors such as prices, technological developments within the wood products and competing industries, and institutional changes. But if population and economic activity rise as described and technological and price trends do not differ significantly from competing materials, major increases in demand for wood can be expected.

The most recent Forest Service projections, for example, indicate that by 2000 the demand for saw logs will roughly double, and nearly triple for

Pre-fab house being erected in Maryland.

331

veneer logs and for pulpwood. Total demand for industrial wood products, that is, all-round products except fuelwood, from domestic forests is projected to increase about 2.3 times.

Implicit in the assumption of constant relative prices underlying these projections is the assumption that enough timber will be available, either from the domestic forests or foreign sources, to meet the anticipated demands.

Huge timber resources are available in Canada and in the tropical regions of the world, and these forests have been supplying an important part of U.S. timber supplies. Total U.S. timber product imports (in terms of roundwood equivalent) rose from 1.5 billion cubic feet in 1950 to 2.4 billion cubic feet in 1970—about 19 percent of total U.S. consumption.

Most of the import increase was in the form of softwood lumber, wood pulp, newsprint, and hardwood plywood. Continued expansion of these imports can be expected in view of growing U.S. demands, the availability of large volumes of timber in the exporting areas, and the relative economics of supplying U.S. markets from these sources.

Timber product exports from the U.S. during the period 1950–70 shot up from 0.1 billion cubic feet (roundwood equivalent) to 1.4 billion cubic feet—equal to about 11 percent of the total U.S. consumption. Most of the exports rise was in the form of logs, wood pulp, paper, and board shipped to Japan and Western Europe. Continuation of the upward trend in exports appears likely in view of limited timber supplies and rapid growth of demand in these areas.

If the above trends do continue, net imports (imports less exports) are not likely to rise significantly. This means the United States must continue to depend on domestic forest resources for its wood supplies.

As of January 1, 1968, the 510 million acres of commercial forests in the United States contained 645 billion cubic feet of timber 5 inches and larger

in diameter at breast height. Included in this volume was 2,490 billion board feet of sawtimber—trees large enough and of suitable quality for manufacturing lumber and veneer.

Timber growth on these forests is a measure of the volume of timber that can be harvested. In response to more effective fire protection and other forest management programs, there have been substantial increases during the past couple of decades in net annual timber growth (total growth less losses from mortality caused by fires, insects, diseases and other agents).

Increase in the net annual growth has been more rapid than the rise in annual timber removals. As a result there are now substantial surpluses of net growth over removals in some sections of the country.

In the South in 1967, for example, net annual softwood timber growth exceeded removals by about 1.5 billion cubic feet including 6 billion board feet of sawtimber. Although some of this surplus has been taken up by larger harvests since 1967, the softwood forests in the South can sustain additional cutting. Softwood forests in the Rocky Mountains and Alaska can also support a small boost in harvests.

Softwood timber removals, however, have been trending upward more rapidly than growth in all sections of the country. If these trends continue, softwood timber demand will rise above the supply in the early 1970's with growing shortages thereafter.

Data on hardwoods show that in the 1970's most of the projected growth in the demand for hardwood saw logs and pulpwood and some of the demand for hardwood veneer logs could be met, chiefly from forests in the Northeast and North-Central States. Beyond the 1970's, however, the demands for hardwood timber also are likely to exceed supplies.

In summation, data on the present and prospective timber demand and supply situation indicate that in the next few years sizable price increases will be needed to bring timber demand into balance with supply. The price increases are likely to be especially large for softwood lumber and plywood.

Such an upward shift in prices could adversely affect national programs to rebuild the central cores of our cities and meet the housing and other building needs of our growing population. It could also add significantly to the inflationary trend in prices.

Part of the projected growth in demand for wood could be met, and price pressures eased, by increasing the utilization or reducing the volume of wood residues, using cull trees, reusing paper and wood debris, and extending supplies through greater efficiency in construction and manufacturing.

In the past two decades coarse wood manufacturing residues have been increasingly used. For example, chip production—mostly from slabs, edgings, veneer cores, and other similar coarse material—has grown from .1 billion cubic feet in 1950 to about 1.5 billion cubic feet in 1970. In addition, there has been some expansion in use of sawdust and other fine manufacturing residues and greater utilization of logging residues.

Even so, in 1968 an estimated 2 billion cubic feet of wood was still left in the forests after logging or land clearing and 2.4 billion cubic feet more was left unused at manufacturing plants.

Of the 58.5 million tons of paper and board consumed in the United States in 1969, only 10.4 million tons— 18 percent of the total—was reused. In some Western European countries and Japan up to 35 percent is reused.

Greater use of residues could, besides contributing to wood needs, improve public acceptance of timber production as vital forest land use. For example, a reduction in logging residues would mean more wood fiber available for use and at the same time improve the sightliness of logged areas. Reduction of logging residues would also cut down the dangers from wildfire and insect attack, and reduce the cost and smoke associated with slash disposal.

Attaining the potential growth in use of wood residues will require effec-tive research and action programs to develop better technology and to lower the costs of reusing waste materials.

New pulping processes, greater use of plant residues, and reuse of paper, fiberboard, and wooden debris from building demolition and old containers represents a sizable potential for meeting the wood demands of the pulp industry. Added benefits are in the reduction of land needs for producing timber, and in water and air pollution involved in waste disposal. These measures would also permit diverting some roundwood production from pulpwood to saw logs and veneer logs.

Projected demands on domestic forests for saw logs and veneer logs could also be reduced through log slicing techniques, thinner saws, and more accurate sawing and veneering machinery that increase lumber and veneer yields.

Still other potential gains in lumber, veneer, and plywood—the products most likely to be in short supply— can be achieved through utilization research. Development of a practical stress-grading system for structural lumber would permit each piece to be used at its full capacity, while possibly allowing a reduction in the size of structural members or an increase in spacing in construction. Research leading to changes in design would more efficiently utilize wood in construction and serve as the basis for changing of archaic and unrealistic building codes.

Although greater efficiency in utilization can meet part of the projected demand for wood, most must come from intensified management of the Nation's commercial forest lands.

Farm and miscellaneous private ownerships comprise some 59 percent of our 510 million acres of commercial forest land. Management of most of these lands for timber production is limited, and average growth per acre is very low. Expanded programs of technical assistance and incentives to increase planting, timber stand improvement, and other management practices could, in time, result in a

333

considerable expansion in the Nation's timber supply.

Many firms in the forest industries have been making large investments in timber management, including the planting of genetically improved stock, thinning, and fertilization. As a result, some of the best managed forest lands are industry owned.

Nevertheless, average net annual growth per acre is much below the potential, and forest industries will have to invest far more on their lands if they are to assure adequate timber supplies at prices close to present levels. In addition, the forest industries must seek ways of increasing production on other privately owned lands.

There also are substantial opportunities to expand timber supplies on the National Forests and other public lands. Sizable investments in such measures as planting, timber stand improvement, thinning, and road construction will be needed. These would make it possible to promptly achieve larger timber harvests as well as substantial long-run increases in timber growth.

Attaining additional timber growth on all lands will depend in part on an adequate program of research as well as accelerated action programs. There is special need to develop more effective programs of regenerating stands with desirable species, propagation of superior trees, determining optimum levels of stocking, and improving protection.

In the past decade, growing numbers of people have been demanding withdrawals of commercial forest land from timber production, or modifications of forest land management, to provide wilderness and other recreation areas. Besides this there is a new awareness and concern that forest management practices insure protection of forested watersheds, control soil erosion, prevent water pollution, and provide for wildlife needs.

This has been formally recognized by the Federal Government in the National Environmental Policy Act of 1969, which established a national policy "to use all practicable means and measures, including financial and technical assistance, in a manner calculated to foster and promote the general welfare, to create and maintain conditions under which man and nature can exist in productive harmony, and fulfill the social, economic, and other requirements of present and future generations of Americans."

To sum up, it appears that the foreseeable demands for timber and other goods and services produced on the Nation's forest lands can be met if the necessary investments are made in management and research programs.

In research, there is a special need to develop improved technology for multiple-use planning and multiple-use land management to achieve the optimum output of timber and other goods and services. There is a related need for research and development in harvesting and manufacturing practices to more efficiently use available timber resources, not only to help meet future timber demands but also to improve the environment.

Together, research and action programs in forest land management and in forest products utilization can do the job.

Manufactured Foods, Fibers

WILLIAM S. HOOFNAGLE and
WILLIAM W. GALLIMORE

AMERICANS have the reputation as the best fed and best clothed people in the world. This stems from our achievements in agricultural production, processing and marketing, and our continued search for new sources of food and fiber.

Left, textured vegetable protein roll. Right, textured vegetable protein bits, for addition to soups, casseroles, and as a garnish on salads.

Most of the foods we ate in the past could be associated closely with the originating products. Beef steak, applesauce, and fried potatoes are examples. In the more recent past we accepted new foods like margarine, coffee whiteners, and artificial sweeteners, whose source is not known unless we read the fine print on the label. This trend toward more manufactured foods is in its infancy, and the kinds of food we will be eating by the year 2000 are almost beyond our comprehension.

Since World War II, the food processing industries have deluged us with new products. Most of the products were designed for consumer convenience and we have been willing to pay any added cost for these services. The past 20 years have conditioned us to readily accept new packaging and convenience foods, and have paved the way toward our more ready acceptance of even newer foods appearing on the supermarket shelf.

Introduction of food items in the

*

WILLIAM S. HOOFNAGLE is Deputy Director of the Marketing Economics Division, of the Economic Research Service.

WILLIAM W. GALLIMORE is an Agricultural Economist in the Division.

past resulted primarily from the food processors' desire to create markets and differentiate their products from those of competitors. Then too, products were developed so that weight-conscious consumers could cut down on fats.

The search for new foods and food products still retains these dimensions. Yet, population increases and the desire to provide adequate food at a reasonable cost are major reasons for our continued search.

The United States may have more than 280 million people by the year 2000, which means we would need almost a third larger supply of food.

Total supplies of food are and will continue to remain adequate. But the price of some foods, particularly those high in animal protein, have prevented low income groups from eating desired amounts of them. Then too, the more manufacturing in foods, the more standardization is needed in the quality and quantity of raw materials. Food processors continually seek new sources of supply that do not fluctuate in price and supply like some agricultural materials now used.

Agricultural products are constantly substituted for each other, but future substitutions may differ from

335

Soy protein food	Protein content (percent)	Price cents per lb.	Estimated volume of 1970 U.S. production million pounds	Current uses
Flour and Grits_____	40 to 55	5½ to 11	325 to 500	Ingredients for baked goods, dog foods, and sausages
Concentrates_____	60 to 70	18 to 25	25 to 30	Making textured products ingredient in processed meats, baby foods, and health foods
Isolates_____	90 to 95	35 to 45	20 to 25	Manufacturing analogs, and for use in comminuted meats such as meat loaf, frankfurters, etc.
Textured items:				Manufacturing analogs
Extruded_____	50 to 55	28 and up	{25	such as: bacon strips and
Spun_____	90+	50 and up		bits, pork, beef, chicken, fish, and similar foods

those in the past. Recent developments in substitutes for meat and dairy products illustrate some of the changes possible in the next 30 years.

The soybean has been the largest source of plant protein used to manufacture meatlike foods and to increase the protein content of other foods. Soybeans have won this distinction by being abundant, thereby providing a low cost source of protein. Four types of soy protein are being used in manufactured foods. The percent of protein, prices, and estimated volume used in 1970 are shown in the table.

Soy flour and grits are used in bakery foods, pet foods, and other products. Their use in these products has long been established and additional use will be gradual. There are disadvantages. Flour and grits have a bitter chalky taste and cause flatulence (intestinal gas) in humans unless the carbohydrates are removed. Used in small amounts, however, they cause no problems.

Soy protein concentrates, in ground or textured form, can be used as extenders in meats such as hamburger and in meat loaf, casseroles, and other foods of this type. These new products are being accepted first in institutional markets like hospitals and schools, and then in the mass consumer markets.

Simulated meats from soy protein isolate are presently on the market and are very similar to the natural products they are manufactured to represent. The technology of spinning fibers from protein powder enables simulated meats to be made from vegetable protein sources.

Undoubtedly other advances will be made in the technology of fabrication and flavoring that will result in better and more simulation of meat and meat products. Soy protein products have an essential amino acid content approaching that of meat, although the methionine and lysine content is lower.

Further refinements are being made in simulated meats from soy protein to obtain a product that has the desirable properties of meat and yet has less of the undesirable properties. Simulated meats are made mainly in dry or frozen form, thus having a longer shelf life than chilled meats. They can be more convenient in the home than ordinary meats—especially when used for flavoring.

Start up and development costs have tended to make soy meats relatively costly when compared on a price per pound purchased basis. However, the cost per serving or amount eaten is about the same as natural meat because there is less shrinkage than with natural meats. Therefore, as the need for soy meats develop either from convenience or shortage of natural meat, the U.S. food industry has the technological ability to produce soy meats to fill this need.

At present, protein from meat substitutes probably accounts for less than a fraction of 1 percent of that supplied by meat. However, some sources have indicated this will increase to 5 or 6 percent by the year 2000. The rate of substitution of vegetable protein for meat will depend in part upon relative prices, labeling regulations, nutritional levels, and consumer acceptance of the products.

Plant oil and protein also are used as substitutes in and for dairy products. Per capita consumption of margarine, for example, is more than 10 pounds compared to less than 6 for butter. One estimate is that coffee whiteners have 35 percent of the market for light cream and probably 80 percent of the whipped toppings are nondairy products.

Substitutes for fluid milk are either 1. filled milk, in which nonfat milk solids are combined with vegetable fat in place of milkfat, or 2. synthetic milk, in which no component of milk is used. The major ingredients in a completely synthetic product are vegetable fat and protein, plus buffers, stabilizers, and other ingredients. Sodium caseinate is a major protein source, but work is underway on locating other sources.

Both synthetic and filled milks have been marketed in several States. So far, market results indicate the need for additional technical work on the synthetic substitute for whole milk. Some synthetic milk has not matched the nutritional quality of whole milk. When consumers became aware of this, they expressed a preference for whole milk even at higher prices.

As the technology and source of materials for fabricating synthetic milk improves, the quantities consumed will depend on the relative prices—if we assume the quality of the synthetic product will not be significantly different from whole milk.

Research is underway on developing protein sources from peanuts, safflower, cottonseed, rapeseed, sesame, sunflower, and plant leaves such as alfalfa. Protein from peanuts and cottonseed has been used for human food purposes but not in fabricated meat items. The research being conducted would open up whole new sources of plant protein extract should it become necessary. Techniques could be devised to make conventional foods from these sources.

Discovery of other protein sources could alter our food supply picture, including the introduction of foods from new sources and in forms not presently used. These protein sources could include certain types of fish and single cell protein.

Currently a protein concentrate can be made from fish, but care must be taken to keep the fluorine content low, usually by excluding the fish heads. The cost of fish protein concentrate and the food standards of a number of countries have limited use of this product. In the future, fish protein concentrate could be an important source of protein and be manufactured into food products, if present problems are eliminated. Development of an acceptable fish protein concentrate would allow the use of abundant, underharvested fish as human food.

Another potential protein source for manufactured foods consists of the single cell protein—yeast, fungi, bacteria, and algae. So far these protein sources have been obtained by using petroleum, sewage, garbage, or wood pulp as the growing medium.

Single cell protein sources have not been competitive in cost in this country with other sources of protein. Purification and achieving a digestible form of algae have caused problems. By the year 2000 scientists may have solved these problems, making single cell protein another source of protein.

Most research on single cell protein sources is being done outside the United States. The Japanese are conducting research on algae and the Europeans are testing yeast and bacteria grown on petroleum distillates as a source of protein.

The source of fiber for many of our products has changed. We no longer think it unusual to wear out a set of automobile tires and never have a flat or blowout. Although our roads have improved, this better service is due primarily to the use of improved fibers in tires.

Synthetic fibers are used in many other products. In 1969, over 46 percent of the total domestic consumption of broadwoven goods was classified as manmade fabrics. This is expected to increase to more than 60 percent by the year 2000. However, with the increase in population and the trend toward more cotton in some blends, cotton is still expected to supply a significant portion of our fiber needs for the next 30 years.

Advantages of synthetic fibers are their strength and flexibility, and they have captured the market in such applications as cord for automobile tires. Other advantages of the synthetics are permanent press and resistance to abrasion. As a result of the development of synthetics and permanent press cotton fabrics, we now wear clothing that does not require ironing or pressing after repeated cleanings. Natural fibers have the advantages of lower costs, moisture absorbency and better heat transfer.

Research is underway in both natural and synthetic fibers to improve their qualities. However, the future of fiber production in the United States may hinge more on research and development of ways to produce a fabric from synthetic material without spinning the fiber and weaving the cloth, both processes requiring much labor and capital. These new processes are experimental at this time, and economic and technical considerations may delay their widespread adoption.

To sum up, consumers will have an ever increasing choice of food and fiber products in the next 30 years. Simulated meat products from plant protein developed for use by groups not eating meat will become increasingly important as a source of food. New sources of protein will be discovered but will probably be used more outside the United States. Both natural and manmade fibers will be improved. Advances will be made in techniques of producing fabric without spinning or weaving.

Although we will have the advantage of being able to use many new products in the years ahead, we will probably still be able to buy the natural products, if we so desire. Witness that butter, cream, wool, and leather are available even as margarine, coffee whiteners, and nylon have come onto the market. Thus, new products of the future will add to, rather than subtract from, our selection of items.

Food and Fiber Employment Opportunities

EARLE E. GAVETT and
ROBERT E. FRYE

WHAT DO a technician in a pharmaceutical lab, an oil refinery worker, a rubber plant worker, a data programmer, a lawyer, a truck driver, a helicopter pilot, a warehouseman, a supermarket cashier, and a farmer have in common?

The answer is: related employment. All these kinds of workers and many more are employed in agribusiness—that is, in manufacturing and distributing farm supplies, in production on the farm, and in processing, storing, and distributing farm products and items made from them. Agribusiness now engages nearly a fourth of all employed persons in the United States.

Farming uses fewer than 5 million workers. But industries that process and distribute farm products employ about 10 million workers, and industries that provide goods and services used by farmers employ about 2 million.

Workers actively engaged in farming went down from 10 million in 1950 to 4.5 million in 1970—a 55 percent drop. Employment in these other industries has changed little since 1950.

With the number of farmers and of farm production workers declining rapidly, what are the prospects for employment in agribusiness? Good, although most of the opportunities obviously are off the farm.

By 1980 we expect fewer than 2.9 million farmworkers on 2 million farms, and by the year 2000 perhaps fewer than 2 million farmworkers on 1 million farms.

Employment in farming has decreased in recent years as agriculture has become more efficient, but there are still many employment possibilities.

For a limited number of entrepreneurs, full-scale farming (farms with annual gross incomes in excess of $20,000) has great potential if one draws on all the latest technologies.

New opportunities in farming also are found where land reclamation is feasible, where abandoned farmland can be converted to new farm uses,

*

EARLE E. GAVETT is Leader of the Farm Labor and Mechanization Group, Farm Production Economics Division, Economic Research Service (ERS).

ROBERT E. FRYE is Leader of the Distribution Analysis Research Group, Marketing Economics Division, ERS.

and where small farm units are difficult to consolidate into larger units and are easily acquired for part-time farming.

While the total number of farms has been decreasing—from 4 million in 1960 to fewer than 3 million in 1970—the number of full-scale farms has been increasing. Farms having sales of more than $20,000 a year have nearly doubled in number since 1960, and are expected to continue at nearly the current number through 1980.

This means that full-scale farming would require 500,000 to 600,000 operators and over 600,000 regular hired workers.

In addition there are, and will continue to be, opportunities for many seasonal hired workers although mechanization has made drastic inroads on seasonal farm employment on these larger farms.

Further, hired workers contribute substantially to the labor input on small farms. Often the operator of a small farm obtains nonfarm employment for himself and hires help to do most of his farmwork. Nearly a fifth of the work on small farms is carried out by hired workers.

Part-time farming provides an opportunity for about a million people to live on the farm and produce some farm commodities, while deriving major income from nonfarm occupations. For many this is the better of both worlds.

For example, in a 1956 survey in Michigan a dairy farmer reported that he was tired of the twice daily routine of milking cows. He sold his herd and got a job in the automobile industry in Detroit, 50 miles away. Even with 2 hours commuting time added to his 8-hour workday, he still had more free time than when he was dairying.

He switched to producing hay, corn, and wheat on his farm. With a modern baler and combine he was able to harvest these crops during weekends and in one week of his two week vacation.

He still had one week's vacation to travel—a week more than was possible while dairying. He could have farmed with even less work and investment by obtaining the services of a custom operator.

Custom operators supply the equipment and labor to perform most any field operation. They baled nearly a fifth of the 1967 hay crop, and we estimate they combined over a quarter of our grain crops.

Here is an opportunity for active participation in farming without incurring a large investment in land.

The rapid expansion of modern highways in the 1960's and the deurbanization of many industries have enabled more farm families to live on the farm and work in industry—with some jobs agriculturally oriented, others not.

This combination of better highways and decentralized industries has permitted many people to remain in the country who otherwise would have pulled up stakes and moved to major metropolitan areas. It has been particularly beneficial to older workers with little incentive to leave lifelong homes and friends, and to those with limited skills.

In the Piedmont and Coastal Plains of both North and South Carolina, for example, many industrial plants are located in the open country. These plants rely on former farmworkers and part-time farmers for their work force.

On a recent trip to South Carolina during the peak of the flue-cured tobacco harvest, we saw few adult men in the fields. Most were employed in nearby industrial plants. Women, children, and aged workers dominated the harvest crews. Such work combinations provide opportunity for substantially increasing farm family income.

As mentioned earlier, farm employment dropped over a half from 1950 to 1970, and is projected to drop more than half again by 2000. Why this sharp decline in farm employment when population has grown and experts project an increased demand for food to supply some 20 million additional families by the year 2000?

Farmers have adopted mechanization and other laborsaving technology at a rapid rate. For example, in 1950 there were 3.4 million tractors, or 0.3 per farmworker. This was a small tractor averaging only 27 horsepower. During 1970, there were 4.8 million tractors. This is an average of 1.2 tractors per farmworker and the tractors are quite different. They now average 43 horsepower each; and many of the new models are in the 100 to 140 horsepower range.

Accompanying the more powerful tractors are a multitude of complex specialized machines to do a better job faster, cheaper, and easier. They have been effective in reducing labor needs. In the 20 years since 1950, farm production per hour of labor has tripled.

The tomato harvester is an example of a specialized machine. Before 1964, when the Bracero Program was terminated, some 40,000 to 50,000 Mexican nationals were admitted each year to pick and load canning tomatoes in California.

These men picked tomatoes and lugged the 50-pound field boxes to the truck. Women were prohibited from lugging by a California law which made it illegal for them to lift more than 25 pounds. Thus, tomato picking was largely a man's job.

The machine changed all that. The harvester lifts the entire plant and shakes the fruit from the vines.

Women sorters ride, standing or sitting, and cull green and defective fruit as it passes over the machine's sorting table.

Employers believe that women are especially adept at machine sorting because of their greater manual dexterity, and because they are less apt to develop motion sickness than men. The result? Output per hour of labor tripled and harvesting costs dropped about $8 per ton, from $18 to $10. Women have replaced many men in the field.

Some harvesters have been enclosed, air conditioned, and provided with music. Many farm jobs are more pleasant than they used to be.

Farmers have prefabricated building systems designed to provide pushbutton livestock feeding and handling facilities. With such facilities, beef feedlots up to 100,000 head capacity per year are being operated with 50 men.

There are a number of 1,000-cow dairies with 10 to 15 workers doing all chore work. Forage and grain concentrates are purchased from other farmers who specialize in crop production, or from feed dealers.

Some dairy farmers have hired women crews and find them ideal milking parlor attendants. Mechanization has eliminated heavy work from milking and made the job attractive. Women admit cows to the parlor, wash their udders, attach milkers, feed grain by remote control, and release the cows from the parlor. They do this while working in a clean, bright, air conditioned area that is gleaming with stainless steel fixtures and glass piping.

Mechanization and specialization have enabled farmers to get their work done without requiring them to work from sunup to sundown 7 days a week as some of us used to do on the farm. The average workweek for all farmworkers is about 39 hours—40 hours for operators and 34 for all hired workers. This is not greatly different from nonfarm employment which averages just about 40 hours a week. On larger farms, however, operators and regular hired workers average about 45 hours a week.

Seasonal farm employment offers job opportunities for many workers. In 1970, monthly farm employment rose from 3.2 million workers in January to 5.4 million in July. Of these, hired workers accounted for 601,000 in January and 1,786,000 in July. Seasonality of crop production causes farm labor demands to increase greatly during the summer months and then contract sharply after harvesttime.

Housewives, high school and college students, unemployed industrial workers, and "moonlighting" nonfarm workers are the major source of seasonal hired farmworkers. Of these, 60 percent (primarily housewives and students) were not in the labor force most of the year.

Seasonal farm employment offers many opportunities for workers who want to travel around the country. During this year's cling peach harvest, women pickers in California told us that they were free—independent—proud. They could work if they wanted to. If they didn't like the job, they could go to another farmer or leave the area entirely.

The women said they would head south shortly to work in citrus during the winter months. They don't want to stay in the Imperial Valley year around "because summers there are too hot." These people felt that they could contribute most to society, make a fairly good annual income, and enjoy themselves while working by following the crops as the seasons progressed.

Yet, for many families who travel the migrant route it is a frustrating and discouraging existence. If crops do not ripen on time or too many workers arrive for the work available, everyone including children may go hungry. Annual earnings are low. Temporary housing (used 3 or 4 weeks a year) is far from ideal. And constant movement from one locality to another during the school year compounds the educational problem for youngsters. Fortunately, the migrant work force is declining rapidly.

Significant labor legislation has recently been passed or is imminent for workers directly engaged in farm production. The Fair Labor Standards Act now covers many farmworkers with a Federal minimum wage. The Crew Leader Registration Act prescribes procedures for handling crews of migratory workers.

Most noncasual farmworkers have

social security coverage and some have workmen's compensation and unemployment insurance. Some farmworkers have become unionized, although they are currently excluded from the provisions of the National Labor Relations Act.

As wages have risen, farmers have looked for ways of reducing labor costs. They have substituted machines for farmworkers. However, not all of the decline in farm employment can be attributed to new machines. Some jobs have moved off the farm.

When we were farming 30 years ago, we went to the railroad siding and unloaded bags of lime and fertilizer by hand onto farm trucks. We hauled the material home and spread it on the fields.

Now, farmers have the fertilizer dealer test the soil and determine nutritional needs of the crop to be produced. He prepares a prescription formula including necessary trace elements for top performance, delivers this fertilizer to the farm in bulk spreader trucks, and applies it at the proper time and rate. Thus, fertilizer industry salesmen, chemists, warehousemen, and truck drivers are directly involved in providing fertilizer. None of these are counted as farmworkers.

Similar job opportunities exist in providing other inputs to farmers. Pesticides are a good example. They may be applied by both ground equipment and aircraft. Most farmers using ground equipment apply their own pesticides; those using aircraft pay to have it done.

Dusting with aircraft started in 1925 with 14 planes being used to protect cotton. By 1939, some 200 planes were treating farm crops. In 1962, over 5,000 aircraft treated 65 million acres logging nearly 1 million hours of flying time.

Since then, aircraft use in farming has increased as new technology has permitted precision application of seeds, foliage fertilizer, and pesticide materials.

Helicopters now safely apply sprays to orange groves within 50 feet of nonfarm residences.

Production of farm machinery and equipment provides employment for approximately 150,000 workers. Their output is channelled to farmers through nearly 16,000 dealers. The average franchised farm machinery dealer has, besides his sales and clerical force, five shopmen—foremen, mechanics, and helpers. Thus, probably 100,000 workers are engaged in distributing and maintaining farm machinery and equipment.

There are growing opportunities for jobs in the farm service sector as new services are provided to farmers.

Farmers, like so many other businessmen, use computer services to aid them in making important decisions. They ask such questions as: Should I continue to feed corn to hogs, or sell the corn outright? How much fertilizer and with what ingredients do I need to obtain the most profitable yield of potatoes? What is the most profitable combination of enterprises with my fixed resources and available capital?

The card puncher, the programmer, the computer operator, and the systems analyst are but a few of the people whose employment in computer services is directly related to farming. Farmers are greatly expanding their use of such services.

In total, about 2 million persons in the farm input industries provide the U.S. farmer with production equipment, materials, and services. They help to make him the most productive farmer in the world.

Producing farm products is only part of the job. These products must be moved from farm to consumer. Many must be transformed from farm commodities to consumer goods. This movement and transformation occurs in the marketing system. Prospects for employment in this area appear bright even though the number of employees has remained stable over the last decade.

In 1970 it is estimated that consumers spent over $102 billion for food which came from U.S. farms.

342

More than two-thirds or $69 billion went for marketing services. Population expansion and rising consumer income point to even greater demand for marketing services in the future.

The wide array of employee abilities and skills required and business opportunities provided may be seen by examining the food marketing system. It assembles products from farms, then processes, transports, stores, and distributes them to retail outlets where they are purchased by consumers. This may sound simple and routine, but it is very complex. Let's go behind the scenes to observe some of the things done in marketing and the scope of opportunities.

As consumers we buy only a small proportion of farm products in either the form or at the place they are produced. We buy bread instead of wheat, steak instead of steer. It's a long way and lots of things are done between the Great Plains farms where wheat is produced and the supermarket where a freshly baked loaf of bread is bought by consumers.

Similarly, the steak you were served when you took your wife out to dinner on your anniversary not only came a long way but also is very different from the 1,000 pound steer that started the marketing process from a Nebraska feedlot. Yet marketing is broader even than this.

Marketing makes it possible for shoppers in a Maine supermarket to buy frozen orange juice processed in Florida and peaches canned in California. It provides to the consumer, on a year-round basis, fruits and vegetables processed in season.

Dinners requiring only heating to serve, fully prepared ready-to-eat foods, and literally thousands of items with built-in cook or maid service are readily available to our Nation's food shoppers. Between shopping trips the consumer may find that some items have been dropped from the grocers' shelves but a larger number of new products have been added.

Today, an increasing proportion of our food needs are being met in retail outlets which collectively we call the "away from home" food market. Besides the conventional restaurants offering table service, fast food establishments offering quick meals or snacks have sprung up all over.

Mobile food services and in-plant restaurants and cafeterias for employees are being provided at job sites. Lunch service is available in most of the Nation's elementary and secondary schools. Food catering services are readily available.

These examples illustrate the broad scope of marketing and the varied opportunities it provides for participation as an employee or businessman. Also, they reflect the many opportunities for employment in industries that supply and support our modern marketing systems.

The largest part of the marketing bill goes to food retailers who sell for home consumption as well as for on-premise consumption. That is, food retailing includes the corner grocery and the supermarket, as well as the restaurant and drive-in.

In the retail grocery business, there has been an almost universal shift from clerk-service to self-service and from credit and delivery to cash-and-carry. The shifting of these tasks to consumers and the emergence and adoption of the supermarket method of retailing has sharply reduced this industry's labor inputs per dollar of sales.

Over the last two decades there has been a sizable drop in the number of grocery stores, but openings and closings have been nearly balanced in recent years. A sharp increase in the number of convenience stores has off-set the large number of small conventional grocery stores going out of business.

Despite the fact that the average size of grocery stores will continue to increase, population growth and demand for more retail services will result in increased store numbers in the next decade.

The nearly 220,000 grocery stores

343

now in operation provide employment for an estimated 1.6 million persons as clerks, cashiers, butchers, shelf-stockers, custodians, and watchmen. In addition, administrative employees including store managers, department managers, accountants, and others with specialized skills are required. Employment opportunities range from part-time to full-time and from semiskilled to highly skilled.

Approximately 190,000 independently owned grocery stores not only offer individuals the opportunity of operating their own business, but also provide jobs for the community where they are located.

A large proportion of food retailing employees, especially those of chains and large independents, work under union contract and enjoy wages and benefits comparable with workers in other industries. In fact, the size of many firms and the level of the technology employed has placed food retailing in competition with other industries for trained people, skilled workers and management abilities.

Over 23,000 of today's grocery stores have annual sales of at least $1 million and account for over 60 percent of total grocery sales. The proportion of total retail food store sales accounted for by corporate chains is increasing. Many large retailing firms now provide opportunities for on-the-job training and advancement to more responsible positions.

The away-from-home market for food, already sizable, appears to be expanding rapidly. Based on a 1966 survey, it was estimated that food and nonalcoholic beverages with annual retail value of $22 billion moved through public eating places and institutions such as hospitals, rest homes, colleges, and universities. The military services, elementary and secondary schools, Federal hospitals, correctional institutions, the in-transit feeders (planes, trains, ships), and boarding houses which served food and beverages with an estimated retail value of $6 billion were not included in the survey.

In the areas covered by the survey more than 371,000 establishments provided food services. Of this total, 345,000 were public eating places of which about 87 percent were independently owned. These food service establishments reported an average of nearly 104 million transactions daily. Some 3.3 million persons including owners worked in these outlets.

In recent years there has been an almost explosive growth in the number of outlets offering fast food service. Franchising of independent operators as well as expansion of chain operations have contributed to the increase. This growth is expected to continue and it will mean that more people will be needed to manage, work in, and supply such outlets.

Next to retailing, food processing accounts for the largest share of the food marketing bill. The processors' share has been rising and will continue to do so as demand increases more for highly processed food than for less processed or fresh forms. While processing of food is a multibillion-dollar industry, its complexity is even more impressive than its size.

Originally food processing was oriented toward processing and preserving. These are still necessary functions. However, food processing today is, and in the future will be, oriented toward consumer desires with emphasis on food preparation, convenience, and packaging in order to provide the housewife with the exact product she wants.

The processor has taken on jobs formerly thought of as duties of the farmer, the retailer, or the housewife. Consequently, today's food processing industry has become more complex, technical, and scientific.

For most food processing industries the prevailing trend is toward centralization, large scale undertakings, and automation. A broad array of specialists and experts are required to operate and manage the modern food processing establishment.

Opportunities are provided for engineers, chemists, food technologists,

344

accountants, lawyers, finance specialists, advertising and marketing specialists, and data processors. Also, many thousands of people with a wide range of capabilities are needed to install, operate and maintain food processing equipment, and to man the production lines.

The assembly, transportation, and wholesaling of food will continue to provide substantial opportunities for employment. However, many of these functions have been integrated into the operation of the processor or the retailer.

For example, the food processor may buy directly from the producer and the large food retailing firm may buy directly from the processor, bypassing the broker or wholesaler. On the other hand, many wholesalers are now providing retailers with accounting, inventory control, management training, merchandising, advertising, and financing services. These were previously performed by the individual retailer.

Although particular arrangements are changing and more change is likely, wholesaling will continue to be essential and provide opportunities for employment.

Transportation plays a vital role in marketing. Suppose that all trains, planes, trucks, barges, and ships came to a complete halt for a week. Producers could not move their products to market, many processors would have to close down, many shelves in the supermarket would be bare and the home pantry would become depleted of a number of foods.

Getting products where we want them, at the right time, and in proper condition requires a well coordinated and dependable transportation system. Even greater dependence will be placed on our transportation system as total demand for marketing services increases along with our population growth.

While employment opportunities in food marketing appear to be expanding, a less brilliant future is forecast for employment in marketing of farm-produced fibers—mainly cotton and wool. The expanding use of many manmade fibers is being made largely at the expense of natural fibers. Thus, employment prospects connected with marketing of cotton and wool will probably decline.

We have roughly sketched the major employment opportunities of American agribusiness. About 17 million persons are currently so employed.

Future job opportunities are increasing for many categories of workers as the demand for farm products expands with population growth. Skilled workers will replace stoop and other unskilled workers and the work environment will continue to improve.

Increasing worker skills and providing workers with new technology permits greater output per worker, however, so we foresee little expansion in overall employment in the agribusiness complex.

Development and the Role of Water

EUGENE C. BUIE,

LOUIS M. GLYMPH, and

WILLIAM H. HENEBERRY

POPULATION growth and general economic development frequently have been linked with the increasing use of water and improvements in its management. Water management can include flood protection, navigation, erosion control, drainage of wet areas, irrigation, provision of high-quality domestic and industrial water supplies, and facilities for water-based recreation, or various combinations of these.

Flood protection has attracted industries, business, and homebuilders and encouraged farmers to switch to higher value crops. Importation of water supplies for agriculture, household, and industrial use has been associated with phenomenal growth in population and economic activity in the arid regions, such as southern California.

Irrigation with ground water has changed agriculture in the High Plains of Texas from wheat and cattle ranching to production of irrigated cotton, grain sorghum and some vegetables, and intensive cattle feeding operations in less than 20 years. In many areas, manmade lakes have provided recreation for local residents and attracted visitors from other locations.

In the cases cited above, interaction between water management and several other physical and institutional factors have contributed to the stimulated economic activity.

In Southern California, a favorable climate and early recognition of the need for additional water for agriculture and industry were important. In the Texas High Plains an abundance of relatively level, productive land, large-scale farms, and a good supply of high-quality shallow water helped in the growth of irrigated agriculture.

Visitors to recreational water developments frequently are drawn by scenic or historic attractions in addition to the water.

Location of industrial plants is influenced by the availability of land and labor, transportation systems, nearness to markets, and State and local tax structures, as well as water availability. Nevertheless, water development and management often have removed some of the roadblocks and stimulated economic growth by increasing and stabilizing production and providing new job opportunities.

*

EUGENE C. BUIE is the Assistant Deputy Administrator for Watershed Planning, Soil Conservation Service.

LOUIS M. GLYMPH is Assistant Director for Watershed Engineering Research, Agricultural Research Service.

WILLIAM H. HENEBERRY is an Agricultural Economist in the Economic Research Service.

Will continued improvement in water management be a requirement for future expansion in economic activity? The answer to this question seems obvious. In most parts of the country, water is becoming more costly as ground water supplies are depleted and fewer sites are available for storing surface water.

Competition among users is increasing, too, with both municipalities and industries taking water which formerly was used for irrigation.

The upward trend in water use is likely to continue because of increasing per capita household use and the expected growth in population.

Water use and management could become more important in the development of rural areas as a result of population movement as well as growth. While demographers expect an increase of at least 65 million in total population in the next three decades, farm population seems likely to drop.

Only 10.3 million people were living on farms in 1969 compared with 15.6 million in 1960. Some of these people moved to small towns or remained in their rural homes after they quit farming, but more of them apparently moved to the larger urban areas. There is a need to reduce this outmigration.

If the present trend continues, metropolitan centers will get larger and the already-serious problems of traffic congestion, housing shortages, air pollution, and waste disposal will be aggravated. Positive action may be needed to stimulate economic activity in small towns and cities and to create new towns where orderly growth can be achieved at lower economic and social cost. Planned water resource development can contribute to this objective.

The U.S. Department of Agriculture has recognized the relationship between dwindling rural population and urban congestion for some time. Many USDA programs are aimed directly or indirectly at achieving a better balance between urban and rural population. These include financing of rural housing, water and sewer systems, and electric power co-ops, and various programs of financial and technical aid for improving soil and water management.

The small watershed program is a good example of a combination of Federal financial and technical assistance to local people in solving water-related problems and encouraging rural development.

Many of the opportunities for water resource development occur in the

Most of the flood plains in upstream watersheds are subject to frequent flooding. In many of the land resource areas these flood plains are the most productive and most suitable farming areas. In some land resource areas they are the only lands really suitable for farming, due to soil or slope conditions, or both.

Protection of these lands from frequent flooding produces more stable farms, ensures more dependable crop yields, and stabilizes the agricultural sector of the local economy.

Ducks on Mississippi flyway.

upstream reaches of the Nation's river basins. Approximately 60 percent of floodwater damage occurs in these upstream areas which are defined as watersheds having less than 250,000 acres. Water supply for many rural communities and small towns is inadequate or undependable.

Opportunities for water-based recreation often do not exist within a reasonable driving radius of many rural communities and small towns.

Timely development of water resources in upstream watersheds and river tributaries can provide the physical basis and economic stimulus necessary to support an expanding population.

Inadequate farm drainage and the removal of excess surface water are critical problems in many areas, including flood plains, coastal plains, lake plains, and other flat lands.

A highly critical problem with respect to agricultural drainage is the selection of proper land use. Many so-called "wetlands" have soils which are not suited to cultivation. They may produce commercial hardwoods or provide habitat for fish and wildlife, or both. Areas of that type should be retained in or returned to such uses.

Other wet soils are highly productive when properly drained. They have good infiltration rates, permit

347

favorable plant-soil-moisture relationships, are easily tilled, and can be farmed at a sustained high level of productivity. Large acreages already are in cultivation and represent large capital investments. Proper drainage permits a more efficient use of the committed investments and better response to fertilizers, timely tillage, and other management practices.

At the same time, it should be noted that some of this land, strategically located, should be left undrained to serve as waterfowl and wildlife habitat.

Surface drainage systems often are not practical because of inadequate outlets. Upstream watershed projects which provide surface drainage must be developed concurrently with or subsequent to downstream or adjacent projects which provide the same services. Coordinated planning and implementation then become essential.

These types of developments provide limited direct employment opportunities. However, in many instances they are essential to the maintenance of small family farms.

Usually, acreages to be irrigated by project-type developments in upstream watersheds are relatively small and crops often are specialized. However, both flood protection and drainage often permit large areas to be irrigated using on-farm ground water developments. That is especially true in areas like the Mississippi Delta.

Where significant areas are brought under irrigation, on-farm employment increases. Both irrigation and drainage require expanded service industries in producing, harvesting, and processing the crops.

Many rural communities and small towns are limited in growth potential by inadequate water supplies. The condition usually occurs where suitable ground water is not available and surface impoundments are costly. Upstream watershed projects offer opportunities for reducing the cost of municipal and industrial water supplies through including them in multiple-purpose reservoirs.

An adequate water supply is essential to both population and economic growth. Towns which have taken advantage of watershed projects have experienced very favorable results.

Waldron, Ark., installed such a project. Afterwards, a small industry located in the town and employs about 430 people. Estimated annual payroll exceeds $3 million. The effect on the local economy is multiplied several times.

Many other towns have had similar experiences. Among them are Carrollton, Ga., and Princeton, W. Va.

Water-based recreation is another service which can be provided through watershed projects. Reservoirs designed and constructed for this goal usually are multiple-purpose. Provisions can be made for boating, swimming, fishing, and picnicking. Some reservoirs have a large enough surface area to permit powerboating and water skiing.

Recreational opportunities created by watershed project developments enhance the community environment. Their availability makes a community a better place to live. They provide an added enticement to industry to locate in the area and attract residents to the community.

Fish and wildlife developments can be included in upstream watershed projects. They may be designed as recreational facilities or as wildlife preserves. The projects can make maximum use of existing natural conditions or create desirable habitat where none exists. They contribute significantly to the environment of the community.

Water quality problems are created when waste effluents from industries, feedlots, slaughterhouses, and urban or residential areas are discharged into local streams. The pollutants can be diluted by water stored in multiple-purpose upstream reservoirs and released during periods of inadequate streamflow.

Watershed projects include plans for proper land use and runoff and erosion control as well as structural

348

measures. Such steps are essential to protecting the watersheds, reducing sediment, and enhancing the environment. Erosion scars are removed; contrasts between open and wooded lands created; eye-pleasing patterns formed by contour tillage, stripcropping, and legume and grass combinations; and suitable habitats provided for upland game and game birds.

Planned operation and maintenance of recreation and fish and wildlife structures can attract migratory waterfowl, both as resting and feeding areas. Objectionable features, like junkyards and strip mined areas, can be screened or covered by vegetative plantings.

Upstream watershed projects and their water resource developments can attract people to these communities as desirable places to live. Needed and desirable water-related goods and services can be provided in the interest of the well-being of local residents.

Job opportunities are increased. The economy is made more stable, and the community improved through recreational opportunities and a more beautiful and desirable environment. Outmigration from communities often is reduced or stopped and inmigration stimulated. A more favorable rural-urban balance can be generated over the long run.

To meet the needs of an expanding population, it is essential that water and related land resource problems be examined on an area basis and the available resources directed to those developments which are most urgent and will provide the widest range of opportunities to local people.

Comprehensive river basin plans provide the basis for scheduling development to meet needs in accordance with the degree of urgency that can be foreseen.

Areas which have growth potential are identified and the nature of their opportunities for water resource development is defined. Regional and subregional population expansions are estimated by target years, such as 1980, 2000, and 2020. Water and related land resource requirements are estimated to meet the demands of future population levels and the expanded economic activity they will generate.

Increasingly, the potentials of alternative developments and uses of water resources are being looked at and evaluated by techniques of systems analysis. It has long been apparent, for instance, that land-use and management practices greatly influence the hydrologic performance of the individual soil-cover-treatment complexes.

Mathematical models of hydrologic and hydraulic components of watershed systems now make it possible to visualize how these influences affect the water regimes of complex watersheds and river basins.

One potential application of such models is depicted on the next page. This shows the results of a numerical experiment to determine the influence of land-use management upon water yield as streamflow in Land Resource Areas represented by research watersheds at Coshocton, Ohio; Hastings, Nebr., and Riesel, Tex., using the USDAHL-70 model of watershed hydrology (developed by the USDA Hydrograph Laboratory, Beltsville, Md.).

Here, three levels of land-use management are considered for watersheds in the 3,500- to 4,500-acre size category: 1. Exploitive land use, farming all lands that could reasonably be put into crops; 2. Conservative land use, farming in conformance with recommended practices; and 3. Converting the watersheds entirely to grass.

The interactions of soil characteristics, stratigraphy, vegetation, tillage practices, and rainfall patterns caused different responses on each research watershed.

Exploitive use of the land caused an increase in streamflow over that prevailing at each location. Conservative use of the land caused an increase of streamflow at Coshocton and Riesel

349

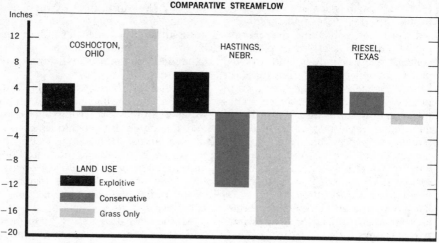

COMPARATIVE STREAMFLOW

From USDAHL—70 Model of Watershed Hydrology

and a decrease at Hastings. Retiring the land to grass resulted in a streamflow increase at Coshocton and a decrease at Hastings and Riesel. In each case, there is a rational physical explanation for the results computed by the model.

Irrigation scheduling—using climate-crop-soil data, computers to facilitate the tedious computations, and field observations by experienced personnel—is a service now becoming available to the modern irrigation farm manager. It is another example of the systems approach in making decisions about the use of our water resources.

Such services, incorporating the most recent advances in irrigation science, have the potential of increasing the management skills of the farmer and his net return at a reasonable cost.

In an average year, the 48 contiguous States receive about 4.75 billion acre-feet of renewed water supply in the form of rain and snow. Capturing this water, controlling, protecting, and using it for the well-being of people, challenges the best of science and technology.

Today's effective water resource development activities comprise numerous decisions and choices from among the various alternatives in the

fields of engineering, agriculture, economics, sociology, and ecology, within boundaries prescribed by laws and customs. But tomorrow's decision processes are likely to be even more complex and difficult because of the mounting demands upon available water resources, and as more is learned about the potentials for meeting them.

Small Watershed Projects Bring Big Dividends

R. NEIL LANE

SMALL watershed projects are furthering the economy and improving the environment of countless local communities.

The Watershed Protection and Flood Prevention Act (Public Law 83-566, as amended) is the principal authority under which Federal assistance is provided on a continuing basis for watershed development on a nationwide scale.

Public Law 566 came into being primarily in recognition of the fact that there was a gap in Federal water and related land resource programs between the conservation work being carried out on farms and ranches and the downstream major river improvements.

Magnitude of this gap is indicated by the fact that of the Nation's $1.7 billion flood damage, about 60 percent occurs in upstream watersheds. But only about 11 percent of the Federal flood prevention and control funds were budgeted for upstream development in 1970.

In 1956, and in almost every Congress since, important amendments to broaden the scope of P.L. 566 have been enacted. Now, with the exception of water quality management, the watershed program being carried out under P.L. 566 provides for coping with all major water resource development needs in small watersheds. This includes preventing damage from erosion, floodwater, and sediment; and furthering the conservation, development, use, and disposal of water.

The 1968 National Inventory of Soil and Water Conservation Needs, compiled by the U.S. Department of Agriculture, shows that project development is feasible for over 8,900 small watersheds encompassing 750 million acres of land.

Although the inventory did not include data on economic conditions, it is certain that in a high proportion of these watersheds the local economy would benefit from multiple-purpose watershed developments. Some case histories follow.

In a small watershed in the rolling Piedmont area of east-central Alabama, in a single decade, 1950–1960, rural population had decreased by

*

R. NEIL LANE retired in 1971 as director of the Watershed Planning Division, Soil Conservation Service.

70 percent. Nonagricultural jobs in and near the watershed did not develop fast enough to absorb the labor force migrating from farms, and many people were forced to seek employment elsewhere or rely on public assistance. Unemployment was substantially higher than the national average.

Several small industrial plants were unable to expand because of an inadequate water supply. One of the larger plants was actively seeking another location because of the lack of water.

Faced with a critical situation, several local organizations joined together and submitted an application for assistance to USDA.

With technical help from the Soil Conservation Service and other agencies, local people developed a plan to protect land resources of the watershed; reduce flooding, particularly on farmland; and impound 653 million gallons of water for municipal and industrial water supply.

This supply of water is considered adequate for present and foreseeable needs, and already plans are going forward to expand existing industry and attract new plants. Reduced flooding is expected to stabilize the farm economy and even reverse its downward trend.

In a small watershed in Arkansas, the median income per family in 1960 was only $3,120, compared with the average for the United States of $5,660. Fifteen percent of the work force in the watershed was considered unemployed in 1960 as against a national average of 6 percent. Much of the employment was seasonal, with only 40 percent working all year and 26 percent working less than half the time.

Because of the lack of local job opportunities, 42 percent of the work force traveled to jobs outside the county. Industrial expansion in the principal city was not possible because water, being purchased from a nearby city, was limited.

The plans for multiple-purpose

development in this watershed provide for watershed protection, flood prevention in both rural and urban areas, and sufficient municipal water storage to meet anticipated needs until the year 2005. The additional water supply together with flood protection will permit use of 200 acres at the edge of the city for an industrial park.

In contrast to the previous examples, agriculture is of minor importance in the economy of a small watershed in Pennsylvania. Plants for textiles and garment and leather manufacturing provide the principal support for the local community of 4,400 residents. Because of the decline of coal mining and the railroad industry, many of the residents commute to areas outside the watershed for employment.

Local interests decided that the rugged, though scenic, terrain that deterred agricultural and industrial expansion would offer an excellent opportunity for outdoor recreation. With funds obtained from the Area Redevelopment Administration, U.S. Department of Commerce, a study was made of the feasibility of a recreational complex centering around a 330-acre lake that would be constructed as part of the watershed project.

This study showed that with full development of the recreation complex as many as 250 new jobs would be created.

Since the first floodwater-retarding structure was constructed in a remote Oklahoma watershed in 1948, applications for assistance from more than 2,900 watersheds—embracing an area of 223 million acres—have been submitted to USDA. Applications continue to come in at the rate of over 100 per year even though assistance can be provided for only about 50.

Federal assistance for carrying out watershed development had been authorized for 1,001 watersheds by July 1, 1970. Installation of works of improvement is completed on 273 watersheds. These figures indicate that the full potential for economic development has been achieved in only a few of the watersheds. But some examples

will illustrate the variety of ways that watershed development is already breathing new life into the economy of local communities.

In one city in a Georgia watershed, the mayor reports that six new industries, employing 450 people, have opened plants since the watershed project was started. Plans have been completed to run a water pipeline to a 140-acre tract of land reserved for industrial development. The assured water supply from the watershed project is credited with securing the new industries.

A city of 4,000 in an Illinois watershed has taken on new life since its project was started. The project provided over 4,000 acre-feet of water storage capacity for municipal use.

This assured water supply stimulated major undertakings including purchase and development of a 132-acre industrial park, construction of a $200,000 sewage treatment plant, initiation of two housing developments, construction of a $500,000 nursing home, and plans to develop a community park around the 240-acre watershed lake.

A local banker credits the lake with having a tremendous psychological effect in creating the optimism now found throughout the local community.

A small New England town was able to develop a million-dollar shopping center on land that was too wet for agricultural or industrial use before watershed development was completed. City officials estimate that in 3 years the tax revenue alone from the shopping center will repay the town's cost for the project.

A city in Kansas is moving ahead with urban renewal in its downtown area as a result of its watershed project.

In a Florida watershed, farmers bought over $200,000 worth of sprinkler irrigation equipment to use water from their project. A new packing plant has been built at a cost of $300,000 and employs 50 people. Farmland formerly worth only $100 per acre now brings $500 per acre, and labor and services are increasing for picking, processing, packaging, and distributing citrus crops grown on these lands.

In an Arizona watershed, reduced hazard of flooding has been credited with increasing the value of crops produced from $200 to $400 per acre; and in a California watershed, from $150 to $500 per acre. Before project development, only one crop per year was feasible because of the flood hazard. With the long growing season and flood protection now provided by the projects, two or more crops of vegetables and fruits per year are grown.

Just outside Washington, D.C., is an example of community development at its best. Periodic flooding and a dwindling water supply had been pinching off chances for community and industrial growth.

Since completion of the watershed project, three new industrial plants employing 500 people have been built. A new community hospital has recently been completed. The added payroll is $1,750,000 annually.

All of this and more has stemmed from a project costing $544,000, with only $189,000 of Federal funds. The project has so spurred economic growth that the community is developing plans for additional water supply, more flood protection, and creation of a large lake for public recreation.

In Arizona a watershed project provided new land for expanding a college campus. In Florida a faltering housing project that had been abandoned because of floods was rescued. Hawaii was able to build low-cost housing in an area given flood protection.

A Louisiana community has a new medical clinic, 48-bed hospital, nursing home, bank, new homes, and plans for a new plant to employ 150 to 175 people.

A cooperative study has been carried out in a county in Oklahoma to measure the amount of secondary local income generated by the additional primary income arising from watershed developments.

This county was selected because a high proportion of the needed watershed developments had been completed, the economy is primarily agricultural, and considerable recreational activity had developed as a byproduct of the 90 floodwater-retarding structures constructed.

Most of the property directly benefited by the watershed developments is agricultural. Thus, it was comparatively simple to trace the impact of increased agricultural income on the local economy. Data used for this study were obtained from checks that cleared through the bank in the county's principal city and county seat.

The studies showed that an increase of $100,000 in farm receipts resulted in $77,845 in additional gross receipts to other local sectors of the economy. In terms of net income, this rise in gross farm receipts resulted in an increase in net income of $26,867 to farmers and $16,457 to other sectors of the local economy.

Two watershed projects in the final stages of completion were studied by a private research firm under contract with the Soil Conservation Service. Purpose of the study was to identify and evaluate benefits which have already occurred and to project the additional benefits expected to occur.

One project covers 240,000 acres in southwest Kentucky. Objectives of the project are to reduce erosion and retard runoff by conservation land treatment; reduce floodwater and sediment damage on about 13,800 acres of flood plain; supply municipal and industrial water to two small cities; and provide water-related recreation facilities for residents of the watershed and surrounding area.

Nineteen of the planned 23 floodwater-retarding structures and three multiple-purpose reservoirs for flood prevention, water supply, and recreation have been completed. About 195,000 acres of land have been adequately treated with conservation measures.

USDA agencies assisted landowners in developing conservation plans and applying needed conservation practices. Total cost of the project to date is $6.1 million.

The researchers conclude that without the added water supply, cities in the watershed could not have achieved their employment growth of the past 7 years. They also say that without the recreation facilities as an added inducement, the growth would probably have been less impressive.

Estimated project development benefits from 1961 to 1967 included 1,300 new jobs, $17 million in wages and salaries which would not have existed without the project, over $300,000 worth of recreational benefits, and substantial changes in land values.

A total of $5.9 million per year in regional income was attributed to the watershed project.

Impressive as these returns are, they are dwarfed by the estimated value of all regional income benefits by 1990. By that time, regional income is expected to total $354 million—more than 50 times the initial investment in the project.

But not all the project's benefits can be measured in dollars. The Boy Scouts now have a 1,100-acre reservation at one of the project's lakes. It provides camping facilities for Scouts from 26 Kentucky counties.

The other project covers an area of 22,300 acres in southwestern West Virginia. Economy of the area centered around coal mining and manufacturing. When the coal mines and railroad shops were closed in the 1950's, thousands of jobs were lost.

At first the project provided for only watershed protection and flood prevention. Later, as P. L. 566 was amended and the local leaders saw additional opportunities for watershed development, the plan was supplemented to add municipal and industrial water supply and recreation.

The watershed is served by the West Virginia Turnpike. It has excellent access to Northern and Midwestern population centers. However, there were two major bottlenecks to development of the community's economy.

One was the lack of suitable land for industrial sites; and the other, a shortage of water. These bottlenecks were removed by the project.

The researchers compiled this list of benefits:

- 1,276 new jobs, with $6.7 million in annual wages and salaries—projected to increase to $49 million by the year 2000.
- Clean, safe water for 16,250 people.
- Sewage disposal for 8,500 people made possible by the project.
- Annual income of $150,000 credited to changes in land value.
- Over $6 million of new public buildings with plans for more.
- More than $20 of regional income for each dollar spent on the project.

New employment and public investments made possible by the watershed project have halted the community's economic and social decline, according to the researchers.

In this day of environmental concern, watershed projects not only improve opportunities for earning a living but also improve the quality of life. In fact the watershed development concept is "tailor made" for improving the environment. Open space, clean air, clean water, natural beauty, mosquito control, wildlife sanctuaries, public recreation areas, home modernization and beautification, all of these and more have come from watershed development.

But perhaps the most important and lasting benefits are those that can be felt rather than seen. Watershed development is often the rallying point for community interest and action. Boy Scouts, Girl Scouts, garden clubs, 4-H clubs, churches, civic groups, and many others have made tremendous contributions to the betterment of their communities by becoming involved in watershed projects.

Out of that effort and out of that association have come a new community pride and optimism to grapple effectively with other community problems. This is the hope and the promise of watershed development.

The Possible Dream

WALLACE L. ANDERSON and

CAROLYN JOHNSTON

ROBERT HOGNER was a 32-year-old dishwasher. He had never held a job paying more than $1.25 an hour. He had never completed high school.

Today, Hogner, a Cherokee Indian, is a welder and maintenance man. By working hard he can earn a decent salary. He is a graduate of an area training class—one of 138 programs initiated or assisted by the Cherokee Hills (Okla.) Resource Conservation and Development Project.

Hogner has heard about the six county RC&D project, of course, but he's not too sure of all its aims. What he does know very well indeed is that it helped him qualify for better pay and a brighter future than at any other time in his life. That's the important point, both to Robert and the people who helped him.

The Cherokee Hills RC&D is one of 78 similar multicounty projects throughout the United States, led by local citizens and aided by USDA and a host of other Federal, State, and local agencies. Its slogan is "Making better use of what we have"—and that emphatically includes people. For example:

Many Cherokee Indian young people want to stay near their homes, but not enough of them have the skills demanded by society for a good job. RC&D people asked for training assistance in the area.

The U.S. Department of Labor provided $1,130,000 for a training program, operated by State people, that began in 1967. Courses include bulldozer operation, tractor and implement repair, maintenance mechan-ics, small engine repair, stenography, welding, and machine-tool operation.

More than 540 people were trained the first 3 years—60 percent of them members of the Cherokee Indian Nation. More than two-thirds of all graduates are employed.

In Cherokee Hills, like all RC&D projects, the aim is to improve the lives of people through better care and use of the area's natural and human resources. The task is great, but the dream is possible.

Here are some tasks—and dreams—from other areas:

Taking the guess out of growth— "Boomtown of the South" they've called Gwinnett County, Ga., just outside Atlanta. People poured in during the 1960's, demanding new schools, homes, water supplies, streets, flood protection, and recreation areas.

RC&D project sponsors for this small (the only single-county RC&D) but complex and urbanizing area sought to encourage a land-use pattern that would meet the needs of an expanding population without sacrificing a quality environment. Working with an advisory board, the Chamber of Commerce, the Atlanta Region Metropolitan Planning Commission, and other groups, they developed a master plan for resource conservation and development.

First, they helped speed completion of the soil survey, fundamental to making wise land-use decisions. Armed with this information, local officials adopted new planning and zoning regulations and restricted construction work in floodplains.

Legislation was passed providing for county-wide sewage disposal. Schools, hospitals, and other agencies received help in sediment and erosion control work on their land. Officials worked out a sediment-control ordinance that, if adopted, will reduce the amount of

*

WALLACE L. ANDERSON is Director of the Resource Development Division, Soil Conservation Service.
CAROLYN JOHNSTON is an information specialist, Soil Conservation Service.

silt going into lakes and streams from construction work.

Flood-prevention work has included building 9 dams; reshaping and reseeding 685 miles of bare, eroding roadbanks; and helping with 184 new mini-lakes or fishponds to provide beauty, recreation, and the control of water runoff.

The careful planning has meant better environmental protection, along with good industrial development. Sixty new industries, employing more than 6,000 people, have been welcomed to the county. RC&D people helped to develop conservation and landscaping plans for 40 of the industries, including land reshaping to handle drainage problems, reseeding, and erosion control.

A new look at the land.—It's hilly country in southern Indiana. Beautiful and green, but tough on the small farmer and small towns that depend on rural trade.

This 4-county area of the Lincoln Hills RC&D project had problems of poor land use, not enough jobs, not enough recreation—and too many young people moving away. The problems and some of the solutions were put together by local people in 130 pages of their RC&D project plan.

Cooperating landowners were helped to convert thousands of acres of poor farmland into better-suited pasture, recreation, or wildlife areas. More than 35,000 acres were planted to grasses for livestock forage. Over 6,000 eroded acres were planted with pine trees and plants for wildlife, a million trees in 1 year alone. Nine square miles of land have become a wildlife haven.

Six new manmade lakes help prevent floods. Four of them have facilities for swimming, fishing or camping, and are extremely popular spots for both tourists and local residents.

Timber growers have cut their culls, planted better trees, taken lumber grading short courses, improved their marketing skills. Several wood-using industries have come to the area and use locally produced wood products.

The entire Lincoln Hills area has been soil-surveyed by the Soil Conservation Service—a major help in bringing about better land use. The information funnels into plans for new homesites, industrial areas, and schools.

RC&D people provided technical assistance on all of these land and water improvements, and the RC&D funds shared the cost on some of them.

With better land use in agriculture, recreation, housing, and industry, the Lincoln Hills RC&D Project is truly of, for, and by the people.

It's no longer all wet.—From October through May it rains . . . and rains . . . and rains in the Upper Willamette (Ore.) RC&D Project.

Roads to the Corvallis airport often were impassable. About 700 acres of cropland were damaged annually, and crop varieties were restricted because of flood conditions. After the waters subsided, roadbeds were eroded, farmhomes damaged.

Teamwork by the city of Corvallis, Benton County Court, Benton County ASC Committee, local landowners, and RC&D people resulted in floodprevention work to drain water from the airport and neighboring farmlands.

Today, heavy rainfall no longer prevents access to the airport. Surface water is handled quickly, and airplane maintenance can be performed in all kinds of weather. DC-9's, scheduled to begin operations soon, can now use the airport safely. And fields once waterlogged produce more and better crops.

It still rains from October through May. But the people of the Upper Willamette are better prepared for it. The rains no longer stay mainly on the planes or grains.

Bigger yields from sandy fields.—Irrigation in Minnesota? The land of 10,000 lakes? Yes!

Farming is a marginal business for many people in the nine-county WesMin RC&D Project. Almost a million acres—a fifth of the whole area—is light, sandy soil. Despite 22 inches of rain yearly, the hot summers damage crops 4 out of 5 years. Irrigation *is* needed.

Pulpwood industry is big in Gwinnett County (Ga.) RC&D project.

Ground water studies were made by the U.S. Geological Survey, and SCS drew up soil interpretation maps. They were put to use. New crops for the area—cucumbers, table beets, snap beans—were successfully tried. Ap-

proximately 150 farmers have begun to irrigate in the past 5 years.

The Staples Vocational School has purchased a farm and used it for demonstrating irrigation equipment and desirable crops. The Cooperative Extension Service arranged 2- and 3-day information sessions.

An increased annual gross income of nearly a million dollars has been one result of irrigation farming. They expect this to jump to $12 million in the next 15 years.

Irrigation has raised crops—and incomes—in west central Minnesota.

You can go home again.—When the citizens of Spencer, W. Va., asked Little Kanawha RC&D Project sponsors for help with flood prevention on Spring Creek, the city fathers were not planning for economic development. But the 70-acre flood prevention lake now under construction also will provide increased water supplies and make possible future growth that should persuade more young people to stay in the area.

Early planning by Spencer officials and RC&D people brought into focus the need for better use and control of

Earl Laney welds new future for himself through training courses in Cherokee Hills (Okla.) RC&D project.

357

their water supply. The area's water source was polluted, and the 4-month storage supply was not enough for home and business use. It did not meet emergency needs of Spencer State Hospital, nor provide the daily requirement of 36,000 gallons of water for the newly constructed Roane County General Hospital.

SCS engineers proposed two dam sites. The one selected met area needs for flood prevention, more storage capacity, clean drinking water, and larger supplies for industry. The city acquired 2,000 acres to construct the dam, and an Economic Development Administration grant and loan helped provide the treatment facilities and a city distribution system.

Tangible results? One local company, dependent upon good water supplies, has added 200 employees and may add 130 more. The new hospital has sufficient water; a 70-unit housing development for elderly and low-income families can now proceed, and an industrial park and recreation area are under consideration.

Adios to apathy.—The Northern Rio Grande country in New Mexico is the land of room enough and time enough. But there are not always jobs enough. Citizens of the small town of Española in Rio Arriba County wanted a better life. How to achieve it in a land whose bounty does not match its beauty?

The Duke City Lumber Company, in cooperation with the Rio Arriba Development Corporation, decided one major step was to build a modern sawmill to use log supplies from nearby national forests.

RC&D people helped coordinate the needed "inputs"—timber surveys and studies of market possibilities for forest byproducts by the State Forestry Department; a long-term lease for the mill site through the Bureau of Indian Affairs; recruiting and training work by the State Employment Securities Commission; and arrangements for housing and utilities by the town of Española. Getting together the people and resources needed for a project is a major task in all RC&D projects.

The mill, completed in 1966, now employs about 200 people, most of them Spanish-Americans. Local people also work in the woods and transport the logs.

The new jobs have created a weekly payroll of $30,000. Economic impact of this one project alone, on one small community, during 1 year, has been estimated at more than $5 million.

The Mud-Fighters.—It is flat, prairie land in southeastern South Dakota. Old-timers remember the "dirty thirties," when the Missouri River was "too thin to plow and too thick to drink." They're working to clean up, and green up, their land and water.

Soil erosion control and sediment reduction to keep good topsoil out of the Missouri River's Lake Francis Case is one primary objective of the six-county Randall RC&D Project.

Project sponsors developed plans for 35 grade stabilization structures, 11 of which are already built. When completed, these structures will reduce sediment delivery to the lake by 25,000 tons a year.

More than 45,000 acres of cropland, which drain directly into the lake, have been seeded to grass. Ten thousand acres more each year, for the next 10 years, will be covered with this green guardian of the soil. Reseeding, combined with better range management, will improve the land for local people and the water for downstream users.

Your pleasure is their business.—Good sports and outdoor recreation developments begin with good understanding, and use of, the natural resources that are involved.

Project sponsors in the 11-county Hull-York Lakeland (Tenn.) RC&D Project have helped provide that understanding for 21 recreational facilities and historical attractions now in operation. These facilities represent an investment of approximately $5 million.

Project sponsors also have helped organize the 200-member Upper Cumberland Tourist Association for this area of both scenic and historical significance.

358

RC&D helped negotiate the purchase and restoration, by the State Conservation Department, of Alvin York's water-powered grist mill and the surrounding 6 acres. The restored mill—operated by Sgt. York's son—now is part of Pickett State Park.

With more leisure time in the next decade, Americans will demand more and better outdoor recreation facilities. The people of the Hull-York-Lakeland area will be helping to meet that need.

Matching needs and resources.—Take one crowded State—New York—whose citizens are eager for more "back to nature" opportunities. Focus on seven counties where certain types of trees are in excess. Add one SCS forester and a sawmill owner who liked his ideas. The result is a new industry: log cabins in the space age.

Much of the South Central New York RC&D area was former farmland, bought by the State in the mid-1930's and planted to coniferous trees by CCC crews at the rate of a thousand seedlings an acre.

Since 150 mature trees an acre is a good ratio for a healthy stand, thousands of these softwoods must now be cut in the interest of good timber management. And—more than 50,000 acres of softwoods, in need of thinning, had timber large enough to produce sizable logs.

The SCS forester, under RC&D auspices, developed plans for sawmill-produced, pre-cut logs from the tree thinnings. A do-it-yourself builder can assemble his own cabin. The logs are planed on three sides and rounded on the fourth, or exterior, side.

A local sawmill owner first put the idea into action. Today, the mill produces—and quickly sells—both assembled and unassembled log cabins for the hunters, fishermen, and "summer people" from New York City who come to the area in growing numbers.

As for the trees: In their 35-year lifetime, they have controlled soil

Memories and property of Sgt. York of World War I fame provide grist for tourism mill in Hull-York Lakeland (Tenn.) RC&D project.

erosion; provided work; produced beauty; and now, in selected numbers, they will make still another contribution.

You can't buy peace and quiet. But a log cabin in the woods is a pretty good start.

Down by that old mill stream.—The population of Connecticut grew almost 20 percent in the last decade. Its more than 3 million citizens want both industries and open space.

A quality environment in the Eastern Connecticut RC&D depends, to a large extent, on protecting and enhancing streams and the adjacent open space for wildlife, recreation, and beauty. Streambelt inventories, prepared with RC&D technical help, can identify areas with permanent streams, flood plains, and associated wetlands; uplands suitable for intensive urban-type development; and land with special qualities for wildlife or recreational use.

Many towns in this three-county area incorporate streambelt inventories into their comprehensive town plans, then work to acquire desirable land within the streambelt areas for preservation and recreation.

Helping people to help themselves. Better use of natural resources. Improving life in possible ways.

These are capsule descriptions of the 78 resource conservation and development projects now in action.

Each project has at least 100 separate "jobs," to which the RC&D people add leadership, technical skills, coordination, or sometimes financial assistance. Each RC&D project is tailored to its own area's needs and opportunities, but all of them help local people to take a new look at their home country.

T. S. Eliot is not a poet of rural America. But he spoke for living, striving men and women everywhere when he wrote:

"We shall not cease from exploring
And the end of all our exploring
Will be to arrive where we started
And know the place for the first time."

The chance to improve home, not leave it. The second look around, to understand, finally, what we have loved all along.

issues for the future

Handling Growth: Some Examples From Europe

BARRY LAWSON and
DAVID J. ALLEE

THE GOVERNMENT in the middle may be the key to solving the problems of our next doubling of population. A review of recent changes in Europe, where some problems we will face may be appearing now, suggests we should look for expanded coordination and planning by States and regional agencies.

Picture where you live as a checkerboard, with each square a unit of local government. Many other forms of social organization have less rigid boundaries for their membership. Obviously the size of an organization is reflected by many things other than the territory it covers. The frequency and importance of members' relationships to the organization are more significant.

A gage of the effectiveness of the organizations is the extent to which they can adjust to changes in the activity patterns of their members. Local governments, tied to geography, face major difficulties in adjusting.

As incomes have gone up, many people have found that their day-to-day lives involve activities in more and more jurisdictions of local government. The private auto and other means of communication have allowed people to spread out their activities. This has also changed the service patterns for many organizations.

Supply and service activities in the larger urban centers frequently have pushed out of business their counterparts at the crossroad communities. Where there is a large population and employment base in the overall region, however, the crossroad community has often been able to shift to a bedroom function.

The old checkerboard pattern was perhaps just right for another level of population, distributed differently and with different incomes and life styles. Now more and more decisions made by one group have an effect on other groups. And there is an uncomfortable feeling that the welfare of the whole region is not often effectively taken into account by each jurisdiction within it.

National governments have increasingly recognized this and taken action to improve the coordination between local governments. Local governments, concerned over their prerogatives and freedom to respond to their own problems as they see them, nonetheless often feel overwhelmed. Either growth is too rapid to cope with or growth is too slow to meet the aspirations of their people.

An intermediate level of organization—a regional governmental arrangement—can achieve the coordination required, yet allow for response to unique local values and conditions.

Further development of the functions of State government can be expected, particularly in planning and coordinating development. Certainly the State government that assumes the power for review of future land development plans and serves as an effective intermediary between national policy and local implementation has so far been the exception rather than the rule.

A review of recent experience in European countries leads to the conclusion that a general trend in the industrial nations is in the direction of three-tier levels of responsibility for future development.

*

BARRY LAWSON is Assistant Professor of Regional Planning at Wayne State University, Detroit, Mich.

DAVID J. ALLEE is an Associate Professor of Resource Economics, New York State College of Agriculture, Cornell University, Ithaca.

National agencies set the broad lines of national policy concerning economic activity and investment. Traditional local government planning authorities continue to conduct planning studies for land use and hold responsibility for most implementation. But a natural political process seems to be leading to a regionalism between national and local whose intermediary coordinative function is made politically palatable to the local and national governments because it is a compromise to either one holding a dominant role.

Europe contains many patterns of settlement, degrees of development, and a multitude of approaches to the development issues.

In the planning or coordinative functions of government, there are two types of administration: those countries which have either strong local or national government with relatively weak but growing regional arrangements, and those few which have fully developed three relatively strong levels. Although an exact categorization is difficult at best, we might include in the first group such countries as the Soviet Union, Denmark, Sweden, and possibly Yugoslavia, Italy, and Spain.

At one extreme is the Soviet Union, where the national economic plan sets the guidelines for all branches of the economy. Physical plans are drawn up for the distribution of utilities and transportation services at the local level, where the scope of detailed plans and the role of local construction committees, as they are called, has greatly expanded in recent years.

In both Denmark and Sweden, on the other hand, much of the traditional power is still retained by the local communities. Any regional association or coordination remains purely voluntary, and until now almost non-influential—except in an educational or persuasive sense.

Perhaps more instructive as prototypes would be France, the Netherlands, England, and Poland.

In France, an effort to achieve a balanced national development to offset the domination of Paris led to introduction of the regional programming idea at the national level in the mid 1950's. By 1960, an Interministerial Committee had been established for coordinating long-range national policy.

Economic planning carried out by the French national government—and made explicit in so-called Five-Year plans—became coordinated with environmental, or physical, planning by 1963. Not only was the experience one of reforming the national government to coordinate policy and shift departments' territorial districts, but it also featured a reform of local administration in which 21 regional planning districts were established.

Regional administrative organizations and consultative bodies in France insure the coordination of the various national agencies, provide for research and implementation, and establish committees for local representation.

In the Netherlands, another type of regionalism exists—at the provincial level. Recent legislation requires that national and provincial plans must be taken into consideration and coordinated through local (municipal) plans. The Netherlands has a tradition of strong municipal government.

This three-tier planning system is monitored by a number of inspectors who are responsible for conflict settlement and achieving agreement among the three tiers.

Municipalities in the Netherlands may make future plans for areas outside their municipal boundaries, both at a general and detailed scale. National legislation permits such planning as well as the subsequent expropriation and acquisition of land. Such "extension plans" receive approval of provincial planners. Without this approval, the national and provincial governments have the power to withhold funds needed for extending of municipal services or otherwise providing for future development of areas outside municipal boundaries.

The socialized countries of eastern and central Europe are not, as one might anticipate, all examples of a monolithic national government devising plans and directing local development from above as in Russia. To the contrary, in Poland each of 17 provinces has an economic planning commission. In coordination with the national plan, draft regional plans are prepared at the provincial level which include a physical as well as strictly economic component.

In Yugoslavia, as a delayed response to a relatively recent decentralization reform which placed control for most activity in the hands of worker-managed enterprises and local communal (like counties) governments, the first regional planning agencies are now developing. They are directed to coordinate republican (like states) government policy affecting the future social, economic, and physical development of each of the three republics and to stimulate and guide intercommunal cooperation.

Another level which is beginning to take form in a number of countries is the metropolitan government encompassing a number of selected functions found unmanageable at the local level and extending beyond the historical boundaries of local government.

The Greater London Council is responsible for preparing and reviewing the area's development plan plus the execution of major development projects. Other similar boards also exist in England, but they have less administrative power.

Stockholm will adopt a similar metropolitan mechanism in 1971. Other cities where the same approach may be seen include Paris, Prague, Madrid, and Copenhagen. Here, as in other examples, the regionalization of local physical planning has occurred largely in response to inadequacy of the local structure to cope with development problems within traditional boundaries.

What type of planning actions are the most popular in dealing with regional development problems? Let's consider just two types of problems: that of regional economic underdevelopment, and control of new physical development.

A recent housing and planning conference sponsored by the International Federation of Housing and Planning called for a development type corporation which had not only financial strength but also undertook a comprehensive and coordinative role. A prototype of this kind of agency, they suggest, is the Highlands and Islands Development Board of Northern Scotland.

This board, representative to some degree of other regional institutions in the United Kingdom, oversees activities of a number of existing bodies, but also has power to intervene in almost every aspect of development. It provides assistance for the location of selected new industries, technical surveys and expertise, and loans to activities of primarily social rather than economic value.

It also provides aid to established enterprises undergoing short-term difficulties, in order to avoid the consequences of unemployment.

By contrast, much French regional planning is focused around projects like port or waterway development, or the guided transformation of agricultural regions.

In West Germany, towns ranking as central places (for retail and other services) in lagging regions are selected for future growth through promotion of transport facilities, utilities, and educational, cultural, and administrative facilities.

Such areas are more likely to have enough density of population so that economically efficient opportunities will be provided for earning a living for the commuting region around them.

In the control of land use and related urban development, the Dutch approach sketched above and the New Town development of England and Sweden are accompanied and made possible by ambitious governmental purchase of land.

By contrast, perhaps the most interesting feature of French regional planning is the strong relationship between the national government and regional districts. This relationship is structured in several forms such as: (1) the promotion of eight to 12 cities as equilibrium metropolises (as in Germany), (2) the control of private investments and development by law and monetary incentives, (3) the coordination of all public investments within the framework of the national plan, and (4) special projects.

Such projects would include port and waterway development, guided transformation of agricultural regions, and Priority Urbanization Zones (Z.U.P.).

Since 1958 the direction of urban development projects has been placed under a single body such as a municipal government, public service corporation, or the like.

These Z.U.P. zones can include entire towns, and combine intensive planning surveys with provisions for financing needed public services. Such a program permits the national establishment of priorities for the government funding of public facilities and the overall choice of new developments throughout France.

Furthermore, land acquisition for development becomes an administrative process at the local level.

It is clear that although a real land shortage does not exist yet in Europe, a concern for this possibility exists (and the response of nationalization, price control, public acquisition of land prior to private development). Of equal concern is avoiding higher public service costs. Both are real economic factors behind physical planning strategy.

Provision of public services over an area much broader than present development projects is felt to be prohibitive in cost.

In the United States, however, all the costs of infrastructure servicing are not taken thoroughly into account at the time of development decisions. Long-run operating costs of facilities and hidden social costs of apparent cost-diffusing devices such as the personal automobile are not brought out. This plus the fact that we as a society believe that speculation in land is a legitimate form of business, even if the increased value is the result of public policy or investment, goes much of the way in explaining major differences in planning approach and resulting physical development.

It is fair to say that a general displeasure exists in both Europe and our own country with the capacity of traditional local governments to face up to the problems of their region, and that there is a need to tackle these problems more effectively. All the examples given are really experiments by society, attempts to find methods for coping with expressed public issues.

This experimentation will continue in each country and the institutional lessons will be learned primarily through trial and error. There is no universal "best way" to approach such problems, and each country has its own appropriate methods based on cultural history, physical geography, and economic realities.

We have tried to highlight the positive trend toward a coordinated, three-level government approach to structure. This experimentation hopes to improve vertical coordination of policy.

At least it serves as a political compromise between two opposite poles of national power and local autonomy and identity.

The fact is that several societies with a political tradition like ours in the United States, with a similar scale of social and economic development, have undertaken to restructure their institutions—many from the local level on up.

And these new arrangements do express and carry out policy more in the national interest rather than in any one group's interest.

This indicates that we must get on with a sophistication of our own organization for guiding our Nation's physical and economic growth and coping with its associated social issues.

Stresses, Strains From a High Population Density

JEAN B. WYCKOFF

O NE HUNDRED MILLION more people in these United States by the turn of the century is a possibility, according to some population forecasts. Three people where there are two today!

What are some of the stresses and strains we can anticipate from vastly increased population density in a country where 74 percent of the population already is crowded onto some 2 percent of the land?

One-half of our least densely populated counties lost population from 1960-70. The nonmetropolitan population is growing at less than half its natural growth rate.

At the same time we now have 33 Standard Metropolitan Statistical Areas (SMSA's), each with over a million population. And the SMSA's are increasing in population not just through natural growth but through inmigration, migration from rural to urban areas.

Within these units of increased population, however, there is a less well-known movement from city centers to the suburbs. Thus, the densities of the city centers are declining while those in the suburbs are increasing.

This distinction in migration patterns and the change in population densities is important, as is recognition of the age composition of the migrants. Those coming from rural to urban areas tend to be younger than the general population, while the movement from city center to suburbs tends to consist of family groups in which the head of the household is advancing in job status and income.

Migrants to suburbia are likely to be well educated, to hold white collar jobs, and to earn incomes considerably above the median for the total SMSA's. They choose to reside in single dwelling units in neighborhoods containing persons very much like themselves.

The resulting homogeneous suburban communities exemplify a type of socio-economic segregation that may have serious future consequences as yet not identified.

Outmigration leaves behind people who are older, are members of small-size households, are less well educated, and earn lower incomes than the suburbanites.

The inmigrant, in contrast, is likely to be a young adult who comes to enjoy the social, cultural, and economic environment of the big city.

Yet another distinction becomes important in considering the central city—the concentration of low-income minority groups in areas of high density and of low environmental quality.

This heterogeneity in the makeup of the central cities increases the complexity of their problems and makes solution more difficult.

Subtleties of changing composition of population within generally increasing densities are very important in assessing impacts.

Many of the impacts of population concentration are readily discernible. Examples include the decline of the natural visual environment, congestion, noise, and pollution of water and air.

Less obvious is the tendency of people to emphasize the individual (themselves) and the private family unit to the exclusion of the larger social group. This occurs even within the environment of decreasing personal privacy and freedom of movement, and increasing social impacts of personal actions. It is manifested by lack of a

*

JEAN B. WYCKOFF is a professor in the Department of Agricultural and Food Economics, University of Massachusetts, Amherst.

sense of "community" and general unwillingness to "get involved."

Such alienation of the private family from the surrounding group tends to rationalize antisocial behavior such as juvenile delinquency, crimes against persons, and crimes against property.

The tendency toward distinction between place of work and place of residence also causes problems. While much employment is located in the central cities, many of those employed there live in adjacent suburban areas. A person who works in one area but lives in another may lack the feeling of "community" for the city. Active interest and participation is likely to be concentrated in concern for his residential community. Thus, he contributes little financial help or talent toward solving problems of the central city which provides jobs.

This results in many suburbanites living in a kind of fantasy world in which the bad (the problems of the central city) is ignored and the good (the environment in which they live) becomes their only conscious world.

Thus the importance of adjusting government institutions to meet the changing needs of expanding population concentrations is emphasized. As growth "spills over" political boundaries, the boundaries must become flexible.

Further, new institutional forms may be required to perform needed services efficiently.

A governmental structure designed to service an urban center of 25,000 may prove completely inadequate for a population concentration of 250,000. While the New England town meeting may have been effective for small, rural communities, it is not doing the job of solving the environmental problems arising from growing population densities.

Institutions for collection and expenditure of funds for public purposes also must undergo rather drastic revisions to meet new needs.

As institutional structures change, participation by individuals in the governing process will likely be quite different. Since the tendency will be toward aggregation, access within the political process will become more limited to the individual. Also, organizing in response to functional needs may include only one segment of society in particular decisions. This can result in further alienation of the individual.

Increased concentration of population also creates strains on many services provided via the public sector. Transportation systems not designed to bear the heavy demands of increased population become clogged and congested. Public safety systems are often found to be inadequately structured and manned. Schools become overcrowded and the quality of education tends to decline.

Urban recreational facilities become overcrowded and deteriorate under intensive use.

Only massive inputs of planning and investment can prevent or correct these situations.

To plan, an explicit definition of goals is required—goals relative to public and private use of our resources, quality of our environment, and provision of public services.

Then too, planning is a group approach to a problem and naturally requires the subjugating of some individual desires.

Tradeoffs among values held by an individual and between the individual and the larger community are required. Certain goals may be mutually exclusive or at least conflicting. Thus identification of the "gainers" and "losers" and the relationship of the gains and losses is important.

As total population density increases, decisions on the use of limited resources, particularly nonrenewable resources, become more critical. Competition between public and private, single and multiple, existing and new, productive and nonproductive use of resources intensifies.

Tradeoffs among spatial arrangements and resultant ecological, social, psychological, political, and economic impacts grow increasingly complex. The illusive criterion of "quality of life" becomes ever more difficult to measure.

Finally, there is some indication that tradeoffs may have to be made among alternative levels of living, technologies, the rate of population growth, and environmental quality goals. If we do realize a population of 300 million by the year 2000, we must begin now to specify these types of tradeoffs.

However, I am unable to accept the general pessimism of some of my colleagues. Perhaps we will develop a spatial arrangement for our population, as yet unspecified, which will minimize antisocial behavior and the negative ecological impacts while maximizing the general quality of the environment and the overall quality of human life.

Perhaps new forms of government will arise to handle the various public functions in a specialized, efficient way not as yet experienced. New technology may make cultural and recreational experience accessible to everyone. Likewise, a social organization may be forthcoming which will reestablish in high density areas the feeling of community which exists in smalltown America—a sense of civic duty.

The complexity of problems associated with population growth and increased density precludes simple dogmatic solutions. Yet, this very complexity provides a tremendous opportunity for innovative and creative thinking relative to new institutional structures, and to organization for development, organization for administration, and methods for obtaining resident involvement.

Assisting residents in recognizing their interdependencies with each other and the natural environment may be a key to accepting necessary changes and to reducing the stresses and strains of increasing population density. Who knows, we may even succeed in reestablishing a "sense of community". Why not?

Planning for a New Life Style

FREDERIC O. SARGENT

As our population increases and the area of the earth's surface remains fixed, the role of planning becomes critical. In the sixties urbanization, population, income, and motorization increased at an accelerated rate and intensified our problems of living together.

The purpose of planning is to reshape the institutional arrangements that organize our life so our expanding population can live together more efficiently and harmoniously on a given area of the earth's surface. We must design our governmental institutions to promote most of the goals of most of the people—the esthetic and recreational goals as well as economic and development ones.

In the seventies planning must become the most important political activity for all concerned citizens and set the framework for managing, allocating, and controlling our natural resources.

To discuss planning in the future we need to recognize two types—the old *conventional* planning and the new *quality environment* planning.

Conventional planning, with which we are all acquainted, is based on a narrow concept of the public interest.

It consists of drawing up utility networks and zoning plans for urban areas and making token efforts to carry them out without a concept of, or commitment to, the long-range general public interest.

Under conventional planning an industrial concern, because it employs a large number of people, pollutes a river and destroys it for recreation, wildlife, and drinking water. A highway cuts through a park because the land is in public ownership and therefore "available."

Some other examples: An interstate highway is located to serve intracity traffic, leading to early obsolescence. An oil company obtains permission to build another filling station when the city already has twice as many filling stations as needed per thousand population.

Youths have no recreation facilities because the municipality "lacks funds" for them. Scattered rural residences continue to pollute streams as there is no planning mechanism for preventing it.

All these public resource allocating decisions are characteristic of conventional planning.

The wave of the future is *quality environment* planning. It is democratic control of land use to conserve the natural resource base for the long run and in the general public interest. It is making ecological surveys before land use is planned.

By quality environment planning is meant establishing and enforcing a maximum limit on the number of commercial enterprises, such as filling stations; or zoning of floodplains for suitable and compatible uses, for instance agriculture and recreation.

It is providing public access to all public water for multiple recreational activities. It is protecting scenic, visual, and esthetic qualities of the countryside, and preventing uglification by excessive signs, litter, and inadequate landscaping. It is eliminating air and water pollution.

Quality environment planning consists of two parts—planning *with* nature and *for* man.

Planning *with* nature—ecological planning—has been systemized, advertised, and demonstrated by Ian

*

FREDERIC O. SARGENT is Professor of Resource Economics and Director of the graduate program in natural resource planning, College of Agriculture and Home Economics, at the University of Vermont, Burlington.

McHarg. It encompasses analyzing the natural resource base and designing man's use to be compatible with and to take advantage of intrinsic quality factors of the natural environment.

Unique natural areas are protected and managed to ensure that they will remain in a natural state for succeeding generations. Natural cycles and processes are protected and encouraged to run their courses.

Planning *for* man means more emphasis on people and their needs to produce a meaningful life, and less emphasis on highway building as a dominant planning activity.

It means that suburban neighborhoods are laid out with walkways to primary schools, eliminating the need for busing. Public lands are provided with public access for pedestrians, bicyclists, horseback riders, cross-country skiers, hunters, fishermen, nature students, walkers, and strollers.

Planning for man entails providing a gamut of recreational facilities from a tot lot in every block to trail systems, community and regional parks, adequate access to public waters and public forests, and protection of natural areas and reserved wild lands and waters.

Quality environment planning requires an environment planning team. Manpower requirements for the team are five to 10 times the manpower used in conventional planning. This increased manpower can be supplied through greater participation by colleges and universities and State and Federal Government agencies, and by higher levels of citizen participation.

The environmental team approach consists of bringing together experts in all relevant disciplines—with each one making his contribution within the framework of coordinated planning.

Colleges and universities will play a major role in providing the team.

Professors and students from geology departments will make soil borings and percolation tests and will

369

interpret topography with reference to ground water location and suitability for various land uses. Ecologists from botany and forestry departments will supervise ecological surveys to identify natural areas.

Resource economists will study the economic base, tax problems, sources of funds, and the economies of government consolidation. Public health students at medical schools will make surveys of use of detergents, water quality, attitudes toward fluoridation. Hydrologists will contribute data on water quality. Cartography students will draft maps to collate and interpret data from the several disciplines.

This college and university participation will supplement data collected by State and Federal public servants, county foresters, county agricultural agents, and soil scientists.

After the team has compiled an inventory, professional quality environment planners will have a basis for designing man's use of land in a way compatible with the environment and acceptable to the people.

Citizen-members of organizations with an active interest in our environment will provide the indispensable broad democratic base for quality environment planning.

Citizen action in support of quality planning may come from any one or a combination of groups. Among these groups there might be a chapter of the Audubon Society, a Parent and Teacher Association, the League of Women Voters, a chamber of commerce, a fish and game club, a professional association of foresters, a regional development-promotion association, an outing club, a community or a student environmental action group, or some other group with an ecological conscience.

Collectively these groups express the general long run public interest in a quality environment.

Both initiative and planning goals must come from these citizen groups. Quality environment planning—planning *with* nature *for* man by a *team* with *citizens'* support—starts when the

members of special interest groups realize that their existence depends upon better social control over resource allocation.

When they understand that we must stop defiling our nest, citizens will participate in planning as a civic responsibility. Citizen leaders will make contributions during regular working hours as well as evenings for personal satisfaction and public recognition.

The new planning will resemble a social movement more than the activities of a single planning firm, planning department, or planning commission. The process will be complex. Initiative for better resource management will come from informed, excited, and sometimes angry citizens. These demands will be taken up by citizen organizations and interest groups.

Environmental planning teams and planning commissions will become the vehicles for attaining the new public quality environment goals. Teams from colleges and universities, all levels of government, and activist citizens will make inventories and draft preliminary plans. Quality environment planners will coordinate this new and more comprehensive planning process.

Dramatic examples of the new planning are provided by recent experience in Vermont. The Green Mountain State until recently has been a quiet hill and plain region devoted to dairying, foliage viewing, skiing, sugaring, and minding one's own business. During the sixties it came under intense pressures from the Boston-Washington megalopolis.

These pressures threatened to turn all mountainsides into ski slopes, all the bogs into reservoirs; to widen, straighten, and pave all roads; to lock up lakeshores in private ownership; to subdivide the State into half-acre lots; and generally to extend urban uglification into the previously peaceful and pastoral secluded scene.

To the rescue came the team approach to quality environment planning with successful accomplishments

Above, Camel's Hump. Below, hiking Vermont's Green Mountains near Stowe.

to date in protecting a mountain, rescuing a bog, acquiring public access to Lake Champlain, planning a subdivision, and planning open space in a county.

Camel's Hump—the fourth highest, most distinctive, and most popular for hiking of the Green Mountains— was right in the path of development progress.

In 1967, a team got together that included a botanist, an ecologist, a historian, a forester, a geologist, a planner, and a resource economist from the University of Vermont, plus interested citizens supported by the local Audubon Society. They collaborated to produce a plan to enlarge and protect the mountain in its natural state without additional ski slopes, roads, cable cars, hotels, subdivisions, or heliports.

The plan was translated into a proposed State statute establishing a State mountain park. Organized groups concerned with the environment supported the legislation. The bill was passed by the legislature in 1968, signed into law, and a citizens advisory commission appointed. Immediately there was better protection for a unique natural area through special management. Also, additional land was acquired.

In 1968–69, a 1,250-acre wetland complex called Victory Bog was dramatically saved from condemnation to flooding. It is now protected as a State natural area, thanks to work by a successful team and citizen support.

The team was led by a museum curator and consisted of a science teacher, a geologist, an ecologist, an ornithologist, a botanist, a fish biologist, and a resource economist. It was supported by four groups of conservation activists.

A plan was drawn up to use the wetland complex—as it had been used for many years—for an outdoor classroom, nature study laboratory, living museum annex, and hunting and fishing reserve. The plan was presented to the legislature with vigorous support

371

by the Fish and Game Department, Fish and Game Clubs, Foresters Association, Audubon Society, and other conservation-minded citizens' groups.

The legislature supported preservation of the bog by a resolution. The Fish and Game Department acquired the bog and reversed the previous sentence of damming. Thus was created one of the best natural science outdoor laboratories and wetland recreation areas in the northeast.

This team approach with citizen action was equally successful in establishing a major park on Lake Champlain in 1970 for South Burlington, a town with no access to its public waters.

The team was from the University of Vermont Resources Research Center, the Soil Conservation Service, the Extension Service, the Vermont Forest and Parks Department, and the Vermont Recreation Board. It inventoried the natural resource base of the town and then produced a conservation and recreation plan in 1968.

Supported by a special town natural resource committee, the plan was adopted by the planning commission. It was also accepted by the townspeople as part of their "master" plan and supported in town meeting by a new appropriation of $10,000.

As a direct result, 100 of the most beautiful acres on Lake Champlain were acquired with 700 feet of beach for a town park. This was a major accomplishment for a previously landlocked and parkless riparian town.

Implementation of other sectors of the plan are following, such as making a river park along the Winooski—the State's major river.

The new planning approach—first an ecological survey by a team, then quality environment planning—works even with a subdivision. In the Kings Hill section of the town of Westford, 17 miles north of Burlington, a developer is using this method.

First an ecological survey was made to identify all natural areas that should be protected and preserved. Then roads and lots were laid out so as not to interfere with the natural areas—the streams, ridges, hilltops, wetlands, the beaver ponds, specimen trees, wildlife habitats, etc.

Innovative characteristics of this ecologically planned rural community include engineered, on-site sewerage disposal based upon soil analysis and percolation tests; narrow, winding interior roads; over a third of the area left in common land to preserve the natural areas; houses located to preserve scenery and landscapes, and make the most of views; plus a trail system linking every house with common land and all natural areas.

Economic success of the development is being demonstrated since it appears that quality environment planning of a subdivision is more salable than the conventional unimaginative lot design.

Open space and recreational land use in Chittenden County, the most populous county in Vermont, is now (1971) being planned by a team of more than two dozen specialists. Fifteen disciplines are represented: history, geology, hydrology, soils, resource economics, botany, wildlife biology, recreation, health, planning, archeology, engineering, forestry, sociology, and economic development.

This team was drawn from the State university, State agencies, Federal agencies, and business, manufacturing, and professional groups. It has collaborated to produce a series of 20 coordinated inventory reports plus two reports proposing a land and resource use, management, and development plan for the county.

The end product will provide the county with a quality environment plan covering recreation, conservation, natural areas, esthetics, and open space. It will also demonstrate the contribution that a broadly based quality planning program can have in guiding development toward quality living in the face of urbanizing pressures.

Quality environment planning for a densely populated, urbanizing America will of course require more than the ecological method, the work of a team, and broad citizen participation applied to specific resource use conflicts or opportunities. It will require new planning concepts which must be applied generally.

The new concepts will concern themselves with how to maintain the quality aspects throughout an urbanizing region. Country roads must remain crooked, hilly, and narrow (and safe at reduced speeds!), wherever there are alternate high speed routes. Subdivisions will be designed to permit primary school children to walk to school.

Streams and waterways must be zoned for the best use—handling large quantities of water, runoff, and recreation. Drainage ways can then be turned into walkways, miniparks, and a trail system.

Street beautification must become a routine step in all planning. Neon alleys will be changed to attractive streets with adequate setback, lines of trees, flowers, and small, attractive signs.

Public access must be provided to public waters. Adequate access will have a salutary effect on land values. A citizen will have less incentive to buy a lakeshore lot when he can have access to *his* lake for all purposes merely by paying *his* taxes.

Both attitudes and behavior patterns must change if we are to rise to the challenge and redirect our planning toward quality goals. People living within a mile of their jobs should walk or bicycle to work. Bus lines must be used to move masses of people in urban areas.

Cars must run on sanitized internal combustion engines or some other nonpolluting power source. Container manufacturers must adopt containers that will decompose or be returned. Municipalities need to provide sidewalks for pedestrians and paved paths for bicycles.

Parallel to the changes in life style will be major changes in the style of our economy. Led by innovating and enterprising corporations, the concept and practice of recycling will be widely adopted. It will be applied to paper, wood, automobiles, water, and food containers. Industry will gradually abandon the concept of planned obsolescence.

Regulatory agencies will turn toward protecting the consumers' interest. Poisons will be removed from mass production and reserved for specialized uses. Mass ground transportation will be subsidized.

Pricing of natural resources will be designed to promote conservation. We will pay for water according to use. Electricity will cost more, the more we use—an incentive to reduce the rate of increase in per capita consumption and the need for more power plants.

And State colleges and universities will become centers for regional quality environment planning—providing the research, the numerous disciplines, the training, and their share of the leadership to the quality environment planning process.

The Future Of Farmers And Farming

W. B. SUNDQUIST

THE PROJECTION of 100 million more people in the United States around the turn of the century provides a strong prospect for expanded markets for food and fiber. So does the expectation of further increases in export markets for such key farm commodities as soybeans, feed grains, and others.

Recent experience has shown however, that expanded markets and even higher farm prices do not mean more farmers or more farm jobs. In fact, farm population, farm employment, and number of farms have all fallen drastically despite recent increases in farm marketings both at home and abroad. And, dairy farms continued to decline in number between 1965 and 1970 despite a 33 percent increase in milk prices received by farmers. Other farm types also continued their numbers decline whether their commodity prices were up or down.

In the two decades from 1950 to 1969, the U.S. population increased by a third, from 151.7 million to 202.2 million. At the same time, total farm employment declined from 9.9 million to 4.6 million persons.

This drop of more than 50 percent in farm employment was accompanied by an even greater proportional decline in the number of man-hours worked in farming. A large number of persons employed in farming also worked at other jobs, either full- or part-time. Others, though still full-time farmers, now work less total hours than they used to.

Large increases in farm size have already occurred and further increases appear imminent. A chief force pushing toward farm enlargement is the larger volume production systems spurred by new technology. This technology has expanded total productive capacity in farming at the same time labor requirements per unit of production have fallen. The adoption of new technology has permitted even the family-scale farmer to increase the size of his operating unit. And, lower per unit costs coupled with the need for more income have encouraged him to enlarge his operation.

Price discounts on inputs like fertilizer and machinery are available to large-scale farmers and they can often receive a premium price for large-volume marketings.

Increased involvement in farming by firms in the farm supply and marketing sectors has also been a factor in increasing farm size, particularly in some specialty crops and fed livestock.

Other strategies that have led to increased farm size include those of minimizing tax liabilities through internal expansion, purchasing land for expected capital gains, and using low equity financing.

Most farm enlargement has been, and probably will continue to be, the result of using new and larger scale technology on family-run farms. Exceptions are mainly in production of specialty crops such as fruits and vegetables, in poultry, and in cattle-feeding. But some field crops, including cotton, also have a number of very large-scale units.

Gross receipts from farm products totaled $28.7 billion in 1950 and rose to $51 billion in 1969. Though future increases may not occur smoothly, total farm sales will almost certainly advance in the decades ahead. Shifts in consumer demand, illustrated by the per capita shift toward more beef and less bread and potatoes, however, suggest that some sectors of agriculture will prosper more than others.

Future expansion in the demand for soybeans and feed grains is closely tied to the increased demand for livestock and the resulting needs for livestock feeds. Meanwhile, large world supplies of wheat and declining per capita demand for cereal grains in the developed countries suggest a more sluggish future market for wheat for food uses.

Much has been said regarding the technological revolution sweeping agriculture. Actually, three distinct revolutions have occurred. These include 1. The mechanical (particularly the shift from horse- to tractor-power), 2. The scientific (including development of new fertilizers, pesticides, and high-yielding crop varieties), and 3. The business management revolution (including use of business organization and management procedures in farming which were already in use in other sectors of the economy).

*

w. b. sundquist, former Deputy Administrator of the Economic Research Service, is now on the staff of the University of Minnesota, St. Paul.

Moreover, the rate at which further change occurs will differ substantially among farm commodities. One way of evaluating future change is to look at the human resources now involved in farming and the potential for their release.

Within the crop production side of agriculture, a total of 3,430 million man-hours of labor were used in 1969. Several crops appear to have great potential for further labor reduction. For example, the 450 million man-hours of labor used in raising tobacco is almost as great as that in producing feed grains and more than $2\frac{1}{2}$ times as great as in total food grains production. Prototype machines are even now available to mechanize tobacco harvest; the only question is, when? Production of vegetable crops requires almost as much total labor as tobacco while fruit and nut crops require more.

Further mechanization and automation in growing these high labor-use crops appears inevitable. Much of the human resource adjustment in the tobacco, vegetable, and fruit and nut crop sectors will fall on hired labor. In tobacco, a large number of small farm operators and their families are also involved. Unfortunately, many workers employed in producing these crops have limited education and training for other jobs.

Continuing trends to more mechanization, modernized business organizations, and larger production units can be expected in livestock. This is particularly true for those components of livestock production, such as cattle-feeding, where the enterprise requires a minimum amount of land but substantial capital and management inputs. Thus, the 2,450 million man-hours used in producing livestock and livestock products in 1969 is in for a big drop in future years. Fortunately, many farmers shifting out of livestock are better trained than those in tobacco and many have good alternatives, either in specialized crop production or off-farm work.

Both the crop and livestock farmers can expect to operate within a more stringent set of regulations in the future. Many of these regulations will be established outside farming. Future land use and other production restrictions are likely for pollution abatement, the conservation of our natural resources, and for expanded industrial, recreational, housing, and highway needs. This is particularly true in the more humid, heavily populated Central and Eastern parts of the country and in the Far West where future demands from the nonfarm population will be tremendous.

But despite the prospect for increased institutional restraints on land use and production practices, there will be no reversing the trend to fewer and larger farms.

As we look to the future of farm people, we must recognize the farm population as very diverse with a wide range of opportunities. This range reflects differences in age, location, education, and in training. It also depends on the type of farming people are engaged in, the profitability of their individual operations, and on whether or not they are hired workers or self-employed farmers.

Income and living standards of the hired work force in farming have been consistently below those of the self-employed farm operators. This relationship is expected to continue in the future even with significant improvements in wages and benefits for hired workers.

Location of the farm population is an important determinant of their future opportunities in both farming and off-farm employment. For example, preliminary figures from the 1970 Census of Population show an absolute decline in the population of several States in the Northern Great Plains region compared with 1960. Here, land-extensive types of farming predominate, both in crop and livestock production, while alternatives for employment outside farming are very limited. Though further population declines may not occur in these States, a continued decline in some of their rural areas is inevitable.

375

In other major farming regions, such as portions of the Corn Belt within commuting distance of urban and industrial centers, employment opportunities outside farming are far more numerous. Some regions, like southern New England and part of the Southeast, have already had a major shift from farm to nonfarm land uses. In many cases it has been accompanied by employment opportunities for farmers and their families in the enterprises to which the land use has shifted, such as recreation and industry, and in the related service industries.

At the same time that changes have occurred on farms, changes have also been underway in the farm supply, marketing, and related service industries. There has been a movement away from highly centralized location of meatpacking and, to a lesser extent, flour milling. This has resulted in a shift from urban to agricultural trade centers of many meatpacking jobs.

In the flour milling industry, on the other hand, the disbursement has been to locations which can more readily service population centers in the East and West.

A different kind of shift has taken place in small towns in farming areas where machinery and fertilizer dealers, creameries and milk plants, and many other agribusiness firms closed out their small volume operations. Firms providing these functions—both supplies and marketing—are now concentrated in larger units located in the bigger trade area centers.

The overall consequence of changes in the farm supply, marketing, and related service sectors has generally been to phase out businesses and employment opportunities in small towns, but to increase total economic activity and employment opportunities in larger regional trade centers.

The economic well-being of the farm population cannot be determined solely, and in some cases not even primarily, by prosperity or lack of it in farming alone. For example, in 1969, average off-farm income per

farm operator family totaled more than $5,250. Realized net income from farming, on the other hand, was just over $5,400. On farms grossing less than $10,000 from farm sales, off-farm income far exceeded net income from farming.

The decade of the 1960's showed a steady increase in the proportion of income of farm families which came from off-farm sources. This trend will certainly continue into the future, particularly on farms grossing $10,000 or less from farm sales. Units in this lower sales class accounted for almost two-thirds of the roughly 3 million total farms in 1969.

On the other hand, the less than 1.1 million farms with sales of $10,000 or more received almost 90 percent of all cash receipts from farming. And since most benefits paid to farmers through the Federal farm programs are closely tied to acreage and production, a high proportion of these benefits also accrued to farms with sales of $10,000 or more.

These and other statistics suggest continued polarization of farm people into two groups: 1. Those deriving their livelihood mainly from producing farm commodities on a commercial basis, and 2. Those relying heavily on family employment off the farm to supplement their farming income. For many farm families, it is more accurate to say that income from off-farm employment is of primary importance and is only supplemented in a minor way with earnings from farming.

In rural areas like the Northern Great Plains where the decline in farm population is not being offset by increases in other lines of employment, severe adjustment problems are cropping up.

For example, per capita costs for providing public services such as health, education, transportation, and fire and police protection are rising at a rapid rate and will continue to do so. Financing these cost hikes through increased taxes levied on remaining farmers is difficult. But the alternatives are those of finding other revenue sources or having a drop in the availability and quality of these services.

Again, the continued pressure for consolidating and upgrading public services as well as their increased cost suggests they will be more readily available in regional trade area centers than in small towns. More farmers will themselves move to regional trade centers in order to have an adequate access to these services.

In contrast, rural areas near urban and industrial centers will have an increase in population. Many of these people will be only part-time or part-retirement farmers or will be employed entirely in off-farm jobs.

Such scenes are already becoming prominent in many areas east of the Great Plains and in some portions of the Pacific States. Here, the reduction in farm population density will be more than offset by an increase in nonfarm rural residents, and development of viable communities with attendant public services is still possible.

Faced with the prospect of fewer and larger farms and a declining farm population, farmers will need to find ways to obtain effective representation in the political arena. Already it has become apparent that the solid political farm bloc which could be identified in the 1930's and 1940's no longer exists.

The modern day California vegetable producer is concerned with wages and institutional arrangements for his hired labor. His product market is primarily a domestic one, and he knows it.

A family-scale wheat producer in North Dakota, on the other hand, is necessarily concerned about such diverse problems as world export markets (which took more than 600 million bushels or 45 percent of the wheat moved during the 1969-70 marketing year) and farm real estate prices (which have tripled since 1950 and now represent 80 percent or more of the capital required to put together a profitable wheat farming unit). Since he hires little labor, questions of unionization and wage rates are not generally important to him.

In California, farmers represent a small minority of the total population but they tend to be large, powerful, and capable of organizing a major part of the production of their commodities. By contrast, in North Dakota —as in the Northern Plains generally —farmers still represent a sizable portion of the total population and wield considerable political strength through the direct voting process.

Beef producers have prospects for expanding markets and favorable future prices. Cotton producers, on the other hand, are facing strong competition both from domestically produced synthetic fibers and from foreign cotton producers.

This wide diversity of situations in farming suggests little likelihood that all farmers will find a common basis for exerting effective political or economic influence. Rather, the major opportunities for most will lie in the direction of special interest groups organized along commodity and regional lines.

With increased regional and commodity specialization, and with the uniqueness of price and market problems for different producer groups, "the average farm in the United States" is not a feasible unit upon which to center farm policy of either a national or a more local type.

Recent farm policy ventures which have resulted in materially improving the price and income position of farm groups include development of effective marketing orders and producer bargaining groups.

Dairy and some fruit and vegetable producers are cases in point. These producers have been able to effectively differentiate their market demand (and product prices) between higher- and lower-value uses such as fluid milk and manufactured dairy products, and between fresh and processed fruits and vegetables. A strong common interest in the policy objectives of a group of producers and their

377

ability to organize effectively so as to achieve these objectives are key requirements for success.

Wheat and feed grain producers present a different situation. Since they produce commodities that move extensively into world trade and are subject to dramatic price fluctuations depending upon the supply-demand balance, some national program to insure a degree of price and income stability remains essential. Moreover, because these crops are produced over large regions and in conjunction with other products, effective price and income policies are likely only at the national level.

In order to achieve effective farm policies at the national level, political representatives from Farm States will need increasingly to trade their support for projects to help nonfarm people.

Broad price and policy issues cannot be effectively addressed at the State and county levels. This does not, however, preclude local help to farmers through effective real estate tax policy, land use zoning, and planning for educational, medical, and other service needs.

In areas of rapid population growth, for example, delaying real estate tax increases until land is sold for higher value uses may effectively aid farmers whose land is in the path of urbanization, industrialization, or other higher-value uses than farming. So may effective land use zoning. At the same time, orderly development of industry, recreational facilities, and housing should be enhanced by such policies.

The political priorities of much of the farm population have shifted materially in recent years and will shift more in the future. Farm families who realize more income from non-farm sources than from farming now have political interests more like those of urban people than like those of their neighbors who operate commercial farms.

They are strongly affected by policies treating wages and worker and consumer benefits (such as mini-mum wages, unemployment benefits, and consumer safeguards). Thus, their personal well-being stands to be improved much more by policies aimed at strengthening the level of economic activity and employment in sectors outside farming than by policies designed to strengthen and stabilize farm income. Their future attitudes toward restraining those farming activities which cause pollution or environmental damage will be more strongly influenced by their role as consumers and beneficiaries of other amenities of rural living than by their role as farmers.

In conclusion, only one thing is certain. Future changes in agriculture will not affect as many farm families as past adjustments already have. The number of farms and the size of the farm population are down dramatically from their high points in the 1920's and 1930's. Even since 1950, total farm employment has declined by more than 50 percent and a decline of that absolute size in the future is impossible.

Georgia Plans for Growth

E. EVAN BROWN and
HAROLD L. NIX

GEORGIA's greatest asset toward orderly growth and development are her 19 Area Planning and Development Commissions. Generally referred to as APDC's, they represent groups of contiguous counties which have joined together to plan for optimum physical, social, and economic development.

The Commissions came about, in part, as a result of long-time educational efforts by pioneering individuals in both public and private agencies. These pioneers helped point to the APDC's as a mechanism for dealing with such problems as a shrinking tax base, loss of population, and shifting economic bases. Local leaders came to realize the economy of pooling resources and sharing services of adequately trained professional staffs.

The first multi-county planning commission was set up in metropolitan Atlanta in 1947 by a special Act of the General Assembly. In 1959, the first nonmetropolitan multi-county planning commission was formed and named the Coosa Valley Area Planning Commission. In 1960, the 1957 General Planning and Zoning Enabling Act was amended to permit multi-county commissions of not less than five counties to develop throughout the State.

By 1970, a total of 19 APDC's were active in the State—covering 155 out of 159 counties. The smallest commission represents five counties and the largest 14.

Enabling legislation provides for forming area planning commissions and authorizes them to elect officers; hire staff; cooperate with, contract with, or accept funds from Federal, State or local public as well as private agencies; to expend these funds; and to carry out cooperative undertakings and programs.

In most instances, representation on the APDC's in Georgia is limited to two representatives from each member county. One is appointed by the county commissioners and the second by the governing authority of the county seat.

*

E. EVAN BROWN is a Professor in the Agricultural Economics Department at the Universtiy of Georgia, Athens.

HAROLD L. NIX is Professor of Sociology and jointly staffed with the Department of Sociology and Anthropology and the Institute of Community and Area Development at the University of Georgia.

Operating funds for APDC's in Georgia are supplied through three major sources. Local contributions are levied at 10 to 25 cents per capita. State matching funds are based on the formula of $2 for every $1 of the first $15,000; and matching dollar for dollar the next $20,000 collected locally. Federal aid has been in the form of matching grants and loans through such agencies as the Department of Housing and Urban Development, the Economic Development Administration, Farmers Home Administration, the Federal Aviation Administration, and Office of Economic Opportunity.

An executive director heads up each area commission staff. The typical staff includes from 10 to 20 technicians and professionals from such fields as economics, geography, law, public administration, and law enforcement, as well as city, area, and industrial planning. The staffs are frequently aided by State and Federal agencies, the university system, and private consultants.

Generic functions of the Area commissions include research, opportunity identification, goal formulation, project development, program coordination, public education, technical assistance, interagency liaison, citizen participation, and leadership development.

Subject matter areas within which Georgia's APDC's operate currently include economic development, tourism, law enforcement, health, transportation, manpower, recreation, agriculture, water resources, waste disposal. The area commissions are charged with area study, planning, and development as well as with providing local assistance in planning to approximately 200 city, county, and city-county planning units. In addition, each APDC reviews and comments on applications by units of local government within their area to State, Federal, quasi-government, or private agencies for loans or project grants.

Commissions have provided the mechanism through which State and

Federal monies were channeled into local communities resulting in water systems, sewerage systems, airports, roads, recreational facilities, law enforcement facilities, community centers, and other public facilities. Also, they provided a focal point for aiding private investors to secure information and additional sources of credit. In some areas, multi-county industrial parks and waste disposal systems have been established.

Accomplishments cited indicate a tendency on the part of APDC's to go beyond their earlier study and planning functions. There appears to be an increasing trend for them to provide governmental services to their member local governments in such areas as traffic engineering, local planning, and consolidated waste disposal.

Every commission in Georgia has had the problem of developing an area image as well as problems of communicating with local leaders and carrying out plans and programs.

The first decade of APDC's in Georgia has seen the emphasis placed upon local planning and technical assistance. The next decade will probably see emphasis placed upon area-wide planning for use of local member governments and the State, upon area-wide administrative services as requested by member governments, and upon selected administrative functions for State agencies as requested by State governments.

Thus, by providing area planning as a guide to both local and State units and by selective and voluntary consolidation of certain administrative functions and services, local government will be strengthened during the decades to come.

Georgia's APDC's also have served as a mechanism for interstate regional planning and development. Because Georgia was one of the first States in Appalachia with area planning and development units, it was one of the first States to receive funding through the Appalachian Regional Commission Act of 1965.

As a result of early action, many projects have been completed in the 35 Georgia Appalachian counties which are organized under five APDC's. These projects include 140 miles of highway, water and sewerage projects; access roads to industrial and recreational parks; and contruction of vocational schools, hospitals, and housing.

The Coastal Plains Regional Commission was authorized by Congress in 1965 and established in 1967. This interstate commission includes the Coastal Plains counties in Georgia, South Carolina, and North Carolina.

Six target sectors of the economy selected by this regional commission for acceleration are marine resources, education and manpower, industrial development, agriculture and forestry, tourism and recreation, and transportation.

Since the coastal area and off-shore waters of Georgia offered substantial opportunities for long-range development, marine resources planning has received major attention. Plans made by the commission provided for an accelerated program of research and education in support of coastal marine resource development.

To carry out these plans on a State-wide basis, Georgia established the Ocean Science Center of the Atlantic Commission (OSCA) under sponsorship of the Coastal Plains Regional Commission. This center is the official State agency to receive and administer funds provided by the commission or from State appropriated funds used for matching purposes. OSCA is charged by the State to develop an oceanographic research complex and to establish a marine extension service.

OSCA developed plans for a research center on Skidaway Island as well as extension and service centers at Skidaway, Brunswick, and St. Mary's. The research center at Skidaway was occupied by the Skidaway Institute of Oceanography in 1968. This institute is part of the university system of Georgia. It is designed to conduct research and provide for development in commercial fishing and aquaculture, marine engineering, mineral exploration, recovery techniques, pollution, and certain fields of basic research.

Marine extension and service programs of OSCA were instituted in 1970 with the employment of several specialists. Their principal functions are to take useful knowledge generated by the research component or other sources and disseminate it to potential users in the coastal area.

The late 1960's has seen development by the university system of two unique centers in Georgia—the Rural Development Center and the Urban Life Center.

The Rural Development Center is at Tifton, Ga. It will complement and expand existing programs of the Coastal Plains Experiment Station, the Extension Service, the College of Agriculture of the University of Georgia, and Abraham Baldwin Agricultural College. A basic purpose will be to coordinate research, instruction, and service functions of these established units so that total resources of the university system will bear significantly on area-wide problems.

The center's program has four objectives: 1. To increase agricultural and forest production efficiency through continued research findings, 2. To advance development of marketing and utilization of farm and forest commodities, 3. To aid community development and solve problems concerning how and where people will live and relate to each other,

4. To further manpower training and utilization to provide more skilled workers in various types of agribusiness that are needed in the area, and to assist general farm workers to prepare for new forms of employment as farm technology takes over their former jobs.

Complementary to the Rural Development Center is the Urban Life Center at Georgia State University in metropolitan Atlanta.

The private sector is deeply involved in planning and development in Georgia in several ways. Private utility companies, cooperatives, banks, and other private interests have promoted and supported the various public agencies in organizing and assisting the Area Planning and Development Commissions as well as local planning units.

Private planning and development is exemplified by the Cotton Producers Association, which ranked 319th in 1969 in business volume in the United States. The CPA has taken initiative in planning and developing, crop, livestock, and catfish production, processing, and marketing.

Illustrative of this development by CPA was establishment of a $6.5 million soybean crushing and refining facility at Valdosta, investment of $200,000 in the largest feedlot facility in the State at Waynesboro, and the building of a large catfish hatchery and processing plant at Quitman.

Another illustration of private planning, with assistance of marine units

Sketch of Rural Development Center at Tifton, Ga. Center was completed in March 1971.

of the Ocean Science Center of the Atlantic Commission, is a private firm's plan for shrimp production. The firm has applied to the Corps of Engineers for a permit to create impoundments totaling 1,200 acres. An estimated 1,000 pounds of shrimp can be produced per acre or a total of 1.2 million pounds with a wholesale value of over $1 million yearly.

In conclusion, Georgia has staked its future on planning its own destiny. Chief responsibility for this planning is placed in three closely coordinated and supportive levels—State, area, and local.

Capstone for planning is the Georgia Bureau of State Planning and Community Affairs. Second or area level planning is carried on by 19 Area Planning and Development Commissions, each consisting of five to 14 member counties. These commisions have responsibility for area study and planning and assistance in state planning. They are also charged by the Bureau of State Planning and Community Affairs with providing local assistance to approximately 200 planning units of local government.

Georgia, with these coordinated levels of planning strongly supported by the public and private sectors, can look to the future with confidence.

Breakthrough: Looking Back From 2000

ALAN R. BIRD and

MELVIN L. COTNER

We wondered how people would get along in the next 30 years. Where would the next 100 million people live? Would settlement patterns be much different in the year 2000 from what they are today? What will living conditions be like?

Many of you have looked at the same questions, going through this Yearbook. By now, you may have firm conclusions. We must confess that our own conclusions are still very tentative. So we would rather not impose them on you.

To close this volume, we offer an agriculture yearbook article for the year 2000 from a historian looking back upon the last three decades of the 20th century. Perhaps such a "look back" will help in visualizing some of the options available to us. Here it is:

We certainly have come a long way since the moon shots of the sixties. Man had begun to regain mastery of the machine. And it wasn't easy.

We began the seventies with a flurry of concern over population distribution and "balanced growth." Fires in the ghettoes, kids blowing their minds on LSD, shootings, traffic congestion, smog, and other happenings had dramatized the problems of urban congestion. And isolated rural poor still lacked the medical, educational, and other services that were generally thought essential to the good life.

The 1970 Census counted more than 200 million Americans for the first time. And people worried about where the next 100 million would live—the 100 million expected by the year 2000 or certainly by 2020 even with widespread and zealous use of the pill and other birth control devices. We needed living space and facilities for 25 million more families.

Why pile up more people in the cities? Why not spread people around and encourage more attractive communities in rural areas that continued to lose people? People voted with their feet and elected life in the cities, even the ghettoes, and the suburbs. Nearly 70 percent located in metropolitan areas. Yet most people claimed they preferred to live outside the cities.

*

ALAN R. BIRD is Deputy Director of the Economic Development Division, Economic Research Service (ERS).
MELVIN L. COTNER is Director, Natural Resource Economics Division, ERS.

The location of jobs and economic activity continued to be concentrated. Market and production forces dictated the location of jobs and population.

Some new communities were built. They tended to be overnight wonders that responded to the needs of national defense. Cape Kennedy, Fla., and Huntsville, Ala., blossomed out and created many new defense or space jobs.

Other communities were satellites of metropolitan complexes. Washington, D.C., and adjoining areas boasted some three million people and gave birth to the expensive satellites of Reston, Va., and Columbia, Md.

But with all our modern technical know-how, the outlook for really new towns seemed dim. When all was said and done, Washington itself was more a new town in its day than any of the creations of the sixties—and this capital city was created in a much less opulent and less technically proficient society.

So we edged through the sixties and seventies with a general malaise about the way we lived. And we watched cities and towns of various sizes gradually grow. As each town grew, it developed its own smog and traffic congestion. It added freeways to reach suburbs which, in turn, spread further because of freeways. Land was used unwisely. Community facilities were costly.

We made some improvements in our environment, but these involved uneasy tradeoffs. As we stopped one environmental problem, two new ones seemed to replace it. Problems of the environment were related to our affluence. The super-rich were super-polluters.

Then it happened. People had always said it would take a crisis to bring about big changes in our way of life. And it did this time too. What happened was the Great Blackout. The winter was severe, power was taxed to capacity. And there was a freak air inversion that blanketed large areas of the country in smog. Traffic came to a standstill here, there, and almost everywhere. Rescue services were badly handicapped. Thousands died.

Commissions, committees, and other groups made the usual investigations. Scapegoats appeared. Disaster relief was authorized and administered. Yet the impact of the Great Blackout lingered on. The people were patently aware of the need to do something more.

So we took a fresh look at the need to improve all our communities. We had communities of different sizes—from sparsely settled areas that would always support some people, to New York City and surroundings bigger than ever. And we always would have communities of various sizes—all in need of improvement.

What's more, there were some poor people in most of these communities and lots of people just above the poverty line. Even wealthy people had their problems. And all people had certain basic needs—and basic rights guaranteed under the Constitution.

The trouble with communities was people—but their strengths came from people, too. People had not learned how to live with technology. People working together needed to evolve a wider range of options for living and working.

So we saw the birth of a series of measures. Federal legislation was modified. Less emphasis was put on categorical grants and more on block grants and other new ways of working with State and local governments. Programs like health insurance and income support for children were made available to all people irrespective of income level and place of residence. These were the enabling measures or people-building measures that, in turn, have brought us many giant steps in community building.

Our positive people-building programs are a model for the world. More than ten million people are now in major retraining programs every year.

We recognized that many people, perhaps professional and other skilled people most of all, need to update their training, to make it relevant to the new world. More than that, many need to change occupations and learn new skills. Unless they do, many jobs linger on and really amount to full-time pensions that don't even have enough therapeutic value to assure peace of mind. Some jobs are abolished but, thanks to the red tape of big bureaucracies, there's often a lag in facing reality—even in big corporations.

Both government agencies and private companies and even universities and trade unions have done a lot more to help people build better communities. Fringe benefits such as retirement and health insurance are much more interchangeable than they used to be. And this has helped speed up the movement of skilled people to new jobs where they can do the most good.

Many professionals can move from Federal or State governments to a university and, in some cases, even to local government staffs without sacrificing hard-earned retirement privileges. And everyone has benefited. Big corporations are working out similar arrangements—and the government is enouraging them.

Universities have begun to meet student demands for relevance, and government agencies have the "new blood" they always sought. Smaller communities have a better chance to compete for the quality staff they always need—and always will need.

We went further than that. We recognized that the heavy demands of professional and technical training bring forth the danger of developing partial people. Our communities and our way of life had tended to prevent balanced living. Many communities have now taken big steps to correct this fragmentation of life. They are truly better places to work and live.

A previously unheard of example is right in Washington, D.C. Under the Mall, instead of cavernous layers of underground parking to compete with mass transit, we now have a great complex of gymnasiums, health spas, indoor tennis courts, handball courts, exercise rooms and swimming pools, along with cinemas and reading rooms. Part of the shorter work week is due to optional health leave which government employees may take during the daytime when they need the exercise most.

Now that we see these Mall facilities and enjoy them, we wonder that it took a national crisis to bring about such obvious improvements.

And the colonnades around the Mall, somewhat Spanish in appearance, blend well with the truly impressive public buildings and give tourists and citizens ready walking access to some of the wonders of Washington in all weather.

We even have truly new towns—with a new purpose. They are a modern version of the land-grant colleges and universities established under the Morrill Act. These new communities take families from all walks of life and all regions and offer them a sabbatical year for retraining, for learning both new working skills and new skills for the productive use of leisure. There is provision for 50 of these new towns—as many as there are States.

Pollution problems were solved. At one time, the rampant use of technology was blamed for many of the environmental insults. And ironically, our ingenious minds developed the needed technology to deal with pollutants. Anything seems possible—where there is a will.

Both cities and rural areas have found ways of working with neighboring communities to the benefit of all concerned. Planning for needed hospitals, schools, and other major facilities is commonly done on a multi-county basis.

Isolated rural areas have found ways of providing all local children with a first-class education, and these ways are quite varied. Boarding schools, special travelling teachers, television and radio, and even relocation assistance for some families all play a part.

More than that, planning activities

Residential plaza in what is expected to be first enclosed community, free from automobiles. New city 2 miles from Anchorage, Alaska, will be called Seward's Success and is scheduled for completion by 1990.

are forward-looking. New housing is clustered near schools and hospitals so that the rural people will be less isolated in the years ahead. Tax rates are set high enough to support urgent community needs.

Thanks to adequate support of planning staffs, local citizens have much better information on what their community needs are and how the needs might be met. Communities were willing to use their tax authorities to underwrite the needed improvements.

People realized that planning and development must be done on a comprehensive basis. Energy and transportation systems as well as water resource improvements and environmental safeguards must be developed in concert. Even land use planning became essential to insure that residential, industrial, recreation, waste management, and agricultural uses are considered to serve the needs of people.

One other problem has been dealt a mortal blow. We can still travel from town to town and be confident of the quality of accommodation and eating facilities, and still more confident of the quality of service on our automobiles and home appliances. But we don't have to face the same humdrum signs for Grampa Hic's Fried Baloney or the Better Deal Motel. We have a series of programs that have brought some individuality back to our communities—just as we've managed to enable people to be freed as individuals.

Ironically enough, part of this new breakthrough to individuality has resulted from a radical change in our migration patterns. In the seventies, we worried about "too many people on too little land." We have now found that encouraging migration was a big help in developing better communities. Many of these migrants have brought new skills and new viewpoints—and they've helped us cement contacts among our States and regions.

Much of the migration was to new towns that serviced the needs of rural people and some went to existing larger cities. And the cities needed them. In fact, there were experts who had claimed all along that a number of our cities didn't have enough people per square mile to enable the cities to provide improved services economically.

Rapid transit systems in our larger cities have become commonplace. Urban planning and development matched up residential housing with the location of jobs. The planned development provided for open space, parks, and yes, even agricultural uses of land near or within cities to make them more attractive and desirable as a place to live and work.

To sum up the experience in the last third of the 20th century, it can be said that people learned to live together.

Thus we give you a proposed chapter for the 2000 Agriculture Yearbook. We challenge you to be a constructive force in decades ahead so our historian friend can write an even better chapter.

385

Photography

MOST OF THE PHOTOS in this Yearbook were taken by U.S. Department of Agriculture photographers. Generally, prints of the USDA photos may be obtained from the Photography Division, Office of Information, U.S. Department of Agriculture, Washington, D.C. 20250. These prints are free to news media; others may obtain prints for a nominal fee. In ordering please refer to the 1971 Yearbook and give the page number.

Photos taken by other photographers are credited below where the sources were known.

Please note that no page numbers appear in the photo section at the front of the book. However, for photo credit purposes, Page I is the first page on which photos (four in all) appear, followed by Pages II and III (with one photo across the two pages), and so on consecutively with Roman numerals through this photo section. Arabic numerals in the credits indicate page numbers in the main part of the book.

Harris H. Barnes, Jr., 257, 264 (bottom), 347.
Blue Ridge Aerial Surveys, 104 (top).
Columbia (Md.), xvi (bottom).
Photography by Daniels, 104 (lower left).
Deere & Company, 259 (large photo).
W. K. Dorsey, 166 (top left).
Farmland Industries, Inc., xii (bottom), 259 (upper right).
Alan Hicks Photography, 236.
IAA Record, 218.
Industrial Photography, Inc., photo by Jack Beech, 66 (top).
Journal of Homebuilding, National Assn. of Homebuilders, 361 (top right), 385.
Kentucky Department of Natural Resources, photos by Thomas A. Smith, vi (2 upper photos), 40, 58, 160 (both photos), 171 (all 3 photos), 183, 238.
Library of Congress, 104 (lower right).
Matrix of Man, Sybil Moholy-Nagy, published by Frederick Praeger, copyright 1968, 8, 11.
Mobile Home Manufacturers Assn., 107.

MOEN Division of Stanadyne, 103.
National 4–H News, xi (inset photo of girl at bottom).
Ohio Agricultural Research and Development Center, 196 (both photos).
Omaha World–Herald, photo by Don Ringler, xii (top).
Rural Housing Alliance, photos by George Ballis, vii (both photos), 93.
St. Regis Paper Company, 66 (bottom).
State of Vermont, photo on endsheets, 371 (both photos).
Structure in Art and in Science, edited by Gyorgy Kepes, art by Eduardo Catalano, published by George Brasiller, Inc., 12.
Sun Newspapers of Lincoln (Nebr.) Inc., viii (lower right).
University of Georgia, photo by Walker Montgomery, 361 (large photo).
Wallaces Farmer photos by Ruth Webber, 21.
Washore Turkey Assn., 387.
Worthington Foods, Inc., xv (top), 335 (both photos).

Index

FOR SALE BY THE SUPERINTENDENT OF DOCUMENTS, WASHINGTON, D.C. 20402—PRICE $3.50

STOCK NUMBER 0100–1459

391

DR. WILLIAM K. WIDGER, JR.
RFD #2, Hillrise Lane
Meredith, N. H. 03253